TASTE an

365

The Diary of a Food Adventurist

Written By
Dr. Stephanie Shelburne

Published by Talking Stick Books, LLC
PO Box 174
South Lee, MA 01260
Office (866) 994-7539
Fax (866) 994-7539
www.talkingstickbooks.com

ISBN-13: 978-0-9991719-0-5

FOR THE LOVE OF FOOD AND FAMILY

CONTENTS

LETTER TO THE READER:

You hold in your hands a labor of love.

This book is the collection of daily entries of my year-long exploration through taste and flavor. An endeavor started on a whim but birthed from the intense desire to help people rekindle their relationships with food and eating.

You will notice that many entries follow a seasonal pattern as well as include culinary and medicinal profiles and in many cases, recipes. Often the entries are written in a quirky, whimsical way as I careened through each day in search of something new. Yes, there will the occasional structural flaw that I have chosen not to correct simply to remain true to the daily (sometimes frantically written) entry.

There's no "right" way to read this book. Think of it as a journal of a year in the life of the pursuit of palate. The chapters are divided into months simply to provide some modicum of organization for you, the reader. Be adventurous.

The tastes and flavors throughout this book represent my daily commitment to finding something new regardless of location or schedule. I invite you to be curious as you engage your senses and allow yourself to enjoy the tastes and flavors of life.

INTRODUCTION – Prelude to Your Palate

Gastronomical knowledge is necessary to every man because it adds to the sum of predestined pleasure ~ Jean Anthelme Brillat-Savarin

Can you remember the last time you really tasted what you were eating? I'm not referring to simply noticing whether your last snack tasted good or even those occasional moments of oohing and aahing with friends at the latest foodie heaven.

Think about the last time you slowed down and savored all the nuances and expressions of taste, flavor, mouthfeel, texture and even synergy of the ingredients that found their way onto your plate and into your mouth? The truth is when you satisfy your palate with real flavors and you truly savor what you are eating, your well-being is all the better for it. You are designed to eat real food and enjoy real flavors—which are pillars of genuine health and well-being.

One thing that has become crystal clear to me in today's world of food and eating is that as the *science of food* has progressed, the *art of eating* has declined.

Attempts to be healthy, eat well, lose weight, and regulate intake, rely mostly on external sources dictating what, how much, and when to eat leaving your poor taste buds to languish from boredom due to lack of stimulation and self-discovery.

Eating well and staying healthy come down to so much more than counting calorie in/calorie out or resorting to "health" foods that are dully flavored, uninspiring, or worse yet, loaded with chemical additives to make them palatable. Neither does eating well mean spending thousands of dollars on so called "superfoods" or supplements.

How often have you heard that your tongue is divided into separate regions for each variation of taste? Did you know it's a myth; and that you have chemoreceptors (taste buds) all over your mouth including the roof? Each taste bud contains anywhere from 50-100 taste cells, all designed to respond to different nuances of flavor. Each taste bud has the capacity to taste sweet, salty, bitter, sour, and umami. Even more interesting is the fact that not only are taste buds located throughout your mouth, they can also be found throughout your gut and other parts of your body. Has it ever occurred to you that taste and flavor might involve oh so much more than simply the basics of sweet, salty, sour, bitter, and savory? Are you aware that typically after about eight (8) bites of the same food, your brain stops paying attention to the flavor? If you remain mindlessly chewing after bite eight, you begin enjoying from memory rather than immediate flavor stimuli. This phenomenon adds to the 'check-out' factor that can contribute to overeating if you aren't paying attention.

We are designed to enjoy food which is why it is difficult to suppress the aaaahs and mmmms when sampling something delectable—it is part of our birthright and quite possibly one of the more valuable untapped avenues for genuine happiness and well-being. The key to accessing this hidden gem? Curiosity.

That's right, your openness to inquiry and your open curiosity set the stage for the ultimate reward your body can experience; involuntary shivers of pleasure. Often when I speak about the pleasures of eating, people tend to think of decadent desserts and the occasional illicit sugar binge. The truth is, your body is smarter than that!

So, here's to exploring your palate, wherever you are…

CHAPTER 1- JANUARY

DAY 1 - SWEET

What better way to start a new year than with a little sweetness?!? Sweet is one of the six basic taste sensations. It is also one of the most easily detected flavors for the human palate. Infants can recognize sweet as one of their first perceptible tastes and studies show that they prefer milk that has a higher sweet density. But before you begin reaching for the sugar dish, it could be useful to understand what we really mean when we talk about sweet as a taste sensation and as a flavor.

Sadly, in today's world sweet has become synonymous with sugar and other manufactured sweeteners rather than being appreciated for the complex notes that can be found in many natural foods; notes that you are, incidentally, designed to want. So, for those of you who seem to be forever fighting the 'sweet tooth' maybe there's peace of mind knowing that you are biologically designed to recognize and search out foods that are dense with the flavor of sweet. It is not only a delight to your taste buds when you find it but also activates one of the more prominent taste centers in your brain. Enjoying sweet is hardwired and babies the world over smile when they taste it.

That doesn't, however, mean you are biologically designed to eat dessert first, rather, more pragmatically, it seems that in nature, sweet density dictates energy density. This may not mean much in today's world but in the days of foraging, hunting and gathering, energy dense foods were highly desirable because it meant exactly that; more energy to do what needed to be done in the day. Also, sweeter foods in nature were, and still are, typically lower in toxins so innately recognized as safer to consume.

You will hopefully be delighted to know that it is not only possible to satisfy your sweet cravings without consuming processed sugars, but also highly desirable. Refining your palate to appreciate the subtle nuances of sweetness in a wide variety of foods will not only enhance your enjoyment but also help our waistline.

Do some investigating and see if you can find the sweet note in foods you wouldn't suspect.

DAY 2 – SALT

It appears that salt became part of the human dining experience anywhere from 5-10,000 years ago. Initially, it may have been introduced as a preservative for foods and then later as an additive to enhance flavors.

The salt molecule can enhance other flavors, which is why it, and synthetic derivatives, are so widely used in the food industry. It's a cheap and easy way to optimize flavor.

Besides being a welcome addition to food, sodium is also part of our intricate electrolyte balance. Too much sodium is a problem and so is as too little.

Sea Salt is obtained through evaporating seawater; it is typically unprocessed and contains other nutrients like potassium, magnesium, and calcium. Many chefs and foodies prefer sea salt because it delivers superior flavor. Table salt is obtained through mining and is then processed to become the appropriately textured product you find on store shelves. This process often strips away any naturally occurring minerals and typically, additives are mixed back in. Whichever salt you choose to use keep in mind that usually, a little bit of salt goes a long way.

DAY 3 – CLOVE

Cloves are powerhouse medicinal and culinary spice. They are in the evergreen family and are actually the dried flower bud of a particular type of evergreen tree. A little bit of clove goes a long way but that little bit can do amazing things. Not only do they spice up your diet and enhance your palate with their culinary versatility, they do it with the smallest effort. Just a couple of cloves, or a slight dusting of them when ground, can add to the complexity of any dish, sweet or savory.

Medicinally, cloves are amazing. Eugenol is the compound that makes them so beneficial. Research has found they help in fighting the bacteria that contribute to ulcers, bladder infections, food poisoning, colds and flu. Cloves help stimulate digestion and circulation and believe it or not, cloves are even better than citronella at shooing away pesky mosquitos.

Lastly, cloves are best known for their anesthetic quality and as a remedy for mouth pain and toothache; managing pain, infection, inflammation, and freshening your breath all in one fell swoop. Bring on the cloves.

DAY 4 - MOUTHFEEL

You might be wondering what the word mouthfeel has to do with taste and flavor. Well, without mouthfeel, food would be infinitely less delicious. Mouthfeel involves things like temperature, texture, and viscosity and it is what makes food "palatable".

Creamy, crunchy, hot, cold, even spicy, they're all aspects of mouthfeel and each supplies its own message to your body and brain about what you are eating and whether or not you want more. Sadly, mouthfeel is often ignored in the world of food and health, however, it plays a critical role in helping you decide what you will reach for when you need a bit of something to nosh on. This is especially true if you are eating for reasons other than hunger. Mouthfeel is directly related to nervous system communication. Crunchy food can help relieve stress, warm and creamy foods can soothe and calm, spicy foods can energize and even cool you in hot weather.

Interestingly, research suggests that people who suffered from chronic inner ear infections as children, may suffer nerve damage that impairs their ability to taste as acutely as their counterparts. As a result, they rely more heavily than they realize on mouthfeel for their food choices. This potentially steers them towards foods with higher fat and sweet content because those two choices generate an unmistakable sensory experience and are more easily recognized as good.

I can say that I am a person easily impacted by the temperature and texture of food, in fact, those are typically the first things I notice and rely on as I eat. It's also one reason I don't necessarily like to combine foods. Guess what? I had many of those pesky little ear infections as a kid. So maybe there's something to this research thing??? You can do your own research and see how mouthfeel impacts your food choices.

DAY 5 – MAILLARD REACTION

"Eating is a necessity, but cooking is an art..."

Take a moment and think about the last time you smelled fresh baked bread. (pause) What was your response? Was it something like an uncontrollable "mmmmmm"? You can thank your brain and our biological affinity for cooked food. The Maillard Reaction is a series of chemical responses that result in the delicious flavor we get when we brown something.

It is the fundamental attraction to cooking. Amino acids and sugars change their molecular structure when heat is added and create a synergistic effect that is also quite often umami in nature, making a delicious flavor that we crave. Research suggests that not only humans but also many other mammals prefer foods that have been cooked.

The Maillard Reaction first stimulates the olfactory centers which then begins to create a desirable feedback loop throughout the rest of the brain and body. Anyone who has ever smelled something being sautéed, whether it be meat or vegetable, can attest to the stimulating effect of the aroma as the perfect chemical reaction begins to occur. Some scientists suggest humankind began to depend on the Maillard reaction from a self-preservation standpoint. It may have been a way to tell if food was safely cooked.

The Maillard Reaction not only occurs in sautéing but also baking and it accounts for the salivation that so many of us experience when we smell fresh baked bread or cakes. You can also find it in roasted vegetables and browned toast.

Here's a little tidbit to note for future reference: if you find yourself craving something cooked, it could also mean that your body needs fat and you could try roasted peanut or almond butter to satisfy your fix.

The Maillard Reaction goes hand in hand with umami, stimulating brain chemistry to a healthier balance. Just be sure that you don't overcook and burn your foods because then you've gone from delicious and healthy to potentially carcinogenic.

DAY 6 – TERROIR

Do not be fooled when someone tells you that flavor is flavor is flavor and all similar foods taste the same. This couldn't be further from the truth! Sure, an apple is going to have many similarities to all the other apples; that's what makes them apples. However, once you start narrowing down actual flavor characteristics and "notes", believe me, a Fuji apple from New Zealand tastes very different from a Fuji apple grown in Washington state.

The difference comes from a little thing called Terroir (pronounced tear waaahr). Sounds snobby, I know. Typically, people are first introduced to concepts of 'terroir' when they enter the world of wine tasting. Educated tasters can identify regions and vineyards from wines just by the telling aspects of 'terroir' hidden in the end result.

As a testimonial to the fact that terroir is not only relevant to the wine world, I was first introduced to the concept not through a winemaker but by a local butcher, who explained it to me in terms of meat flavor, when I lived in Alameda, CA. He was committed to sustainability, local sourcing, and educating the public so he would hold monthly tastings where he invited people to learn about things like the difference between grass fed, prairie raised, corn fed, etc, etc... It was completely fascinating to try and identify the subtle variations in flavor imparted by the difference in the rock, soil, and grasses from pasture to pasture. Makes sense really if you think about it. (pun intended)

I moved on to discover terroir differences in other foods, all completely fascinating. Chocolate, coffee, fruits (hence the difference between a NZ Fuji and a WA Fuji), vegetables, you name it and ultimately on to wine. I am so in love with the idea and concept of terroir that I have visions of one day forming a geek tasting club where all we do is spend time identifying terroir in the foods we share.

So, what exactly is terroir? Originally, it was a wine term to denote the influences found in regions or micro-regions where particular wines are grown. The term has since been expanded upon and now is used to describe the territory or environment in which a food is raised or grown. The influences of the soil, the weather patterns, the cultivation patterns; they all impact terroir.

This explains why the flavor of wine changes from harvest to harvest. There will be some basic notes that are the same because of things like mineral content in the soil, basic geographical influence, and cultivation processes; however, weather patterns and influences of surrounding flora and fauna can change a taste from one year to the next.

Terroir is also entering the conversation in the world of functional medicine. Savvy and progressive researchers, doctors and scientists are starting to recognize the value of terroir to your own internal terroir, called the "microbiome". Consuming foods from good, healthy soil not only increases the nutrient content but also, through micro-particles that remain on the food, increases the healthy bacteria in your gut. There is some pretty major research going on right now investigating the potential for increasing immune function, improving mood, and decreasing inflammation just through interacting with the terroir from a healthy landscape.

Reviving the landscape and supporting the healthy bacterial growth could make all the difference to not only the flavors in our food but the health and wellbeing of our bodies, minds, and spirits.

DAY 7 - BITTER

The taste of too much bitter evokes an almost universal facial expression. In the same way that sweet is biologically important and influential, bitter interacts with the brain and body in a pretty major way. Some people never grow to like bitter and some people grow to crave it. Interestingly, the love or hate of bitter doesn't seem to depend on how sensitive of a taster you are. One might assume that someone with super-tasting capabilities might really avoid those bitter flavors in their foods but this isn't always the case. For some, bitter is quite an alluring taste even with the funny face. So, what is it about bitter?

Well, bitter, like sweet, stimulates a cascade of responses all throughout the body. It has been asserted that we developed the capability to taste bitter elements of food to warn us away from potentially poisonous or toxic foods. New research suggests this isn't really the case. In truth, bitter taste receptors are located all throughout the human body, not just in the mouth. That's right, you have "taste buds" everywhere. In fact, believe it or not, the presence of bitter taste receptors in human reproductive organs could have quite a bit to do with fertility. Crazy, huh??? This makes bitter, in my opinion, one of the more interesting taste sensations.

It also seems that bitter is necessary for our overall health and wellness. Many of the foods with bitter components are active cleansers and detoxifiers, not to mention great digestives. Consuming a small amount of bitters in your daily diet can also help reduce acid reflux, heal intestinal lining, and decrease overall systemic inflammation.

So where can you get some of these good bitter flavors to add to your diet? Well, you can buy ready-made bitter formulas, like digestives' or you can try things like arugula (rocket), dandelion, chicory, kale, and bonus...coffee and chocolate. (that's dark chocolate or cacao and coffee low in acidity).

Note: people often confuse bitter and sour. If you want to know how to tell the difference try dipping a piece of lemon in salt. You will be left with the flavor of sour and no bitter.

DAY 8 – VANILLA (RECIPE)

Real Vanilla is anything but plain. Vanilla comes from the seedpod of an Orchid. It is sweet and slightly spicy depending on where it is grown and it often has a back flavor that is smoky or woody.

Real vanilla is more expensive and difficult to extract. Much of what is on the shelves today is Vanillin, a synthetic version produced from the waste material in paper milling. Vanillin's main constituents come from some of the precursor ingredients to petrochemicals. I prefer to use genuine vanilla.

You can make your own vanilla extract quite easily, you just have to wait the 6-8 weeks it takes to soak and voila!... vanilla. Vanilla is a flavor that gives the illusion of sweet, so you can add to drinks or foods to provide sweet to the palate without actually adding sugar. Here are two easy recipes for your own extract:

> VANILLA EXTRACT:
> Take 7-8 seedpods, cut them open lengthwise to reveal their seeds. You can cut them in half lengthwise as well. Place them in a bottle, or cut them in half and place them in a jar, cover with alcohol (Bourbon, Brandy or Vodka) or if you want an alcohol free version you can cover them with food grade glycerin. Make sure they are fully covered with liquid. Tighten down the lid and put them somewhere out of the sun, make sure to shake them up every few days. In about 8 weeks you will have delicious vanilla extract.

DAY 9 – UMAMI

Umami is a complex combination of stimuli that results in a very distinct, yet challenging to identify, flavor. Umami is sometimes referred to as savory, which could be true, since typically savory means anything that isn't sweet, but not everything that is savory is umami. Ultimately, umami is its own distinct thing.

So, what is it that makes umami, well, umami? It is actually an experience that happens when glutamate, disodium inosinate, and disodium guanylate tickle your neurons and create an "I like that" response. Sounds pretty scary though, right? Disosodium anything doesn't really sound like food and flavor. Believe it or not, those chemical compounds occur naturally in certain foods and combinations of foods. For example, parmesan cheese, ripened tomatoes, mushrooms, and cooked meat all contain that chemical combination that makes your brain say "Yum".

Umami is not a new flavor although it may have a relatively new name. Prior to being umami it was just sort of unidentified. Umami is a really important part of your diet and palate. The complexity of umami contributes to stimulating the chemistry of salivation, digestion and satiation. When you are slowing down and really savoring your food, umami can help signal the "that's enough" bell.

Studies show that when people are unable to detect umami in their foods, it can contribute to appetite loss and even the inability to assimilate nutrients. Research suggests that one reason humans love Umami so much is that we are exposed to it as our first meal. Human breast milk has a high amount of glutamate in it, significantly higher than any other kind of milk. Not only our palate but our neural networking is shaped by the consumption of... wait for it... U mommy's milk.

So, if glutamate (in other words, MSG) is a naturally occurring substance that we love, why all the bad press about it? Synthetic glutamate and glutamate in ultra high doses, may enhance the flavor of your food but they also work as excitotoxins. Basically, excitotoxins stir your brain chemistry and keep you reaching for more even after you are full. Not to mention a plethora of other inflammatory ailments that contribute to chronic disease. Getting your umami fix from natural sources is always the best bet. Pass the cheese, please.

DAY 10 – SOUR

Have you ever tasted something or even smelled something so sour that it caused an immediate rush of saliva and an involuntary tightening of your jaw? That's because the taste receptors that recognize sour are intricately tied to the largest of the cranial nerves in your head and face, known as the trigeminal nerve. Taste sour and you can count on some involuntary facial contractions that can even influence your eyes!

The sensation of sour is created by the acidic quality found in particular foods. In a way, it's more of a sensation than an actual flavor, which is true of other sensations of taste. Sometimes people confuse sour and bitter but they are not the same and impact the taste receptors and our body differently. Sour is acid oriented in foods that contain acids like sauerkraut, yogurt, lemons and pickles; whereas bitter flavors come from amino acids and peptides. Sours, just like bitters, are a healthy addition to your diet.

DAY 11 – CUMIN

Cumin is one of my all-time favorite spices. Smelling the earthy, pungent scent as it begins to heat induces instant salivation and anticipation of deliciousness. Cumin is found in curries and chili flavored foods. (not to be confused with the chili/capsicum). It is one of the most popular spices in Mexican cuisine.

Cumin smells spicy as it cooks and often people assume it is going to be hot like a chili, but there is no heat in the lovely little cumin seed. The health properties of Cumin can be attributed to the compound cumin aldehyde as well as other antioxidants. It is great for digestion. It's packed with iron. It even enhances immune function. Research also suggests that Cumin may be beneficial for preventing things like diabetes, osteoporosis, tuberculosis, cancer, and even helping in the treatment of epilepsy. I use Cumin in many of my foods, from scrambled eggs to soups and stews, even in tea.

Note: Cumin should not be confused with Black Cumin Seeds or Curcumin; they are not the same, not even close.

DAY 12 – ONION

The onion is a bulb. It has a pungent flavor that is sharp when fresh and uncooked and mellows almost to sweet depending on cooking style and type of onion. It is the amino acid sulfoxides that makes your eyes water when you cut an onion.

Onions can enhance the flavor of a dish, either towards savory or even sweet, without adding salt or sugar. The result you get will depend on how the onion is prepared and the type of onion.

I have not always been a fan of onions but now I must say I enjoy them immensely in a wide variety of dishes. There are even some onions that I enjoy raw. There are many varieties of onions, my two favorites being shallots and chives. Onions also contain delicious little health boosting properties like quercetin and other flavonoids and polyphenols making them a nice addition to your diet.

DAY 13 – PUNGENT

Pungent isn't necessarily a taste in the way that sweet and salt are, in fact, I would say pungent is more of a mouthfeel and linked to a quality of food. Foods that are pungent are often spicy or have the quality of opening up the senses.

Chilies are pungent. Ginger, black pepper, and horseradish are also examples of pungent foods. Pungent foods quite often work on a different neural pathway through the palate. Pungent foods can also stimulate the release of endorphins, which could be why some people love to torture their taste buds with hot and spicy foods. Wasabi, which is a type of radish, is a great example of eating hot food and then getting the follow-up endorphin rush.

As a side note; true wasabi is becoming quite rare and most of what you get next to your sushi is a different class of horseradish and some green food coloring. Still the impact can be quite stimulating if you're up for experiencing a wasabi bomb.

In many cultures, pungent foods are an important aspect of a healthy diet. For example, in the ancient system of Indian medicine called Ayurveda, pungent is one of the six flavors needed to maintain balance and wellbeing. Pungent foods stimulate digestion, as well as encourage detoxification and metabolic function. This can, in turn, also enhance immune function. Pungent foods are often antiviral and antibacterial. So how do you get pungent foods in your diet? Include things like ginger, black pepper, garlic, radishes. chilies, and onion.

DAY 14 – THE IMPORTANCE OF FLAVOR

When you learn to be curious about flavor, you in turn, invite curiosity towards life. When you learn to savor a morsel, you learn also to savor a moment. Life is not always sweet, it can't be. It would be as out of balance as eating a diet of nothing but sugar every day. Sometimes life has bitter moments and sour moments and savory moments. It has ever-changing textures and temperatures. We need these things, even when they are uncomfortable, to live a balanced life.

Today's flavor isn't a flavor, rather it is about the importance and symbolism of flavor and taste. I work with taste and flavor and food and mood, not just because I love good food, but also because I realize when we are able to include a variety of flavors in our diet we not only enhance our health but we are also able to navigate life with much more resilience.

Several years ago, when I first started studying the intersection of eating disorders and trauma, I came across a study that fascinated me. Women who were suffering severe symptoms of post-traumatic stress disorder from sexual trauma, so severe that they were inpatients in a mental health facility, were invited to participate in an eight week cooking program. Each day they learned about, and had experiences with, taste, flavor, smell, palate. They learned how to combine flavors and tastes, and identify texture and mouthfeel. As they grew curious in the kitchen and opened their sensory repertoire, the symptoms of PTSD decreased substantially.

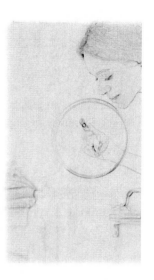

There was an absolute correlation between their willingness to be curious and experience new sensory information and stimulation and its direct influence on the balance and resilience of their nervous system and brain chemistry. Fascinating! And so began my mission of finding ways to help people increase their palate as a way of healing their bodies, minds, and spirits.

DAY 15 - RETRONASAL

Nope, it doesn't mean your nose is old school. Retronasal is one of the ways we can taste the various 'notes' in the food we eat. Generally speaking, retronasal olfaction is activated when we eat food. While we chew, the chemical compounds that are being heated and mashed up begin to waft through our mouth cavity and up into our nasal passages. It's like smelling, only backwards since the 'smell' originates in your mouth. This is also why some foods just don't taste right when you plug your nose or have a cold. If you want to try to isolate this retronasal effect the next time you taste something you can do it by following these simple steps:

Inhale as you take a bite or drink of something (make sure that it's an easy natural inhale and you aren't eating something with powdered sugar on it! (For example, this is NOT an experiment to perform while enjoying beignets in the French Quarter)
Roll it around on your tongue to make sure it is warming up and the volatile compounds are being released.

Swallow and exhale. What do you taste?

If you're really a taste geek you can make this into a game with your fellow geeky friends by naming as many immediate flavor thoughts that come to your mind without censoring them. Another bonus of investigating your retronasal experience? You have to slow down and actually savor your food. Happy tasting!

DAY 16 – THYME

Contrary to popular belief you can indeed have too much thyme on your hands...but only as a flavoring. Thyme is an herb. It's in the evergreen family and it is both culinary and medicinal. I have just plucked a small leaf of thyme to chew on as I write so it can inspire me. I find thyme to be crisp, savory, and slightly pungent. I like it as far as culinary herbs go and often add it to eggs, soups, and stews.

For me, a little bit goes a long way as it can end up having a very earthy flavor that can overpower the meal.

Medicinally, thyme is one of the most studied herbs. It's main property, Thymol, is an amazing anti-microbial and can be used in a variety of ways to get rid of germs and increase immune function. It is most notable in recent history for its benefit as a mouthwash (Listerine has it) and as a topical antibiotic. Try adding a little thyme to your day, just a nibble and see what you think.

DAY 17 – ASTRINGENT

Have you ever eaten something and had the sensation of it drying out your mouth or decreasing your saliva? That's the quality of astringent. Astringent is more of a mouthfeel than a flavor. When a food is astringent it causes contraction of the tissue in your mouth.

Tannins are astringent. It took me a while to learn that it was a feel and not necessarily a taste I was looking for it when trying to decipher the tannin content in a wine. It's the tannins that make a wine feel dry to your palate. Swiss Chard, spinach, and persimmons are some foods that come to mind that can have a strong astringent quality.
You can feel them in your mouth and on your teeth. Some people describe it as a chalky feeling but what it's really doing is absorbing liquid and tightening the tissue.

Tannins are in tea, coffee, and most berries as well. In Ayurveda foods with an astringent quality are important for balance and cooling. These foods also help purify the blood and give the liver a boost.

DAY 18 – CAPSICUM (CHILI PEPPER)

Today's flavor comes straight from the breakfast table at the Cedarbrook Lodge in Seattle, WA. A nice, tiny, personal bottle of Tobasco Sauce, I'm sprinkling on my morning eggs. The heat from Tobasco Sauce comes from the chili pepper and vinegar combination.

Capsicum is in the nightshade family but has plenty of health benefits. As a compound, and in moderation, it aids in digestion, boosts immune function and increases circulation. It's also great as a topical treatment for pain and arthritic conditions. I put a sprinkle of cayenne in my morning dose of warm lemon water and honey. It's a great way to wake up and start the day in the winter months.

DAY 19 – BLUEBERRY

Another morning at Cedarbrook Lodge. I walked into the dining hall and my senses were immediately tantalized by the smell of fresh baked blueberry cake. So, today's flavor is all about the lovely blueberry even though they are out of season. Blueberries are high in awesome phytonutrients that have antioxidant and anti-inflammatory qualities. Polyphenols, quercetin and resveratrol all fall into this category.

Blueberries have an astringent quality to them so they can have a particular mouthfeel, especially when they are newly ripening. Blueberries have a beneficial impact on your whole body and research demonstrates that eating a cup of them a day can increase cardiovascular, cognitive, and endocrine health.

Unfortunate Blueberry fact: Most of the time when you are eating a conventional food with blueberries in it, they aren't really blueberries. Instead they are bits of sugar with blueberry flavoring. Note to self: if you're going to add blueberries to your diet, make them fresh and, optimally, seasonal, sustainable or organic. I've inspected the blueberry cake here and it does indeed sport real blueberries but I'm going to opt for the local, sustainably raised eggs for my breakfast and I'll just enjoy the luxurious smell of "home-baked" goodness.

DAY 20 – MUSTARD SEEDS (RECIPE)

Today's flavor comes direct from Penzey's Spice Shop on the way to Pike Place Market in Seattle, Washington. Spice heaven!! Mustard seeds are another pungent addition to palate-pleasing meals. Like many of the culinary herbs and spices, it also has medicinal qualities. Research has demonstrated the mustard seed has a beneficial impact on the gastrointestinal tract and colon.

The glucosinolatic compounds inhibit the growth and spread of cancer cells. Mustard seeds also have anti-inflammatory properties and a digestive. Mustard seed oil can be used as massage oil to relieve pain in muscles and joints.

Here's a fun recipe for making pickled mustard seeds which can be an amazing condiment to make simple meals spark.

PICKLED MUSTARD SEEDS:
¾ cup whole yellow or brown mustard seeds
1 cup white vinegar
⅓ cup sugar
½ teaspoon salt
a pinch of red pepper flakes (optional)
Place mustard seeds in a small heatproof bowl or jar, like a pint mason jar and set aside. In a small saucepan, combine vinegar, sugar, chilies or pepper flakes and salt. Place over medium heat and bring to a boil.

Pour the hot liquid over the mustard seeds. Stir and set aside at room temperature for 4 hours. You will have about 1 cup. Transfer to a covered container. Store and refrigerate.... use a spoonful when you want to jazz up your plate.

DAY 21 – STAR ANISE

Inhaling the heady scent of star anise, I am reminded of earth, soil, and sunshine...oh and also Ouzo! Star Anise is the fruit and flower of a small evergreen shrub. From a culinary perspective, it can be found as a predominant spice in many Asian foods.

Often the whole star is used as an infusion, much like the bay leaf, and removed upon serving. Star Anise tastes like licorice and is similar to anise and fennel. It is indeed one way to add licorice flavoring to strong, alcoholic drinks such as Ouzo and Absinthe.

From a medicinal perspective, Star Anise has many lovely qualities. It is antifungal, antimicrobial, and antiviral. There has been quite a bit of research suggesting that Star Anise is effective in fighting candida albicans. It also has great antioxidant properties. Word of warning, if you are going to use Star Anise you absolutely want to make sure it is the Chinese variety, known as Illicum Verum, and not the Japanese variety, Illicum Anisatum, which is toxic and can cause some pretty significant reactions.

DAY 22 – ROSEMARY

"Parsley, Sage, ROSEMARY and Thyme...La, la, la..."

Rosemary is another evergreen herb, which also happens to be a member of the mint family. Rosemary means "Dew of the Sea"... I love that. In the culinary world rosemary contains a volatile oil that can add a kind of lightness or openness to dishes. Definitely, it has the potential to overpower if too much is used.

In the medicinal or health world rosemary is a fantastic addition to your botanical pharmacy. It has antioxidant and anti-inflammatory qualities. It is great for circulation and skincare. It is antiviral, antifungal, antimicrobial. It is also great for digestion and immune function. Research suggests that rosemary increases brain health and is effective in fighting free radicals that contribute to disease.

Rosemary is refreshing and lifts spirits, so very useful in mood disorders like depression. Keep some rosemary handy if you are preparing for an exam...sniffing rosemary increases memory.

DAY 23 – TARRAGON

Tarragon is a great herb that is, I believe, easily forgotten or overlooked in most kitchens in America. It is one of my favorite herbs. I love its subtle licorice flavor and the grass-like texture. Another fun factoid, the name Tarragon is derived from the Latin Dracunculus, which means "Little Dragon" ... I bet that's why I love it.

Medicinally, Tarragon has some similar properties to Anise, but loses them once it is dried. So, the best use of tarragon for medicinal properties is fresh or in vinegars or teas. Tarragon is also part of the wormwood family. Some of its great qualities include the fact it is high in antioxidants, it stimulates digestion and it protects against heart conditions. Recent studies also suggest that Tarragon can be helpful in lowering blood sugar. One of my favorite ways to have Tarragon is just to chop up some fresh leaves over my eggs in the morning. It's delicious....

DAY 24 – CORIANDER

If any of you have seen the movie , 100 Foot Journey, you may remember that one of the secret ingredients in the famed omelet that won Madam Mallory's heart was coriander. She gasps as she savors the first bite, exclaiming at the mastery of creating something so piquant, savory, yet fresh and light.

The fresh and light note definitely comes from the coriander. Coriander has a very interesting flavor, it is earthy yet citrusy all at the same time. It seems that coriander is one of the worlds' oldest flavorings with traces of coriander seed found in spice containers from around 7,000 BCE.

From a culinary perspective coriander has a great synergistic impact, influencing the other herbs and spices in a dish without overpowering. In fact, if you've been too heavy handed with another spice you can add more coriander and it will balance things out.

From a medicinal perspective, coriander is on the A-List. Research demonstrates that it helps with digestive issues, blood sugar issues, and cholesterol issues. It is anti-inflammatory and also helps with skin conditions like psoriasis and eczema.
I have a digestive tea that I make and sip when I've overeaten or just feel out of sorts. It consists of coriander, fennel, cumin, and ginger. If I want to give the illusion of sweetened tea, I just add cinnamon. Give it a try...

DAY 25 – FENNEL

Fennel is another amazing herb and food. The seeds, stalk and bulb are all edible and quite delicious in various aspects of a meal. Fennel has a light licorice flavor and is delicious both raw and cooked. The seeds are great for digestion and can be munched on after a meal to help smooth digestion. They are also great in tea.

I love to eat the bulb and stalks as a snack or as a great addition to a meal. My current absolute favorite use of fennel bulb: Fennel au gratin! It is definitely an amplified yum factor dish. If you're up for some food traveling, a trip to Nathan Outlaw's Fish Kitchen in Port Isaac, Cornwall is a definite must for amazing fennel au gratin. Or you can just experiment in your own kitchen until you find your own baked, cheesy perfection.

Medicinally, fennel is awesome. The seeds are great for relieving cramps and menstrual pain and actually outperformed the use of Non Steroidal Anti-Inflammatory Drugs in studies for PMS. It's also awesome for IBS and Crohn's disease and so many other inflammatory conditions and ailments. The bulb and stalks are full of phytonutrients and antioxidants. It's rich in potassium, folate, and fiber. It's a great addition to your diet if you struggle with things like anemia and decreased immune function.

DAY 26 – CARDAMOM (RECIPE)

Whenever I'm feeling a little out of sorts, I take a green cardamom pod and smash it between my fingers, letting the scent wash over me. Not only does it remind me of holidays and all things magical, it opens my senses with its slightly menthol back note and calms my mind. It also makes me hungry for rice pudding...

True Cardamom is called the Queen of Spices and has been around for centuries upon centuries. When put in food or drink that is shared with guests, Cardamom is a symbol of generosity and hospitality. I believe the aroma alone helps the heart open and creates a spirit of generosity and care. A small amount goes a long way and it can be used in savory and sweet dishes to add an interesting depth to the dish.

From a medicinal perspective, Cardamom is awesome. In fact, it is so awesome that in the 1970's there was a research institute based solely on investigating its medicinal properties. That institute has expanded since then and these days focuses on many herbs and spices.

Cardamom itself is amazing for calming the gut and stimulating balanced digestion. It does this by stimulating the parasympathetic nervous system. Remember the Parasympathetic is the 'rest and digest' side of your nervous system function.

Cardamom is also beneficial in the treatment of ulcers and colon and bowel issues. It's effective in the treatment of asthma and helps clear up sinus problems and infections. Cineole, which is one of the active chemical compounds in cardamom, is great in the treatment of hypertension and other cardiac issues. Just make sure if you are attempting to use Cardamom to help with your health that you are using true green Cardamom, the Queen of Spices.

If you're into making your own teas and coffees at home here is a really lovely ROSE AND CARDAMOM LATTE recipe:

> 1 c. milk (goat, cow, or nut)
> 2-3 shots of espresso
> 3 tsp. rose water
> 1/8 tsp ground cardamom

Put the cardamom and rose water in the milk as you warm and foam it. Once it is warm pour it in the bottom of your mug, then add the espresso. Top it off with the last of the foam from your steamed milk. If you don't have a milk steamer you can heat it slowly on the stovetop and use a small whisk to create foam and help the protein molecules expand. Divine!!

DAY 27 – SAGE

"The desire of sage is to render man immortal"

Salvia Officinalis – Salvia comes from the latin "to heal" so no surprise the first recorded use of sage is as a medicinal intervention. Apparently, it wasn't used as a culinary herb until around the 16th century. Sage has a long list of potentials as help for healing and wellbeing. Research demonstrates it is good for calming the mind and boosting cognitive function. Studies also show it helps prevent age related memory loss. Sipping on sage tea can help soothe a sore throat. Rubbing a decoction of sage tea on skin can help sooth skin conditions.

White sage also has spiritual properties and is used in several traditions, including First Nations, to clear the energy of a people or of spaces. Bruising fresh sage between your fingers and inhaling can boost mood and calm the mind. It's aromatic and has an astringent quality. I love cooking with sage, keeping in mind that a little bit goes a long way. It is mostly suited to savory dishes but I must admit I recently had the singular pleasure of tasting some sage and nutmeg shortbread cookies that were off the chain delicious.

DAY 28 – ROSE (RECIPE)

The rain is falling gently here in the desert, with it comes delicious smells

of a rain swept landscape. It seems to me that this morning calls for a delicate fragrance and flavor. As I was mulling over which flavor/taste to share with you today I reached into my cupboard for the ingredients to make a cup of rose petal and raspberry leaf tea.

Opening the jar of rose petals, the fragrance expands into the room, mingling with the fresh earthy smell of the rain. Perfection. Subtle and sublime. So, today's taste is the Rose Petal also called the "Gift of the Angels".

From a culinary perspective rose has long been a subtle addition to a variety of gastronomic creations found throughout the Mediterranean and Middle Eastern cultures. It can bring an interesting earthy note to both savory and sweet dishes.

Medicinally, Rose petals and hips are useful for a variety of reasons. It is antimicrobial, antiviral, antiseptic, anti-depressant, antibacterial, really the list goes on and on. It is the astringent quality of Rose that makes it useful in skin conditions, digestive issues, and circulation and cleansing.

Nutritionally, it has many nutrients that are beneficial to the body, Vitamin C, B, E, and K, not to mention the bioflavonoids and antioxidants that help keep your body balanced. Rose also has aphrodisiac qualities due to its influence on hormone balance and can be useful to stimulate libido. Research also suggests that inhaling the scent of rose influences the central nervous system and boosts mood, focus, and self-confidence.

Here's a delicious recipe for ROSE AND TOMATO HARISSA.
It takes a little time to make but once you have a jar you can keep it in your fridge for about a month and add it to different things

　　5 or 6 ripe tomatoes, halved
　　1 c fresh red chilies diced
　　4 cloves garlic, unpeeled
　　olive oil (to cook)
　　dash sea salt
　　freshly ground black pepper

2 tsp cumin seeds
1 tsp coriander seeds
1 tsp smoked paprika
1 handful rose petals, washed
3 TBS rose water
2TBS caster sugar
1 splash red wine vinegar
1 TBS extra virgin olive oil

Although you could chop all of this by hand, it will take you a while, so I suggest using a food processor. However, if you are doing it by hand you might want to wear some rubber gloves to protect you from the chilies as their juices might irritate your skin.

Preheat your oven to 150°C/300°F. Toss the tomatoes, chilies, and garlic in the olive oil and spread on a large roasting tray. Make sure the tomatoes are turned cut side up. Season with salt and pepper. Place in the oven and roast for about 1 hour, shaking and rotating the tray occasionally.

Remove the tray and allow everything to cool. Once cool enough to handle you can peel and deseed the chilies. You may want to wear gloves. Peel the garlic cloves and place in the food processor with the chilies. Pulse until roughly chopped, then add the cumin, coriander and paprika, season well with salt and pepper and pulse again.

Next, add the tomatoes, rose petals, rose water and sugar, and pulse until you get a chunky paste, with lovely flecks of tomato and rose petals.

Transfer the paste to a bowl and stir in a splash of red wine vinegar and the extra virgin olive oil. You should have a beautiful, deep, reddish paste. Have a taste - you want a good balance between the heat of the chilies, the smoky paprika, the sharpness of the vinegar and the fragrant rose petals. Season again and add another splash of vinegar, if needed. Once you're happy with the taste, spoon into a sterilized jar and keep in the fridge for up to a month.

DAY 29 – BAY LEAF

Bay leaf is in the eucalyptus family, which is why it has that menthol smell before it is cooked. Cracking a dried leaf of bay and inhaling the volatile oils, clears the head and boosts your mood. But what does it really do for food? How does it taste? Well, before cooking it and even shortly into cooking it tastes like it smells, kind of menthol-like and a little bit sparkly. However, if you allow it to continue cooking and mellow the volatile oils, it can give your food a subtle complexity that delights the palate. Bay leaves should always be removed before consuming whatever it is they were added to, whether that is soup, stew or even tea. One bay leaf goes a long way, so unless you are making a meal to feed a large family more than one is rarely necessary.

From a medicinal perspective, the Bay leaf is truly amazing. Research suggests that the mighty bay leaf is a powerful antioxidant; equal to the qualities found in green tea. Studies show that it has the potential to improve insulin sensitivity making it valuable in the management of insulin resistant syndromes and type 2 diabetes. Bay leaf also has anti-inflammatory properties and is useful in pain management and other inflammation based ailments. It is antibacterial, antimicrobial, and antifungal. No wonder the bay leaf has been used for centuries as a symbol of vitality and courage.

DAY 30 – SAFFRON

Saffron has been described as slightly sweet, earthy and pungent. Too much can become coarse and bitter. I think Saffron is a really lovely spice. In fact, it's one of my favorite scents and flavors. It is subtle yet powerful. Saffron comes from the inside of a Crocus flower. It takes roughly 75,000 threads to produce one pound of saffron so you can see why it can be expensive and precious.

To me, the scent of saffron is warming and heart opening. It has a complex volatile oil signature giving it a variety of possibilities for flavor; ranging from sweet and grassy to bitter. Just a pinch of saffron goes a long way. To get the best out of saffron you must take your time and encourage the flavor. You can try slightly roasting it first in the oven or soak it in warm liquid for 15-20 minutes before adding the resulting liquor to whatever you are cooking.

Saffron also has some pretty great health properties including; improving mood and combatting depression as well as balancing hormones for women. I wear an attar (perfume paste) of saffron for mental clarity and heart opening when I'm feeling out of sorts. It always works beautifully to inspire a sense of calm and a nice deep, grounding inhalation.

DAY 31 – COFFEE

Ah, coffee... I was a latecomer to the world of coffee but have learned to appreciate its virtues quite thoroughly. Coffee is considered a bitter on the taste spectrum. Although, in its green stage is relatively devoid of aroma or even real flavor.

It is the roasting that allows the oils within the coffee bean to be released and enhanced. The lighter the roast the more you can taste the actual bean and the terroir of the bean. The darker the roast, the more the flavor of the roasting itself begins to influence and you have darker more complex flavors, called 'notes'. Coffee often gets a bad rap because of the caffeine but it also has its benefits, especially in the green and light roast stages.

As a bitter, in moderation, it can be good for digestion. It also contains antioxidants and polyphenols that can help decrease the potential of ailments like heart disease and type 2 diabetes. As is true for many foods, there is ample research for and against the consumption of coffee. I think as you learn to listen to your own body you can decide what works best for you

CHAPTER 2- FEBRUARY

DAY 32 – GINGER

Slicing into a root of fresh ginger is sensory delight. The sound of crisp and juicy combines with the pleasantly sharp and revitalizing scent followed by the slightest hint of earthiness. Ginger to me tastes both sharp and sweet. It is spicy and pungent. The genus name for the type of ginger we most often consume is Zingiber Oficinale. I think the zing in Zingiber is very appropriate. Ginger is a zingy spice and one of the most abundant spices that I use all throughout the year.

From a culinary perspective ginger is super versatile demonstrated by its ability to be an amazing addition to a cookie, cake, bread or stir fry. While I love ginger in all its culinary guises, it is really its medicinal value that makes it tops in my kitchen pharmacy.

Medicinally, ginger is amazing. It's antimicrobial, antibacterial, a stimulant, diaphoretic, expectorant, analgesic, anti-inflammatory and oh so much more. What does that really mean for you? There is actual a pretty substantial amount of research on the properties of ginger for a variety of uses. It is effective in decreasing nausea, stimulating digestion, and quelling stomachaches and heartburn. It is also effective for increasing immune function; hence the cold busting properties. Studies show it can help decrease the symptoms of asthma and lower cholesterol.

Current research shows that the chemical properties in ginger are effective cancer fighting agents. They down regulate the body's ability to metastasize cancer cells and then effectively kills them off. Ginger also combats e.coli and parasites can help ward off food poisoning and other food related issues.

How to use ginger? You can cook with it, or make it into a tea or take it as a medicinal paste. I tend to have a pot of ginger on the stove all throughout the winter season, replenishing it as I use it. When I'm having stomach issues, I take about a half-teaspoon of ground ginger and mix it with some honey until it is a little ball and have that with a nice cup of tea or warm water.

DAY 33 – LEMON

When life gives you lemons, make lemonade; although, truthfully, I prefer lemon pie.

Lemons are refreshing and revitalizing. They are a combination of astringent, sour, bitter, and some, like the Meyer Lemon even have a hint of sweetness.

From a culinary perspective, adding lemon to foods can help the flavors brighten and become more complex. If your dish is missing a little something, reach for a little lemon before you reach for the salt and it can add just the right notes. Research suggests that adding fresh citrus to foods can help people with difficulty tasting and smelling enjoy their food again. The volatile oils in the citrus open the nasal passages and stimulate the taste buds, allowing for a little more enjoyment.

Medicinally, lemon has a long list of benefits. It aids in digestion and stimulates peristalsis. It is antiseptic, antimicrobial, and antibacterial, so it helps with wound care and can help tissue heal without scarring. Lemon is a great addition to ginger and honey to make an awesome tonic for cold and flu. Most mornings, I sip on a cup of warm lemon water with honey and a pinch of cayenne. It's a lovely wakeup routine, stimulating the stomach, pancreas, and liver.

DAY 34 – MUSHROOMS

I must admit; I have not been a fan of mushrooms until recently. Historically, I found them to be too earthy and a little bit spongy or rubbery, which doesn't sit well with my finicky texture focused palate. Then one day, I happened to be in a noisy little market/eatery in Manhattan called Eataly. The chef was trying to convince me to try the mushroom dish on the menu. I equally tried to convince him there was no way he could make a mushroom that I would voluntarily eat.

The challenge was on.... one plate of Shiitake mushrooms sautéed in EVO and garlic later and I had to admit he'd won the bet. Not only that, but I went home and tried to recreate them, multiple times. I now have a much greater appreciation for mushrooms, which is good because many of them are really quite good for you.

Not all mushrooms are created equally. Common mushrooms like the Crimini or Portobello are great additions to dinner but don't have anywhere near the health boosting properties that the Asian varieties have. Through the years, I have had many a healthmonger hawk the virtues of Asian mushrooms to me and I just have not been able to bring myself to try them... until now.

Ample research shows that shiitake mushrooms lower cholesterol, have anti-tumor and antiviral properties. Reishi, Enoki, and Maitaki mushrooms boost immune function, have cancer-fighting properties, help against liver disease, are antiviral, and help balance the nervous system to fight fatigue and stress. This is just the shortlist!

The beauty of it is you can add these little gems to soups, stews, make tea out of them, grind them up and put them in things. A little Reishi mushroom powder in your morning coffee can go a long way towards enhanced health. This is a go to cold weather remedy for me.

DAY 35 – CARROTS (RECIPE)

As I was wondering what flavor to choose for today, I absently chewed on the end of a carrot before it went into the food processor. Crunchy, sweet, earthy... I love the texture of carrots. From a culinary perspective carrots, even though we call them vegetables, are often considered a "sweet" when added to dishes. This morning's carrots were being crunched up to make yummy pancakes; sweet and savory.

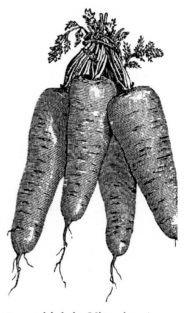

Medicinally, carrots are fabulously rich with phytonutrients and other health giving properties. We all pretty much know that they are packed with beta-carotene which helps with things like vision and cardiovascular. But did you know that carrots have other antioxidants, like polyacetylenes, that help inhibit the growth of colon cancer cells? Carrots are high in Vitamins A and K. They also have a low glycemic load, making them a good choice for a snack. In Ayurveda medicine carrots are considered an awesome choice for recovery from illness. When cooked they are easy to digest, nourishing and they contain a good amount of fiber to help detox the body. Carrots also nourish the liver and help reduce inflammation.

Here's a grain free recipe for carrot pancakes that I think serve up a pretty delicious breakfast. This is a single serving recipe so if you are making for more than yourself you will want to double up. Also, the spices are optional. I recommend playing with different spices to see what suits your palate best.

CARROT PANCAKES (GRAIN-FREE)

2 eggs
1 carrot (grated or crushed)
2 Tbs of yogurt (almond, goat, whatever...)
1-2 Tbs of coconut flour
½ tsp of olive oil
pinch of sea salt
1/8 tsp of baking soda
1 Tbs of pecans or walnuts (optional)
pinch of cinnamon
pinch of garam masala

Mix all ingredients and let them sit for a few minutes so the baking soda can activate. Then cook them up on a griddle. I eat them plain because they are so flavorful but you can definitely add whatever else you want.... Enjoy.

DAY 36 – HIBISCUS

"I put hibiscus flower in every cup of tea I have. It's sweet, sexy, and cleansing." ~ Mario Batali.

Making hibiscus tea is a sensual experience. The smell is pungent and refreshing, with a little bit of earthiness. Pouring the hot water over the petals encourages the red ribbons of color to quickly expand and become an almost iridescent shade of red as it works its way through top to bottom of your cup. Hibiscus is a tropical flower and has a beautiful red color when the dried leaves are brewed into tea or added to foods. The taste is quite astringent and for some people sweet and others sour.

Personally, I find hibiscus to be quite sour so when I use it in a tea I include other herbs, like rose or lavender to soften it. In warm climate cultures hibiscus can be found in quite a variety of foods and in some places the petals are candied and eaten as a sweet treat. I have not yet cooked with hibiscus, other than brewing it in tea but now feel quite motivated to try it in a traditional chicken soup.

Medicinally, Hibiscus is loaded with Vitamin C and certain acids like acetic acid that can be beneficial for digestion and to help balance blood sugar. Studies show that hibiscus is also useful in lowering cholesterol and maintaining healthy blood pressure levels.

DAY 37 – LAVENDER

I must admit that I have a love it, hate it relationship with Lavender. In my early years as a massage therapist I found there was a point when the smell of lavender became repelling (which,interestingly enough, is one of its beneficial qualities). It was the flavor of lavender that retrieved me from the brink and salvaged our relationship.

Most people think of lavender as a relaxing scent. Interestingly, it can also be stimulating in larger doses since its main influence is nervous system balance. The flavor of lavender is refreshing and light. My first culinary experience with lavender was in a tea accompanied by lavender shortbread cookies. They were absolutely divine. The influence of lavender was subtle and gave a refreshing, earthy, almost sweet note to each bite. I have since become a fan of adding lavender to the right tea combinations and various sweet and savory dishes.

Medicinally, lavender is awesome. It is antiviral, antifungal, anti-inflammatory, and antibacterial. In fact, the name lavender is derived from the latin "Lavare" which means "to wash". In the herbal medicine world, Lavender is beneficial for conditions like nervous exhaustion, depression, headaches and high blood pressure. It is also a useful bug repellent.

DAY 38 – NUTMEG

Nutmeg has a warm, spicy aroma and flavor. For me the aroma of nutmeg conjures images of cool weather and holidays. It's a rite of passage from summer to fall when I start to sprinkle nutmeg on my coffee or hot cocoa. Nutmeg is a powerful little spice and a pinch goes a long way. From a culinary perspective, nutmeg's spicy, earthy, pungent quality can add to both savory and sweet dishes alike. A dash on the top of a hearty soup or stew can change the whole flavor dynamic.

Medicinally, nutmeg has a quiet influence. It is not one that you would typically hear about as part of the kitchen medicine cabinet, however, studies have suggested the nutmeg can be helpful in combatting high cholesterol. It has been used to kill human leukemia cells. It has anti-anxiety properties and helps also with depression and memory loss.

Because Nutmeg stimulates the central nervous system it is also considered an aphrodisiac increasing libido and sexual drive. Nutmeg appears also to possess anticonvulsant qualities, aiding in the prevention of epileptic seizures. And has mild hallucinogenic properties in higher amounts. Just keep in mind, a little bit goes a very long way... in higher quantities nutmeg begins to take on a narcotic effect and ultimately toxic quality.

DAY 39 – CINNAMON

Cinnamon is bold and spicy, yet sweet and warming. The Queen of Sheba purportedly wore Cinnamon attar (an essential distillation) to enhance her sensuality. Cinnamon was also banned in many Christian convents because of its warming, aphrodisiac quality.

Cinnamon is actually bark from a cinnamon tree and is sweet, warming, and slightly bitter. It also has some pretty great health properties such as helping control blood sugar, eliminate candida, improve digestion, and it is a great anti-microbial. Just be sure that you're using real cinnamon called Cinnamomum verum. Most cinnamon is actually cassia, which doesn't have the health properties of real cinnamon and can even be toxic.

Because cinnamon has a warming, sweet flavor it can be used to give the illusion of sweetening. My favorite addition to my morning cup of coffee is a blend of cinnamon and vanilla. Enhance your sensual reality with some cinnamon...

DAY 40 – BUTTERNUT SQUASH (RECIPE)

Butternut squash is one of the most popular of the winter squash family. It's a rare restaurant or bistro that doesn't feature butternut squash soup on its menu in the winter months. The beauty of butternut is that it is versatile. It's even delicious raw; cutting it in half reveals a beautiful tangerine color and a fresh, crisp, and slightly earthy scent.

In its raw state, the meat of the squash is slightly crisp and tastes clean, with a hint of chalky back note. In this state, it can be grated and added to salad, chunked up and turned into delicious raw food cookies, or blended in a Vitamix into a health filled raw food soup. However, if one really wants to evoke its namesake quality then baking is the key. Once baked a butternut squash is buttery and slightly nutty. The texture and mouthfeel are smooth and soft, with just enough grain to keep it from being mushy. One of my favorite ways to eat butternut squash, besides as a raw soup, is baked and then coated in butter with cinnamon and garam masala (an indian spice compilation).

From a health perspective, butternut squash is absolutely packed with Vitamin A and other phytonutrients. It contains a good balance of minerals with potassium being the most prominent. Butternut squash also contains a decent amount of Vitamin C and is a good source of fiber. It is relatively low in glycemic load and pretty low in calories considering the amount of delicious flavor and other attributes it packs into your diet.

Research suggests that foods like butternut squash that are high in potassium can help decrease blood pressure. The vitamin A makes them a great resource for healthy skin, while C can improve immune function. The fiber in butternut squash helps with blood sugar maintenance, healthy peristalsis and digestive function, as well as protecting the colon from cancer.

QUICK AND EASY RAW FOOD SQUASH SOUP
3 cups of cubed raw butternut squash
2 cups of coconut water or other liquid (1/2 coconut milk, ½ water is good too)
1 cup of soaked cashews
1 stalk of celery
½ avocado
1 clove of garlic
2 tsp of cinnamon
¼ lemon with peel
pinch of salt to flavor
pepper to flavor

Blend all ingredients in a Vitamix or other powerful blender until all smooth and warm....usually takes about 10 minutes.

DAY 41 – CARAWAY

Today's flavor presented itself as I was savoring the most delicious sourdough rye bread and small batch butter at the Red Lion Pub in East Chisenbury, a tiny village in the county of Wiltshire UK. Incidentally, the sourdough baked goods from this place are all absolutely divine and cultivated from their beloved starter culture, which proudly bears the name Gilbert. Slathering the warm fresh baked bread with butter and great anticipation, my first bite did not disappoint. Delicious! Hearty rye with the earthy crunch of caraway and the sweet cream butter.

Caraway seeds are in the same family as cumin, anise, and fennel, however, they have their own distinct flavor. They have a slightly nutty, subtle licorice flavor that becomes nuttier and less licorice after they are cooked or baked. Caraway is very commonly found in Rye bread. Some older recipes suggest their addition is to help digestion and minimize the potential for belly bloat that can sometimes result from eating bread. Caraway can also be a delicious addition to foods that call for a middle-eastern flair, such as roasted cauliflower and even egg dishes.

From a medicinal perspective, caraway seeds are useful for digestion; combatting issues like nausea, indigestion, heartburn, and stomachache. There is also research that suggests caraway seeds and oil are useful as an antibacterial and antiseptic remedy. Some studies suggest caraway is beneficial for hormone balance in women and also for cardiovascular issues. caraway can be eaten in foods, brewed in tea or the oil can be added to a bit of honey.

DAY 42 – SWEET CHESTNUT

My research in metabolic nutrition and individual metabolism has inspired a super curiosity about traditional food ingredients, by traditional I mean food items that are native to the landscape, local, regional and even prehistoric. What was the diet of our prehistory? Is it available in today's environment and how might eating a more "traditional" or prehistory diet impact metabolic nutrition and well-being? These are questions I am determined to find the answer to, however, I think it will take longer than this short flavor of the day.

Foraging in the Savernake Forest in the UK during the early Autumn, I came across some chestnuts and wondered about them as a food source. I began a search for chestnut flour and traditional chestnut recipes. Later, while in the local Purton Farm Shop, I came across some locally foraged chestnuts and even some chestnut flour. Hooray! The chestnuts are now roasting away in the wood burning stove as I'm typing and will be done any moment, for a full flavor description.

From a culinary perspective chestnuts are great additions to soups and stews and even tasty just roasted (as noted in many a holiday song). They have twice as much starch as the potato but are fibrous and have enough other great vitamins and minerals to make them a good lower glycemic food option. They are packed with vitamin C and other minerals like potassium and magnesium. They are also a good source of essential fatty acids, however, mostly omega 6 so if you already have a diet heavy in omega 6, they can end up contributing to further imbalance.

Lastly, it is critical that you cook the chestnut before eating since they are quite toxic if consumed raw. Pulling my chestnuts from the fire, I am first aware of their sweet, slightly nutty aroma. Their skin is bursting and crackly, making it easy to peel back the layers and reveal the white roasted flesh. My first taste of chestnut gets a mixed review. The meat is sweet and slightly nutty but the mouthfeel is entirely not what I expected.

However, after a few more nibbles my first chestnut does indeed start to grow on me...proof that you should always give something at least nine bites before you decide if you like it or not (neurologically, this is how long it takes the brain to get past immediate historical bias and conditioning). I've decided chestnuts are acceptable to my palate so now on to experimenting with chestnut flour.
Note: It is important to remember there are two types of Chestnut – the edible Sweet Chestnut I've described and the altogether inedible Horse Chestnut that is so large and unwieldy it used in the UK for an ancient sport called Conkers. Go figure...

DAY 43 – HAZELNUT (RECIPE)

Today's flavor is another foraged treasure from the Purton Farm Shop in Wiltshire UK. These hazelnuts, also known as filberts, were an exceptional find and I was excited to take some back to the kitchen to see what could be done with them. I am a fan of hazelnuts and have often used hazelnut flour in various grain free recipes with much success. (I'll share an awesome cookie recipe at the end of this post).

Since I was still feeling very investigative I wanted to prepare these hazelnuts as close to tradition as possible, at least as far as I can imagine. Hazelnuts were apparently a major staple in the diet of our ancestors as early as 8,000B.C.E. There is evidence of charred hazelnuts in huge quantities in prehistoric midden pits in many locations throughout Europe, Britain, and North America.

So, in keeping with imagined tradition, these hazelnuts were destined for the fire.... Sadly, it took several attempts to figure out timing and placement, with quite a few of these precious little gems becoming no better than charcoal. I will not simply describe their 'flavor for the day', rather I will share the entire sensory experience of the one's that survived the flames.

First, let me say, as someone who occasionally toasts hazelnuts in the oven or on stovetop, that toasting them in the shell on a flame, seems to make a huge difference in the quality of their flavor. Their aroma as they begin to roast (and prior to burning) is really delightful; nutty, earthy, and slightly sweet all in the same moment. Once I rescued the appropriately timed nuts from the coals, I allowed them to cool slightly before breaking them open. As they cooled and I could more readily handle them, I smashed the shell and retrieved the flesh...delicious! They were toasty and crunchy as well as slightly chewy and sweet, with a slight pungent nuttiness. Very delicious. I think the hazelnut adventure was a great success.

From a culinary perspective, Hazelnuts are great additions to dishes both sweet and savory. When dried and ground they also make wonderful flour for use in baking. Toasted hazelnuts are very versatile and are great just tossed over vegetables and sprinkled on things like oatmeal.

Medicinally, the hazelnut is a great source of fiber and essential fatty acid. They also provide a good boost in minerals and vitamins, like folate and iron, and they are a fabulous source of Vitamin E. Research suggests that hazelnuts have a higher Proanthocyanidin (PCA) content than the almond, making them an amazing resource for defending against free radicals. One caveat; you need to enjoy the hazelnut with its skin on to gain all the good stuff. And now for that delicious cookie recipe for

HAZELNUT COOKIES.
6 Tbsp grassfed butter, softened or ghee
4Tbs of honey
1 large egg
1 tsp pure vanilla extract
1/4 tsp baking soda
Pinch of sea salt
1 1/2 c. hazelnut flour
1/2 c. chocolate chips

Preheat oven to 350 F.
In a mixing bowl, add the butter and honey. Mix on medium speed until thoroughly combined and creamy.
Add the egg and vanilla extract and mix to combine.

In a medium mixing bowl, combine the hazelnut flour, baking soda, and sea salt.

Add the hazelnut flour mixture to the wet ingredients and mix to combine.

Fold in the chocolate chips to incorporate.

Using a small cookie scoop, scoop out the mixture onto a cookie sheet (or two) lined with parchment paper or a silicon mat.

Bake for 8-9 minutes or until golden brown. Allow to cool slightly before transferring to a baking rack to cool completely.

DAY 44 – KEFIR(RECIPE)

Today's flavor is a cultured milk product called Kefir. I found a lovely jar of small batch cultured kefir in the Sunshine Health Store while wandering the back streets of Stroud in the UK's beautiful Cotswold area. (I also found a goldmine of the best Welsh chocolate imaginable but that's for a different day). I was a little hungry and craving something refreshing and bright and when I spotted the little jar of kefir in the refrigerator section.

Often people think Kefir is the same thing as yogurt only runnier, not so. While it's true that kefir is a cultured milk product, it is fermented from a different 'source' and as such produces different bacteria for the gut. Research suggests that for colon health, kefir is superior to yogurt. The flavor of Kefir is tangy and bright; just what I was going for. It gives a hint of acidity but remains smooth and ends with just a note of sweetness.

I find Kefir more palatable than yogurt when it is a whole milk, plain version. Just like yogurt the goodness of Kefir is sort of lost if it is low fat and packed with sugar-laden flavors. So, don't waste your money purchasing flavored and sweetened options. Your best bet is to get the whole milk plain product and then if you need you can add other things to give it flavor. Kefir is typically smooth and creamy and runny enough to be a drink, rather than eaten in a bowl like yogurt. In fact, Kefir could be a lovely replacement for regular milk in cereal or porridge.

How is Kefir different from Yogurt? Kefir is cultured from a product similar to cheese whey called a kefir grain. The fermentation process is different so it contains quite different bacteria. It is simple to make your own and it is great to enjoy on a daily basis. The other upside of kefir is that by the time it is fully fermented, the grains have typically consumed most of the milk sugars in the host milk and you end up with a more easily digestible product.

Medicinally, there are studies that suggest consuming at least ½ cup of kefir a day can help boost immune function, increase digestive health, and nervous system balance. Kefir contains beneficial yeast, bacteria and a multitude of vitamins and minerals.

OVERNIGHT OATMEAL AND KEFIR

1 cup kefir
½ Tablespoon chia seeds
¼ cup oatmeal, any kind, old fashioned, steel cut, rolled.
Optional: you can add fruit
Optional: syrup, honey, stevia

Mix Kefir and oats (and rest of optional ingredients) in a jar. Place on the lid and let sit overnight. Voila!
You can heat oatmeal up in the morning, slowly with very low heat so you don't kill the good stuff.

DAY 45 – PIMENTA BIQUINHO (LITTLE BEAK PEPPERS)

Today's flavor comes straight for my lunch plate at Truffles Brasserie in Bruton, Somerset, UK. Quite hungry after meandering the back roads hunting for raw milk, we happened upon this little bistro treasure just in time for lunch. My order came with a side of "leaves" (salad in the U.S.). A nice presentation of arugula, baby chard, and two different types of tomatoes. Or at least what I thought were tomatoes until I took my first bite with relish, expecting the flavor of sweet cherry tomato...Surprise! Not a tomato, but definitely intriguing.

It had the mouthfeel of a small pepper, with tough outer skin and chewable attached seeds, only this was sweet and tangy and completely devoid of any heat or spice. Second taste revealed a bright and almost fruity quality, yet definitely pepper. What were these delightful little things?
I inquired with the server and left armed with a name to investigate further.

Pimento Biquinho, or little beak peppers, are from Brazil. They are a type of capsicum and are in the nightshade family with tomatoes and eggplant. The little beak's have a zero heat rating but are big on chili flavor, so if you've ever wanted to know what a chili actually tastes like, these are a great way to get familiar without torching your palate.
Interesting note, the little beak pepper and the habanero are in the same family... both ends of the spectrum.

The little Pimenta Biquinha is rich in antioxidants, vitamins C, B-6, and

A together with a variety of minerals. Research suggests that these little peppers provide the benefits of capsicum without the heat of capsaicin (which is what makes peppers hot).

Don't forget, choosing to eat at places committed to local and sustainable food will help build your local economy and your health. Can you find local and sustainable food options in your area? A perfect little find in the town of Bruton. Truffles Brasserie is committed to serving food from within a 10 mile radius and proudly preparing local, sustainable and delicious... Just in the nick of time!

DAY 46 – RAW MILK

After an adventure wandering the English countryside to find raw milk, I have to sing its praises. This particular raw milk is from the Guernsey breed of cow. They are a lovely red and beige with big, soft, brown eyes. As soon as we returned to base camp, I poured a small glass of the coveted elixir with great excitement and anticipation. I was not disappointed. Raw milk from a Guernsey cow tastes like sunshine and sweet grass, with a hint of nuttiness, totally delicious and amazing. The mouthfeel was really lovely, very creamy and smooth. I thought perhaps it would feel fatty or overly rich but was pleasantly surprised to find it so satin smooth on my palate.

I have been fascinated by the "milk" argument for quite some time, not only the politics of it but also the truth about the health value of raw milk. There is so much confusing information out there. So, just as we were headed out hot on the trail of the actual milk product, I have been for many months hot on the trail of the "truth" about milk.

From a health perspective, it seems to all comes down to two things; actual health vs. politics and shelf life. For this entry, we will steer clear of politics, although at some point trying to feed yourself well indeed becomes a political statement.

From a health perspective, the deciding factor comes down to a particular protein molecule and how the milk is processed. Different cows produce different milk proteins. Some cows produce milk that contains a beta-casein variant called A1 and some cows produce a beta-casein variant called A2. A1 beta-casein has a higher correlation with inflammation and disease while A2 beta-casein has a higher correlation with health due to proline and collegen. So the questions becomes does your milk product contain beta-casein variant A1 or A2?

If milk is not raw, then it is more than likely pasteurized and perhaps even homogenized. Pasteurizing milk means heating it so that any bacteria or harmful pathogens are removed. The downside? Many of the good bacteria and enzymes are removed with the bad. Homogenizing milk means applying enough pressure to force the fat globules in the milk to break into smaller more uniform components. This is why homogenized milk never develops cream on the top and has a thicker or more viscous mouth-feel. The downside? Homogenizing increases the potential for an allergic reaction due to the alteration of the protein laden fat molecules and it also decreases the actual milk flavor and increases potential for oxidation. Oxidative Xanthine a by-product of this process has been shown to contribute to cardiovascular disease.

I love raw milk and plan to continue purchasing it from reputable sources as often as I can.

DAY 47 – ANCHOVY

"Add anchovies to almost anything, in moderation, and it will taste better." J. Mcinerney

I have to admit that I am only newly acquiring an appreciation for the salty little anchovy. A little bit of this tiny cold water fish goes quite a long way adding a salty and complex quality to culinary endeavors. Initially, I was afraid to try anchovies because of their strong smell and not so attractive appearance. I continued to avoid dishes that had them in the ingredient list. When I finally did take the leap and taste something with these power-packed little beauties I was pleasantly surprised. Salty, pungent, and oily, the anchovy also sports very good health qualities. Like other small cold water fish, the anchovy is packed with Omega 3 fatty acids, protein, and other great nutrients.

Omega 3 fatty acids are beneficial for heart health, as well as brain and nervous system health. Omega 3's help balance mood and decrease systemic inflammation. Just six to ten ounces of cold water fish a week can make a huge contribution towards health and wellness. Sticking to the smaller fishes, like the anchovy, sardine, and kipper (mackerel) will also help decrease the risk of mercury in your diet.

It's good to keep in mind that anchovies are prepared by being first salted in brine and then packed in oil or salt. They can be high in sodium if too many are consumed but that is typically not an issue because they have such a strong flavor just a small amount is all that is necessary.

DAY 48 – BRUSSELS SPROUTS

"Brussels sprouts are misunderstood - probably because most people don't know how to cook them properly." ~ T. English

Okay, I must confess I have a thing for miniature vegetables; and while Brussels Sprouts aren't really miniature because they're exactly the size they're supposed to be, they look like little tiny cabbages which makes them seem miniature and therefore loads of fun.

Brussels Sprouts are pungent and bitter. They can taste earthy and a little bit sulfurous if not prepared correctly or if they are too old and large. Brussels Sprouts are in the cruciferous family, which can make them a little bit bitter when they are more mature but it also makes them wonderfully good for you. I've lately gotten in the habit of throwing a handful of these little beauties in my handheld food processor and then quickly frying them up as a sort of veggie hash. It's quite a delicious and healthy addition to breakfast.

From a culinary perspective Brussels Sprouts are pretty versatile. It's just good to keep in mind that they can be quite bitter depending on how they are prepared and how old they are. They can be roasted, steamed, fried and any number of other modes of preparation. Cutting the core out can make them quicker and easier to prepare but if they are young, leaving the core intact increases nutrient value and texture.

Brussels Sprouts are in the same family as broccoli, kale, and cabbage. They are packed with fiber and phytonutrients; making them great additions to a healthy diet.

Research suggests that some of the phytonutrient qualities in the Brussels Sprout in particular, improve the internal structure of our white blood cells. This increases immune function and aids in the protection of DNA stability; which in turn ups their cancer preventive qualities. Brussels Sprouts also help decrease inflammation; cleansing the blood and detoxifying the body.

DAY 49 – GARAM MASALA (RECIPE)

Today's flavor is actually a combination of flavors...a blend of spices to be exact. Not only is it a mix of spices but the combination varies from region to region in India. Garam Masala should not be confused with curry...they are not the same, although in some cases curry dishes may contain a spice blend similar to or the same as some of the variations of Garam Masala.

Basically, Garam Masala means 'warming spice' it is typically a little bit sweet and savory and can also be hot. My favorite blend combines cardamom, cinnamon, black pepper, cloves, cayenne, coriander, fennel, and cumin; nicely warming and all together in one lovely splash of flavor. I have to admit I use Garam Masala on just about everything! I splash it in eggs, dash it over veggies, pinch it into my porridge and sautee it with just about everything else.

The flavor of Garam Masala is spicy, sweet-ish, pungent, and also refreshing because of the coriander. It sort of covers all the bases and just generally makes things delicious. Tonight, I sprinkled some into the chestnut flour pancakes I was making and it bumped them up a culinary notch from awesome to double awesome (yes, I said I would give an update on the chestnut flour.... mixed it with water, pinched in some Garam Masala, fried them up in coconut oil...holy moley!! Double YUM!)

From a medicinal perspective, according to Ayurveda medicine, Garam Masala is an awesome tri-dosha (fine for all three body types) blend. It hits all the flavors necessary for a balanced palate and helps increase digestive fire. Each of the various spices in a blend of Garam Masala has its own unique medicinal quality ranging from pain relief and anti-inflammation to mood balance.

Here's an easy recipe for an interesting tri-dosha snack
TRI-DOSHA LADOOS
2 cups dry-roasted Sesame seeds
1/2 cup soaked Chia seeds (1/2 cup after soaking)
1/4 cup soaked Pumpkin seeds
1/8 cup soaked Walnuts
approx 5- 6 Medjool Dates
1/2 handful Raisins
1/2 cup shredded Coconut Flakes
1 ½ tsp of Garam Masala (if you just want sweet flavor you can use a blend of cinnamon, cardamom, and a pinch of nutmeg)
Pinch of Himalayan salt

Blend the chia seeds, dates and raisins in a food processor, add the other ingredients; give a few quick pulses to make a rough mixture. Form this into balls, roll in coconut and refrigerate. Eat in a few hours after all ingredients have set.

DAY 50 – BEET/BEETROOT (RECIPE)

Aaah, the lovely Beetroot; known to some as just plain old Beet. Either way, Beet or Beetroot, is an earthy and delicious addition to your diet. Beets are one of my absolute favorite veggies (actually, I think I say that about most veggies). It is versatile and beautiful! Beets are awesome grated and raw in a salad, or pickled, or baked or roasted. And, believe it or not, they are the magical ingredient in one of the best chocolate cake recipes I've ever had.

Eaten raw Beets are crisp and earthy. Cooked they take on an even earthier quality that pairs well with pungent flavors, like goat cheese or tarragon. I love cooking with beets because they have such a lovely red color, which can stain if you aren't careful but still is quite beautiful. I'm not a fan of cooked tomatoes so I often use beets as a replacement for them in chili or other sauce recipes that call for tomatoes.

From a medicinal perspective, beets are obviously amazing. They are packed with nutrients like Vitamin C, Potassium, Betain, and are high in fiber. They are good for reducing inflammation, preventing cancer, decreasing blood pressure, and increasing stamina. 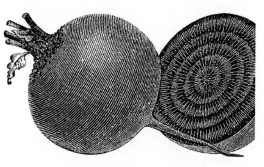 The high levels of potassium make them an aphrodisiac food. And now for the most amazing recipe ever....

GRAIN-FREE CHOCOLATE BEET CAKE

3 cups of roasted and grated beetroots
4 eggs
1/2 c. coconut oil
1/2 c. raw honey (you can use date syrup or date sugar instead)
1 TBS vanilla extract
1 tsp baking soda
1/2 tsp sea salt
1/2 tsp ground cinnamon
1/4 tsp ground nutmeg
1/2 c. raw 100% cacao powder
1/3 c. coconut flour (for a slightly fluffier and dryer cake, use 1/2 cup coconut flour...I'm going to try using chestnut flour as well)

Preheat oven to 350F

Put the beetroot, oil and eggs in a food processor and process til smooth.
Add the honey, vanilla, baking soda, sea salt and spices. Blend well.
Add the cacao powder and coconut flour and mix until well incorporated.
Pour into a greased cake pan of choice.
Bake for 35-45 minutes, or until an inserted toothpick comes out clean.
Cool completely before cutting.

DAY 51 – WATERCRESS

Who'd a thought it? Watercress is a cousin of the Brussels Sprout. It's a member of the Brassica family, and cruciferous, which means it is also related to wasabi, radish, mustard and even broccoli. This is what gives it the peppery, spicy tang. Watercress is interesting at first taste. It is initially refreshing and piquant then introduces a bit of a zing, especially the more mature plant.

For today's flavor, I have been nibbling on baby watercress. It is not as peppery as its adult counterpart but still has a refreshing quality. Watercress is apparently one of the first known leafy veggies that consumed by humans. It grows in water or partial water environments. I can imagine cruising along the riverbed foraging for dinner and grabbing a handful of fresh green cress. For now, I just purchased this watercress in the market.

From a culinary perspective, watercress is a great addition to salads and other fresh vegetable dishes. I tend to throw it on top of eggs or other dishes as a refreshing topping. I love it on a sandwich or as extra flavor in a collard green wrap. It's also awesome in pesto! It also makes a lovely soup served hot or cold.

Medicinally, watercress is packed with phytonutrients. It is blood cleansing, anti-inflammatory, cancer preventive...in fact, all the wonderful things that Brussels sprouts were and more. Watercress is packed with Vitamin A, C, and K. It also is great for your eyes since it is full of lutein. Grab a handful of cress and give it a try!

DAY 52 – HONEY

"well, said pooh, what I like best..." and then he had to stop and think, because although eating honey was a very good

thing to do, there was that moment just before you began to eat it which was actually almost better than when you actually were eating it, but pooh didn't know what that moment was called..."

Today's flavor is honey, which in truth has so much variation one could do 365 days of flavor just focusing on the different terroirs of honey each day. Honey is produced by bees from the nectar of flowers. It is a by-product of their vital work pollinating the plants and flowers in our fields, orchards and pastures. It undergoes quite a process moving from flower to bee to beehive.

Currently, my kitchen counter sports eight different types of raw and sustainably produced honey. These are referred to as 'varieties' and derived from the flora and fauna specific to particular landscapes. I have cherry, lavender, pine, wildflower, henge, manuka, sage, and pumpkin blossom, each tasting distinctly different. I prefer raw honeys so they also have a great mouthfeel and viscosity. Honey is in the sweet category but depending on the variety or soil derivation it can also contain pungent and earthy elements.

From a culinary perspective honey is versatile and can be used as a replacement for other sweeteners, although it is still made up of monosaccharides so don't be fooled into thinking it doesn't impact blood sugar. The impact is slightly less if it is in its raw form but still best if used in moderation. I personally feel that honey is a blessing and it is the product of very hard work by busy bees, a little bit goes a long way and respects the work they've done.

From a medicinal perspective, honey is completely phenomenal! It has so many amazing properties I will only be able to just touch on a few of them here. First of all, honey is amazing for ailing skin; wound healing, burns, sunburns, acne, rashes, and even eczema. There is quite a bit of research demonstrating that applying honey to diabetic foot ulcers can speed on healing time and minimize scarring. I use honey when I've got a sunburn or burn. I also use it as a restorative facial when my skin is feeling dry.

Raw honey is packed with all the enzymes, nutrients, minerals and vitamins. It is antibiotic, antimicrobial, anti-inflammatory, and antifungal. Research suggests that honey can increase the hemoglobin count and help manage anemia. It fights infections, especially throat and chest issues such as strep throat and bronchitis. The list really goes on and on and on...

I think honey is good for the soul and a taste or two of good raw honey can put many things in perspective. And now my plug to save the bees! Be mindful of where and how your honey is produced. Be aware of the environment and how we can cultivate bee friendly environments.

DAY 53 – AVOCADO (RECIPE)

"The Avocado is a food without rival..."

The inspiration for today's flavor comes from my delicious second breakfast in Jamie Oliver's Café/Shop Recipease. The morning is bright and beautiful. We are sitting in a sunny window overlooking Notting Hill Gate Road in London. We have just finished a romp through the Notting Hill Farmer's Market and decided to stop for a coffee and small snack. Spicy Avocado smashed on toast for me, please!!

Avocado is such a versatile food. Personally, I love the mouthfeel and texture the most and the fact that it can enhance any number of dishes with just the right amount of delectable fat and flavor. The creamy, smoothness feels almost refreshing and there are some days when that first bite of Avocado is satisfying like nothing else could be; definitely for me, the avocado is an 'mmmmm' factor food. This morning's delight is smashed up with spices, herbs, some fresh jalapeno and small tomatoes and served on a slice of homemade sourdough toast. YUM and thank you!

From a culinary perspective, Avocados are often viewed as a side or a topping. Perhaps topped up on a salad, or sandwich, or served as the infamous guacamole. However, Avocado can do sooooo much more than that. From my stint as a raw foodie, I learned to use Avocado when I wanted to give something some complexity and a little added oomph; blending it in soups, sauces, and even making cakes and puddings with it. (Stay tuned for the most amazing chocolate pudding recipe)

From a medicinal perspective, Avocados are considered a super food! They are packed with nutrients like potassium and lutein, vitamins B, C, and E. They are high in fiber and fabulous fats. Research suggests that eating avocado helps curb systemic inflammation, which in turn helps with different inflammation related ailments like arthritis, fibromyalgia, and even diabetes.

Avocados are great for your skin, your digestion, and especially your brain! The fatty acids help balance hormones and neurotransmitters that impact your mood. The only downside to Avocado? They are high in fat so, avoid eating them with processed foods. If you are a fast metabolizer, they are a great source of energy. If you are a slow metabolizer, it's good to know when the best times to eat them are. Stay tuned for more info on that! For now, here's the most amazing chocolate pudding recipe:

CHOCOLATE PUDDING

1 ripe Avocado
2-3 TBS of Cacao (not hot chocolate powder)
2 tsp of date syrup or ¼ c. of soaked dates (or a few drops of stevia)
2 TBS of Coconut milk (or cashew, almond, etc)
Pinch of sea salt
Dash of Vanilla
Mix it all up in the blender until it's smooth and creamy!

DAY 54 – BASIL

The ancient Egyptians and Greeks believed Basil would open the gates of heaven, so placed a sprig of basil in the hand of the dead to insure a safe journey and open passage.

Basil is incredibly fragrant. The smell is vibrant and refreshing; tinged with earthiness and a little hint of spice. Smashing a little bit of basil between the fingers and inhaling can uplift the mood in a matter of seconds. Interestingly, the taste and flavor is less intense than the smell so full enjoyment of basil depends also on the retronasal effect. Most people are familiar with basil because of pesto but there are many, many types of basil that are popular in other ethnic cuisines. One of my favorites is Thai purple basil; which has a slightly citrus taste to it.

From a culinary perspective, basil is an awesome addition to dishes both savory and sweet. Basil can be chopped and added fresh to salads, sprinkled over eggs, pizza, and sandwiches. It can be pureed and added to soups, stir-fries, and other dishes. I especially love basil in the summertime and tend to add it liberally to foods for its refreshing flavor.

Basil is as packed with nutrients and phytonutrients as it is with flavor. It is really high in Vitamin K, A, and C. It's also a great source of magnesium, manganese, calcium, and iron. Research suggests that volatile oils from Basil provide cellular protection against oxidation and intra-cellular inflammation. Basil is also has great anti-microbial qualities. Studies also show that Basil is helpful for increasing cardiovascular health.

DAY 55 – WALNUTS

"Walnuts can be eaten raw, as they are, or toasted to bring out more of their flavor"– BBC Food

Walnuts are getting more and more critical acclaim. They are high in Omega 3 fatty acid sand also in copper and manganese. Not to mention being a good source of fiber and a help with balancing blood sugar because of their lower glycemic load. Just a quarter of a cup a day can work wonders for your brain and body.

Walnuts can taste bitter and have a bit of a bite to them, especially if the lining or "skin" is on them, or they can be sweeter, with an almost creamy, vanilla back-note. I find them also earthy and slightly acidic; this comes from the tannins and phytic acid. Walnuts are packed with flavonoids and other nutrients, which makes them exceptionally good for you.

From a culinary perspective, walnuts are delicious in both sweet and savory dishes. Although, I think most people think of them as something to add to the sweet side. I toss them in yogurt for breakfast or sprinkle them on salads. I also love to add them to baked goods; cookies, breads and cakes. They are an excellent addition to entrees as well. They can even be a mainstay in vegetarian dishes like walnut lentil patties; which are delicious and protein packed. Today's idea for walnut's as the flavor for the day came from sampling pickled walnuts. That's right, pickled walnuts! The jury is still out on what I really think about them but it was worth the bold try.

From a health perspective, as I noted, walnuts are amazing brain food. Research suggests just consuming that quarter cup a day can decrease oxidative stress and help preserve telomeres length. Telomeres are the protective coating on the end of each DNA strand. They protect your DNA structure and help preserve health and well-being; protecting against things like depression and ailments related to premature aging. Walnuts are also great protection against systemic inflammation, which can lead to cardiovascular issues and cellular aberrations. Next time you need a snack, you could be well advised to grab a handful of walnuts.

DAY 56 – ARUGULA (ROCKET)

This flavor for the day comes straight from my breakfast bowl. Arugula, also known as rocket, is in the Brassicaceae family. Like its relatives, it is an awesome digestive bitter and adds well to many a culinary endeavor. I eat Arugula almost every day in some form or another. Whether I am topping it with eggs for breakfast or adding it to my airplane meal ...it's an awesome go to for flavor and nutrients.

Arugula like all other foods differs depending on terroir and type. Wild arugula tends to taste more peppery and spicy. It's my favorite. Conventionally grown arugula tends to become more bitter, the more mature the leaves are but it can also have a sweet, grassy back-note to it. Today's arugula was young and wild; a peppery, spicy addition to my soft-boiled eggs and avocado. You can also make a pretty awesome arugula pesto by following traditional pesto recipe but mixing the basil with some arugula and even spinach.

From a medicinal perspective, like its Brassicaceae cousins, Arugula has many health benefits. Its bitter nature makes it an awesome digestive. It is packed with vitamins A and K to name just two of many. It contains sulforaphane, which research is demonstrating has some pretty amazing cancer fighting qualities. Sulforaphane inhibits development of enzymes that contribute to the progression and spread of cancer, most notably colon, skin, and prostate cancers. The Vitamin K is great for preventing Osteoporosis and the Alpha Lipoic Acid helps manage blood glucose levels and decrease oxidative stress. All around good stuff going on in a handful of rocket!

DAY 57 – ASPARAGUS

Asparagus is a hit or miss vegetable for me. I love it seasonally and I love it when it is prepared deliciously... who doesn't? For me, deliciously means firm yet tender, crispy enough to feel a slight snap with each bite, but cooked enough to eliminate the sometimes ropey or chewy quality that can happen. The taste of asparagus varies slightly with the age of the stem, the season, and obviously, the method of preparation. Young asparagus has a fresh, almost grassy taste, while more mature asparagus stems can taste much more complex even having a hint of bitterness.

My favorite way to prepare asparagus is to quickly parboil it, coat it in olive oil and then grill it, either in a pan on the stovetop or under an actual grill. This is the best of all worlds, the grassy, springiness of the stem accompanied by the much sought after Maillard Reaction. Delicious. But then I also love asparagus soup....so I guess, as I said, as long as it's delicious, I'm game. This morning's asparagus was part of an egg scramble. Slightly sauté the asparagus first, add in some eggs, and finish off with some goat cheese. What a lovely way to start the day.

From a medicinal perspective, asparagus has quite the history. Initially, it seems asparagus was known as an aphrodisiac, listed in several cultural writings throughout history as early as the 10th century. Although, this is technically scientifically unconfirmed for regular asparagus, in Ayurveda, the "herb" Shatavari (which is a type of asparagus and packed with phyto-estrogens) is used regularly for both men and women as an intervention for reproductive and sexual issues. So, perhaps there is something to the aphrodisiac claims.

Even if that isn't the case, asparagus has a multitude of other amazing qualities. It's high in Vitamin K, E, and C, as well as Folate, Beta Carotene, and Selenium. It has great antioxidant properties and helps decrease oxidative stress. It's high in fiber and can help regulate blood sugar. It's also packed with Oligosaccharides, which are considered a prebiotic and helps to populate the colon with healthy bacteria.

Oh, and that crazy after effect that we all know about??? It's caused by Asparagusic acid, which is a compound of chemicals that contain sulfuric components; all perfectly harmless even if slightly stinky in a horsey sort of way.

DAY 58 – EGGS

Myth busting alert! First myth buster: eating eggs causes high cholesterol...nope. Second myth buster: eating only egg whites will make you healthier and skinnier...nope. Truth? Enjoy the entire egg and know that it is full of healthy goodness (unless, of course, you have an allergy).

But let's talk about the flavor first. Having consumed mostly supermarket eggs for much of my life, I was completely unaware that eggs actually had variations in flavor. It wasn't until I had the opportunity to eat farm fresh, straight from the chicken, and various kinds of chickens at that, that I realized there was way more to this egg thing than I originally thought.

Fresh eggs generally have a deeper golden, almost as golden as a sunset, hue to their yolk. They taste much more complex; meaning there are more nuances to the actual flavor of the yolk and white. The flavor of a fresh egg is impacted by the terroir of the hen so sometimes it might taste earthier or sometimes sweeter. Either way, if you can get your hands on fresh eggs. I highly recommend it! If not, you can still appreciate the flavor of market eggs.

For me, it's more about the texture than the flavor when it comes to market purchased eggs and I definitely leave the yolk as runny as possible for better mouthfeel. Interestingly, runny yolks are healthier. Today's breakfast was two, seven minute steamed soft eggs and they were delightfully perfect with fresh arugula and spinach. I also love them with peas.

So now, back to the myth-busting! Medicinally, eggs are a little treasure of delicious health. So, why the cholesterol reputation? It all comes down to poor science, or rather poor delivery of science by the pop culture media. Yes, eggs do have a high cholesterol content, but the actual empirical data does not support that consuming them impacts your blood plasma and cholesterol counts. In fact, quite the opposite.

When most of the surveys and studies were done back in the late 1960's and early 1970's, no one was looking at the entire content of the breakfast consumed. They were simply looking at cholesterol levels, looking at an egg's cholesterol under a microscope and somebody decided $2 + 2 = 4$. Unfortunately, in this case, it didn't and it doesn't.

So, what's the major contributor to cholesterol impact and blood serum wackiness? The combination of breakfast items that tends to include saturated fats with simple carbs such as white bread and sugary items like jams and jellies. Who's the real villain in those old research studies? Sugar! Not egg yolks.

Eggs are a great source of quality protein. They are full of lutein and choline, both of which are required nutrients for brain and body health. They are also packed with B vitamins and even omega 3 fatty acids. All of which support reduction of oxidative stress and systemic inflammation, while supporting healthy neural networking and immune function support.

A couple of caveats: studies suggest (and I firmly believe) eggs carry the stress of the hens that laid them. Research demonstrates that eggs from conventional facilities where birds are highly stressed imparts stress chemicals into their yolk and white. This in turn, contributes to systemic inflammation and upset in your body. Choose range-free, pasture raised, sustainably cared for, whenever possible. Also, if you've ever actually seen a chicken lay an egg, it is absolutely a process worthy of respect...ouch! So, eat with appreciation and purchase so that your dollar provides the best living arrangement possible for these little treasures.

Lastly, cooking the yolk with high heat changes the protein composition and can contribute to digestive issues and poor nutrient assimilation. Notice that I wrote "high heat" so the focus is on how you cook the yolk, not necessarily that you cook it. Low and slow will produce a better taste as well as a healthier meal. So here are top ways to cook eggs:

Soft boil slowly with steam
Poach
Fry - low and slow
Scramble - low and slow
Hard boil – you guessed it, low and slow

Try this7- Minute Steamed Egg technique. It produces amazing soft boiled eggs every time.

Put about ½ inch of water in a saucepan with a lid and bring to boil. Lower the heat to simmer and place eggs in the pan. Put on the lid, set the timer for 6-7 minutes (depending on how cooked you want the yolk). Prepare for perfectly cooked whites and nice runny yolks. Once the timer sounds, quickly run the egg under cool water so you can handle it to crack and also so it will stop cooking. Enjoy!

DAY 59 – GREEN PEAS (RECIPE)

Fresh green peas are a treat. They are crisp and sweet with tiny little flavor explosions in every bite. The starch and fat give them a nice mouthfeel and make them delightfully palatable.

From a culinary perspective, peas are also extremely versatile. They are delicious fresh, raw, cooked, mushy, in soup, in stew, and even in desserts (believe it or not). In my childhood, peas and I got off to a very rocky start, however, they are now one of my favorite go to veggies. I have them several times a week with various meals and snacks because they are so versatile and delicious. In the spring one of my absolute favorite recipes is a nice green pea and mint soup.

Medicinally, peas are amazing and contain some very unique nutrients making them secret champions for your health. Sadly, peas are often maligned and avoided because they are assumed to be too high in starch. They do, indeed, contain a higher starch content than many other veggies but they most assuredly counteract any ill effects with their high fiber, high protein, and numerous phytonutrients.

In fact, peas have their own unique phytonutrients and are gaining huge interest in the health research arenas. They have awesome antioxidant and anti-inflammatory properties. Research is demonstrating their power in regulating blood sugar and decreasing the potential for Type 2 Diabetes. There are also studies showing that eating just one cup of peas a couple times a week helps fight against various gastric cancers.

The other bonus of peas? They are super-helpful to the environment (obviously when grown appropriately). They help balance soil content, decrease erosion, and boost beneficial bacteria. The dwarf varieties also make great container plants, allowing you to have your own little patio harvest if you live in urban areas. I love peas!!

SERIOUSLY DELICIOUS SPRING PEA SOUP
1 bag of frozen peas (or 4 c of fresh)
½ sm. onion
1 clove garlic
¼ c. of milk (milk substitute works just fine)
Broth (your desired thickness)
Salt and pepper to taste
Fresh mint

Sautee garlic and onion. When translucent pour in broth. Once heated add spinach and peas. Let simmer until soft and dark green. Use a hand mixer to blend soup until creamy consistency. Add milk and mint, continue to blend. Add salt and pepper to taste.

Note: If you do not have a hand mixer, let cool and pour into regular mixer and reheat.

This is also a great raw recipe. When I make it raw I use ¼ of the onion, less garlic and I replace the broth with coconut milk. I also add an avocado for a creamy consistency. Blend it all in the Vitamix and voila!

CHAPTER 3 - MARCH

DAY 60 – DANDELION

Yep, those little, tenacious weeds that infuriate the average gardener or lawn keeper are a *delicious* and *nutritious* food. As I'm writing this flavor for the day, I am sipping some lovely dandelion root tea and enjoying the earthy, bitter complexity. I'm also enjoying knowing that it is toning my liver and supporting my digestive function.

Dandelions are nutritionally amazing and sadly underutilized in the culinary world. All parts of the dandelion are edible which makes them versatile for a variety of uses. Dandelion greens in a salad can bring a refreshing complexity by providing a bitter but still palatable back note. The edible flowers can be a delicious and aesthetically pleasing addition to a salad or plate. The greens and the root can be sautéed, added to sauces, soups, and stews and even blended into pesto.

Medicinally, dandelion is a great overall tonic herb. It is packed with Vitamin A, K and C, as well as, potassium, calcium, iron and other fabulous nutrients. Recent research has demonstrated that the chemical compounds found in the pesky, yet oh so fabulous, dandelion are the perfect cocktail in the fight against cancer induced cell mutation. Its efficacy has been demonstrated in studies with leukemia, colon and stomach cancers.

Dandelion is also antimicrobial and antibacterial. Its diuretic quality helps relieve the body of excess fluid while also toning the liver and kidneys. Research demonstrates that it is as effective as several of the typically prescribed pharmaceutical interventions without the adverse effect of depleting potassium and aggravating the cardiovascular system, which is a common side effect of the pharmaceuticals.

My favorite dandelion uses are in salads, sautés, teas and soups... oh and also to make wishes.

DAY 61 – COCONUT

I used coconut oil to sauté some broccoli stems for breakfast. It gave everything a subtle and delightful flavor. I use coconut oil for much of my cooking and baking because of that little extra slightly sweet and nutty back note it provides. Coconut can be a great addition to culinary experiments. Toss it on just before serving or fold it in just before baking and it adds a few extra dimensions to whatever you are preparing.

There is quite a bit that can be said about coconut especially since it seems to be one of the trendy foods that are touted to cure anything and everything that ails you. Coconut is good and there is definitely research that demonstrates its amazing qualities but as always, it might not be right for every body. There is way too much to be said for the space of this short article on flavor so I will keep it short and sweet.

The benefit of coconut is in part due to its medium chain triglyceride which research suggests can help lower cholesterol, balance blood sugar, and stabilize thyroid. Coconuts also contain lauric acid which research is showing to be a very effective anti-bacterial, anti-fungal, and anti-microbial. It protects against oxidative stress and eliminates free radicals. It is also low in sodium, high in potassium and other vitamins and minerals, high in fiber and can be a great way to stabilize your appetite.

In short, coconut is all around good stuff. Things to pay attention to: coconut milks tend to contain additives that are not so great, so it's easier to just make your own. Imported coconuts often are required to be treated with pesticides that you don't really want in or on your body. Go organic whenever possible, avoid additives (including the BPA lining on cans) and avoid overly processed coconut derivatives, which really just end up being a source of sugar and not good stuff.

DAY 62 – RAW MILK JACK CHEESE

Another flavor courtesy of my morning breakfast bowl and initially I thought to just write about cheese as a general flavor. However, I quickly realized the error of my ways when I thought about all of the amazing kinds of cheese out there in the world just waiting to be sampled. So, we will start with Raw Milk Jack Cheese; which is rich and creamy and tangy and ever so slightly pungent all at the same time. This particular small batch Jack Cheese has the added benefit of being from a Jersey Cow, pasture centered, grass-fed. So, it tastes fresh and a little bit zippy.

Jack cheese is historically considered a "country cheese", hence the original name Queso del Pais. According to "The Cheese Lover's Companion", while many attribute the name of Jack cheese to Monterey, California businessman David Jacks; it seems to have originated in Spain and been brought to America by Franciscan Monks in the 1700's. Interestingly, the drier, more aged, version of Jack cheese that some of you might be familiar with became popular during WWI. Apparently, delays in shipping forced a longer aging time and produced quite by accident a delightfully piquant, crumbly version of this mild cheese.

Cheese is often seen as an indulgence to be avoided by the some proponents of health; however, it has plenty of benefits (if it's real cheese and not cheese product). Cheese is a good source of protein, calcium, Vitamin B12, and if it's from grass fed cows, it contains even more good stuff. If it's from heritage breed cows then it has the added power of the A2 casein molecule, which has a variety of health benefits. Cheese is umami and satisfies the palate. Research suggests it also helps regulate blood sugar.

One caveat; if you're going to eat it make sure it is full fat and naturally processed so you are really getting the benefit of the cheese without the contamination of additives and chemical processing.

DAY 63 – SWEET POTATO (RECIPE)

First, let me say I just finished eating the most amazing sweet potato and hazelnut pancakes. I will include the recipe at the end of this post. They were really delish and super quick and easy to make! Obviously, today's flavor comes again from my breakfast plate; it's the lovely and versatile sweet potato!

Despite the name, sweet potatoes are only distantly related to the potato and not part of the nightshade family as sometimes thought

(Convolvulaceae vs. Solanaceae). So, if you've been avoiding sweet potatoes because you believe they are inflammatory due to nightshade toxins, rest assured you can start enjoying them again. They are, in fact, quite the anti-inflammatory food. Sweet potatoes are another amazingly versatile food, being fabulous additions to both savory and sweet culinary endeavors. I love the sweet potato in all its guises. I love it raw and use it often in raw recipes, especially during the spring and summer. Cooked and pureed sweet potato makes an amazing base to thicken soups and stews while adding fiber and an amazing array of nutrients. Of course, it also turns into amazing sweet treats.

A raw sweet potato has an earthy freshness to it. Because the starch is not yet broken down, it can also have a chalky quality that tends to disappear when pureed with good, healthy fats like coconut oil or even butter. I love the crisp, snappy feel of raw sweet potato. To me it also has more complexity in its raw state. As sweet potatoes are cooked, they become sweeter and creamier; developing deeper, nuances sweet flavors the longer they are exposed to heat.

Medicinally, sweet potatoes are one of the darlings of the anti-inflammatory world. Research demonstrates that they are packed with phytonutrients known to decrease oxidative stress and improve immune function. They are loaded with vitamins C, A, and B and minerals like magnesium which helps regulate the stress response and contributes to overall nervous system balance. Sweet potatoes are also filled with beta-carotene and other anti-carcinogenic antioxidants, making them a delicious way to fight cancer-causing influences.

Sweet potatoes are not yams; although the names are often used interchangeably. True yams are part of the grass and lily family (Dioscoreaceae), while sweet potatoes are in the Morning Glory family. Sweet potatoes are less starchy than yams and have higher nutrient content; although yams are a little higher in protein and fiber.

And now on to that recipe: (this serves 1 so you will want to increase if there are more of you or use as a side dish and add other items)

SWEET POTATO AND HAZELNUT PANCAKES (GRAIN-FREE)

½ raw sweet potato grated
2 eggs
2 tbs hazelnut meal
1 tbs coconut flour
1 tsp olive or coconut oil
pinch of sea salt
pinch of baking soda
spice to taste – I used garam masala this morning for a savorier quality but anything goes.

Grate the sweet potato in a bowl then add the rest of the ingredients. Let ingredients sit for a few minutes while pan heats. Add coconut oil to pan and then add pancakes in little spoonfuls. Flip, cook, serve, eat... I usually eat mine with a little bit of yogurt drizzled over the top.

DAY 64 – GRAPEFRUIT

Tasting grapefruit is always a bit of an adventure. There are so many possible variations in the sour, bitter, and sweet combination that you just don't know until you take that first bite. Grapefruit smells refreshing and boosts your mood just by inhaling it.

In fact, Grapefruit essential oil is one of the scents frequently used in hospitals in France because of the mood enhancing properties. Grapefruit comes in a variety of colors; each having their own nutritive properties to accompany the basics of a typical grapefruit. Red Grapefruit have the highest amount of lycopene making them a better choice for cancer fighting properties.

From a culinary perspective grapefruit is an interesting citrus to work with. Depending on the color and intensity of flavors, you can make or break a culinary endeavor when you introduce a little bit or a lot. Pink grapefruits tend to be sweeter, red and white ones, depending on how they were grown and when they were picked, can run either side of the spectrum. Sweet, bitter, or sour. Grapefruit is a great palate cleanser and it also makes a great addition to salads, side dishes and small plates.

From a medicinal perspective grapefruit is pretty amazing. It is one of the most hydrating fruit choices, second only to watermelon and it contains ample amounts of vitamin C and fiber. Because it is also high in potassium and other vital minerals, it is a great resource for athletes.

Research suggests that it is helpful in regulating blood sugar, lowering cholesterol and decreasing the potential for arterial plaque and other cardiovascular issues. For a while the grapefruit was touted as a weight loss gem, in fact, research suggests that it really is. The phytonutrients, hydrating qualities, and fiber all contribute to balancing metabolic function for most people.

The only caveat? Research demonstrates you must actually eat the fruit to reap the benefits. Supplements or juice do not provide the same outcome. Certain research has also suggested that eating grapefruit can inhibit uptake of certain prescription drugs so it's good to check with your doctor...although, research also demonstrates the amount of grapefruit one would have to eat to do so is pretty huge.

DAY 65 – PICKLES

Eating a small batch, all naturally preserved bread and butter pickle on toast with cheese is the impetus for today's flavor. I got turned on to cheese and pickle sandwiches this summer while roving the English countryside for eating experiences. Suffice to say that cheese and pickles became a fast favorite and on occasion, I feel compelled to recreate the experience in my own kitchen.

Today was one of those occasions. The combination of cheese and pickles is so amazing because it provides a hint of all the flavors plus the bonus of retro-nasal and delectable mouth-feel. The pickles are sweet, sour, a little bit bitter and salty too, the cheese is smooth, creamy, and umami.

The combination is seriously addicting.

Pickling is the process of preserving food with either brine or vinegar. It is a process of lacto-fermentation that, so long as it occurs without air, preserves the food item while inhibiting or destroying the potential for harmful bacteria. Pickling has been around for thousands of years in every culture. Flavor is derived during the pickling process depending on what other herbs and spices are added to the mix. Although, simply adding salt and allowing the process imparts its own unique flavor, as with a simple sauerkraut recipe.

Pickled foods provide a variety of taste experiences. Sweet, savory, puckering! Fermented foods also can add a complimentary digestive boost, which makes them a great addition to any meal. Pickling food is easier than you might think. For the most part it's a matter of putting all the ingredients in an airtight container and waiting for them to do their thing. I love making sauerkraut and I am now on a mission to pickle a variety of other things so they will be ready for summertime fun.

Medicinally, eating lacto-fermented foods is a bonus all the way around. Research suggests that eating ½ cup of fermented food a day increases immune function and helps in the battle against any number of flu viruses. (one intriguing study involving chickens and the avian flu demonstrated that the chickens being fed sauerkraut were immune to the avian flu virus despite having it introduced to their system). Fermented foods also help balance the Ph in your digestive tract and body, which in turn can contribute to a more balanced mood pattern. Naturally fermented foods can also help in the battle against systemic inflammation, which is a major contributor of most illnesses and chronic ailments.

Caveat: Make sure you are eating naturally fermented, pickled foods. Most items in the supermarket have been pasteurized and the good stuff no longer exists in them. Opt for those in the refrigerator section, typically containing the world "raw" in them to signify they have not been pasteurized. Or better yet, get experimental and make your own!

DAY 66 – TANNINS

If you are a wine or a tea consumer, chances are you have heard of tannins and maybe even discussed their presence in your beverage of choice. Tannins are naturally occurring polyphenol compounds that play an important role in the growth and health of many plants.

It took me a while to understand what I was 'tasting' for when I searched various foods for a tannic experience. My mind was looking for flavor when I should have been looking for mouthfeel. Once I realized it was a feel rather than a flavor I can now more readily pick out the tannic quality in foods. Tannins are astringent and can be bitter, they're most noted for their ability to take the moisture from the tissue in your mouth and tongue. It's this process that can also enhance the perception of bitterness.

Want to find out how to taste for tannins? Prepare two cups of black tea, steep one for two minutes and the other for four minutes. Taste and feel the difference. What do you notice about each cup? Want to neutralize the impact of the tannins? Add some fat. This is why tannin rich wines pair well with cheese and cream can 'smooth' a cup of coffee or tea.

Tannins play a fascinating role in the plant world. They regulate growth hormones; sending the vital signals to do things like pollinating and ripening. They are also a deterrent to predators, with the bitter astringent quality acting like a toxin in some cases. They are responsible for some of the brighter colors, like the red in a pomegranate skin, and act as sunscreen. Tannins are also antimicrobial; they protect the plant from 'infection' and help it to heal more quickly.

For humans, tannins have a mixed review. Originally, tannins were viewed as an "anti-nutrient"; in fact, it was assumed they were carcinogenic. However, lately research is demonstrating that assumption is not accurate and tannins can play a vital role in health and wellness. Humans can benefit from their antimicrobial and antifungal qualities. Other studies suggest that tannins can help balance blood lipid levels, decrease blood pressure, aid in blood clotting, and regulate auto- immune response. Depending on the type of tannin, they also have amazing antioxidant properties, helping to decrease oxidative stress and the potential for cell mutation.

DAY 67 – LEEKS (RECIPE)

My first positive experience with Leeks was in the form of soup. Initially, in my youth I avoided eating them, knowing they were in the onion family and having a hearty dislike for all things onion. My acceptance and fascination of leeks came, not so much through a sudden enjoyment of their flavor, rather through the cleaning and cutting process. Cutting them and then separating all those tiny rings is enjoyable.

I now love cooking with leeks, because they are such a delight to prepare but also because of their flavor. They are not like onions at all, as they possess their own sweet, earthy, and slightly sharp when raw, qualities. They sweeten as they cook. They are, however, like garlic and onions, and others in the allium family, in their nutritive properties, so it's best to cut leeks and then let them sit for a few moments so all the beneficial qualities can activate. I use that time to separate all their little rings so I have a lovely pile of leek circles that inspire me to artistic endeavors. (: Sautéed leeks are a quick and easy go to for a healthy addition to any meal, but soup is one of my favorite ways to eat them.

Medicinally, Leeks have many of the same beneficial qualities that onions and garlic have. They are high in phytonutrients that help protect cell structure and reduce low-level systemic inflammation.

LEEK AND CAULIFLOWER SOUP
2 TBS Coconut Oil
3 TBS Butter
3 Leeks
1 head of cauliflower chopped
3 cloves garlic, finely chopped
8 cups broth (I use bone broth or mineral broth for added nutrients)
salt and freshly ground black pepper to taste
1 cup heavy cream (optional)

Gently heat a large pot for soup, then add coconut oil and butter, when melted add the garlic, leeks and then cauliflower. Sauté for about 10 minutes. Once they are lightly browned and softened, add the broth and bring everything to an easy boil. Reduce heat, cover, and simmer 45 minutes.

Remove the soup from heat. Blend the soup with an immersion blender or hand mixer. Season with salt and pepper. Mix in the heavy cream, and continue blending until smooth.

DAY 68 – OATS

Some days a warm, nourishing bowl of oatmeal just hits the spot. My favorite way to eat oats is as the entire groat; soaked overnight and then slowly warmed in the morning. They are chewy with a slightly sweet, nutty flavor. If groats aren't available, the next option is steel cut, which still has more of the healthful benefit of the whole oat.

I have found that the more processed the oat, the less complex the flavor and the less nutrient density. This morning I had steel cut oats that I had soaked overnight in yogurt. I slightly warmed them rather than cooked them (to keep all the enzymes alive) added some honey and strawberries and it made the perfect, nourishing breakfast. Oats are a hardy and hearty little grain that do well in a wide variety of environments, from a growing perspective and record of them in the human diet is found all throughout Europe, Asia, and North America.

From a health perspective, oats are little rock stars! As with any food, the closer they are to their natural state, the better they are for you. They are a great source of fiber and various vitamins and minerals. Studies demonstrate that the inclusion of oats in your diet can help with cholesterol, decrease the potential for colorectal cancer, and help balance blood sugar.

Oats are also a great prebiotic, increasing the production of short chain fatty acids that aid in helping you have a happy belly. Some people are sensitive to the phytic acid that remains in the oat even after it is smashed, squashed, and mutilated to become a quick breakfast option; the easy remedy is soaking them overnight to break up the cell wall.

In a nutritional world that is pushing towards grain-hating, I think it's a shame to avoid the hearty little oat. Oats on occasion are a smart option for most palates and bodies.

DAY 69 – CACAO

If you are a chocolate lover, a genuine chocolate lover (not to be confused with a sugar and milk lover) then you will know that cacao is the real deal. It's where it all begins in the world of chocolate. Cacao beans come from the cacao tree and they are what eventually get turned into chocolate.

True cacao is bitter, complex, and earthy. I say complex because there are notes of sweet and almost smoky flavors mixed in with the obvious bitter, if you can stay with it and let it mellow out as you chew and savor. Of course, the various nuances of flavor are dependent on the terroir, making the world of cacao as mysterious, and sometimes as pretentious, as the world of wine.

Cacao becomes cocoa and/or chocolate through a multi-stage process that includes fermenting, roasting, separating, drying and depending on the desired end product, a multitude of other actions. Suffices to say that at the end of all of that processing, most of what we know as chocolate has been so diluted that any of the potential health benefits no longer exist.

From a health perspective, I'm sure you've all heard that a little bit of chocolate a day can be good for you. Well, that should actually be " a little bit of cacao" a day is good for you. It's the raw cacao that is imparting any health benefits, which is why there is typically a caveat that the chocolate needs to be 80% or more and not the run of the mill chocolate bar off the conventional market shelf. (I find most people don't really pay attention to that part).

Truth, cacao is very good for you. It is extremely high in flavonoids and antioxidants. It has fiber. It helps regulate the nervous system and balance serotonin. Research demonstrates that it can be beneficial in the battle against insulin resistance. Its bitter quality enhances digestion and it protects your cardiovascular system. What's not to love??? Well, it is quite bitter and it's a taste you may have to cultivate. But it is well worth it.

Little added endnote: So lately I've been on an all-natural everything kick, including body products. I started using raw cacao powder as a foundation for my face... Love it!! Smells great, feels great, and my skin looks fantastic. Only sayin....

DAY 70 – OREGANO (WILD MARJORAM)

A little bit goes a long way... at least that's my flavor experience of oregano. It is earthy and a bit pungent. Fresh oregano can also stimulate hints of pine or citrus due to the natural chemical compounds. Oregano is in the mint family, which is known for its volatile oils.

From a culinary perspective, oregano's earthy quality makes it pair well with foods that tend to be acidic, like cooked tomatoes or eggplant. It adds well to meat dishes and can bump eggs to a whole new level. Roasted roma tomatoes with a sprinkle of parmesan cheese and fresh oregano is an exceptional treat.

The chemical compounds that give it the pine or citrus impression are indeed oils that contain those notes. Limonene, pinene, and thymol are just a few of the compounds that give fresh oregano its pungent bite. These compounds are also what give it the awesome reputation for being such a benefit to health. The volatile oils make oregano a powerful anti-bacterial, anti-microbial, anti-fungal intervention. Research suggests that oregano oil is a useful intervention for respiratory infections, gastro-intestinal issues, and systemic inflammation. Some studies suggest that even the vapor is powerful enough to kill a wide variety of pathogens, even some of the 'superbugs' created by our over use of synthetic antiseptics.

Oregano is a nice addition to food either dried or fresh, however, each taste a little bit different so it's a good idea to familiarize yourself with the flavor notes found in both fresh and dried so you can add just the right amount. (I've made the mistake of adding too much and creating a dish that tasted like dirt... not yummy!!)

DAY 71 – MASCARPONE

Mascarpone is considered a cheese; an Italian cream cheese to be more specific, however, technically it's curdled cream. It has a smooth and creamy mouth-feel and a sweet, slightly tangy flavor. It's lighter and smoother than cream cheese and goes well in a variety of dishes. Mascarpone can sweeten a dessert without actually adding sugar or other sweeteners. A classic example is figs, with Mascarpone and touch of balsamic vinegar. Quick, easy and delicious! It hits all the flavor notes and delights your palate.

The health benefits in Mascarpone cheese are dependent completely on the quality of the cream used. Heritage cow cream and a naturally derived citric or acetic acid (lemon juice or apple cider vinegar) would have the most beneficial qualities; all the benefits of quality milk.

DAY 72 – FAT (RECIPE)

Fat; we love it, we hate it, we crave it, and we need it. Fat is one of the three macronutrients that our body needs for health and well-being. The flavor of fat will, of course, vary depending entirely on what kind of fat it is. What gives fat its distinctive mouthfeel? Fat is a lipid. It is not water soluble, so it is not as easily broken down by saliva. The fat molecules end up rolling around in your mouth like miniscule, silky-smooth beads.

Tiny science lesson: The concept of fat can be confusing because it's used to describe different things. Fat can be a word describing a type of tissue, which is what we talk about when we talk about the fat on our bodies or from an animal; or the word fat can be used to talk about a particular cell type, which actually begins to encompass all types of fat. Fat tissue is made up of fat cells.

Molecularly, fat is a triglyceride; which simply means it is a combination of three fatty acids and one glycerol molecule. The properties of a 'triglyceride', whether healthful or harmful, are dependent on the structure of the fatty acids. This is why the science around triglycerides and fat consumption can be so confusing...we really have to know what kind of fatty acids we are talking about before impact can be identified.

Interestingly fat, as a tissue, is considered an organ, expressing its own biochemical messages to your brain and body via hormone secretion and other chemical signaling. The amount and type of fat you carry on your body influences your nervous system and all the other systems in your body.

Your brain and body need healthy fats to stay balanced and well. So, although it may seem counterintuitive that you would lose fat by eating fat, if you're eating the right kind of fat, it's absolutely true. Good fats include; omega 3 fatty acid rich foods (sardines, salmon, anchovies, flax seeds, pumpkin seeds, walnuts, avocado), medium chain fatty acids like coconut oil, palm oil and ghee, as well as some mono or poly unsaturated fats like olive oil. Animal fat from quality sources are also good fats, butter, lard, tallow, and even duck fat.

What can happen if you aren't eating enough fat? Not only can it make you fatter, but it can also make you depressed, anxious, fearful, and contribute to any number of mood disorders, including panic attacks. One more fun factoid; eating fat (the good kind) stimulates your opioid receptors and in higher amounts can contribute to feelings of euphoria. It appears that in various ancient cultures, high fact consumption may have been the secret ingredient in assisting priests/priestesses in accessing altered states of consciousness for ritual purposes.

PEANUT BUTTER CACAO FUDGE

1 c. virgin coconut oil, melted (melt on really low heat)

1 c. high quality raw cacao powder or good cocoa powder (the quality of this ingredient makes a huge difference in the taste)

1/3 c. raw honey (you can use date paste or 6 pureed dates, if you're keto conscious, you can leave the sweetness out)

1 tsp. vanilla

dash sea salt

1/3 c. chunky natural peanut butter (or more to taste)

Add all ingredients except peanut butter and beat on medium to high heat with a hand or stand mixer for 5-7 minutes. Mixture should be smooth and glossy. Add peanut butter and blend until combined.

Scoop mixture into a glass dish and refrigerate to set. Once set cut into small squares and enjoy. These keep for a while if you keep them in an airtight container in the fridge. Lovely little squares of energy to nibble!

DAY 73 – FENUGREEK

Not commonly found in western cuisine, Fenugreek is a great little addition to many different types of dishes. I am sipping some Fenugreek tea at the moment, attempting to single out the various flavor notes. It is nutty, with a slight astringent and bitter quality (reminding me of celery) and has a refreshing pungency that resolves into a hint of sweetness. It smells a little like maple syrup, which is, interestingly, one of its commercial uses. It can be added to manufactured sugar syrups to give them the illusion of maple.

My tea is made from Fenugreek seeds, which can also be soaked and sprouted and then added to fresh foods. You can also use the leaves and stems in a variety of culinary endeavors. Fenugreek is a common ingredient in many Middle Eastern, Indian, and Asian foods. It's frequently found in curries and other sauce dishes, as well as, baked into breads.

From a health perspective, Fenugreek has been used for centuries upon centuries as a health intervention. Little side note; it's also one of the herbs used by the ancient Egyptians for embalming.

Research suggests that Fenugreek is beneficial for balancing blood sugar, decreasing inflammation and reducing the potential for kidney stones. Sipping Fenugreek tea is a great way to clear bronchial phlegm and aid in relieving issues of sore throat, congestion that can accompany flu or allergies.

Fenugreek also contains diosgenin which is a chemical compound used to make synthetic estrogen. It can be effective in balancing hormones for both men and women. Fenugreek tea can be a great way to kill that cold, balance hormones, and improve insulin production and uptake... oh and it's reportedly an aphrodisiac.

DAY 74 – LEMONGRASS (RECIPE)

Aaaah, inhaling freshly sliced Lemongrass. It is a balm to the soul; bright and refreshing. Lemongrass smells like lemon but somehow not. It has its own complexity; citrus, with some earthiness. Lemongrass tastes as bright and complex as it smells...and like most things with volatile oils, a little bit goes a long way. Lemongrass has a citronella quality that can overpower foods if you use too much (this is also one thing that makes it a great insect repellent).

It's popular in Asian and Indian foods, and can bring an extra dimension of flavor, openness, and brightness to foods. It also makes a very refreshing tea to sip hot or cold. Simmering and sipping a few sliced rings of lemongrass makes your house smell divine and your belly happy.

From a health perspective, Lemongrass has some great qualities. It is antibacterial and antifungal. It has mild astringent qualities so it is helpful for skin conditions. It aids in peristalsis and overall digestive balance. Research suggests that it helps relieve stomachache and spasms. Studies also demonstrate that Lemongrass aids in lowering cholesterol and can help balance blood sugar.

The aromatic quality of lemongrass makes it a great mood enhancer and it also contains chemical compounds that contribute to parasympathetic stimulation. In other words, sipping some lemongrass tea helps calm and relax your nerves and can promote a deep and uninterrupted sleep.

COCONUT CURRY SOUP WITH LEMONGRASS (RAW)

Love this soup in the spring and summer months... I don't like cold foods so I heat it slightly. For the most part all ingredients can be just thrown into the Vitamix and voila you have soup. Spinning it in the Vitamix long enough will also heat it and then the coconut fat can emulsify making it a creamy, delicious delight. All the ingredients can be adjusted to suit your taste, that's what makes it easy.

4 cups coconut milk (blended coconut water and meat)
2 Tablespoons ginger, minced
1 Tablespoon coconut oil or coconut cream
2 Tablespoons olive oil
1 small clove garlic, crushed
2-3 medjool dates, pitted and chopped
2 Tablespoons lemon juice
2 teaspoons curry powder
1/8 teaspoon red chilli powder
1/2 teaspoon shallot
1 Tablespoons Nama Shoyu (or tamari)
1/2 teaspoon sea salt
2 stalks lemongrass, minced
1/2 small orange bell pepper
2 Tablespoons cilantro, chopped

DAY 75 - SPINACH

"I'm strong to the finish cause I eats me spinach"...Popeye, the Sailor Man

Ah, spinach...a food that can be utterly delicious and refreshing or completely disgusting; depending on how it's prepared. I still don't know how I feel about Popeye convincing me each Saturday morning that canned, slimy, sodium packed spinach was really a delicious treat. But I do know that now I'm all grown up spinach is one of my favorite foods. Make that raw spinach, since I still can't abide the cooked stuff.

Raw spinach, especially baby leaves, has a refreshing, earthy quality. It can be slightly bitter and sweet at the same time. It also has an astringent mouthfeel that gets more prominent with maturity. Young spinach leaves have a minimal mouthfeel but mature leaves can taste almost chalky if eaten raw.

The chalky or astringent mouthfeel is due in part to the presence of oxalic acid. Oxalic acid is the plants' way of protecting itself against predators, so in a sense it is a minor toxin. In raw spinach, the oxalic acid binds with the available minerals and other phytonutrients, making them much less available. So, yes, spinach is good for you and, yes, it's a good idea to pay attention to how you prepare it to access all its natural goodness.

I like raw spinach so I help the cell wall break down by massaging the leaves and breaking them up. This, in turn, begins to neutralize the binding effect of the oxalic acid on the good stuff. Cooking also breaks down the impact of oxalic acid, so a quick dip in some boiling water or a quick sauté, would help the nutrient availability without over doing it and giving you a slimy end result.

From a health perspective, spinach is right up there with other green veggies, like broccoli and kale. It packs a nutrient power punch, with vitamins, minerals, and other phytonutrients that help with things like balancing blood glucose levels, minimizing oxidative stress, and increasing bone density. Research suggests spinach is effective in blocking the carcinogenic impact of grilled foods so it could be useful to add a handful of baby spinach leaves to that backyard barbecue burger. Or you could try one of these veggie burgers:

SPINACH BURGERS

1 bag of thawed and well-drained chopped spinach (squeeze all the liquid out)

2 eggs

½ c shredded cheese

½ c rolled oats (I use organic rolled oats... I also tried using chestnut flour and it worked well)

1 tsp red pepper flakes

1 tsp salt

1 small shallot minced

1 clove garlic - minced

Mix all ingredients in a bowl. Shape into patties and cook over medium high heat

Patties are done when crispy brown and firm

DAY 76 – APPLE

Did you know there are literally thousands of different types of apple? With that in mind it's a little challenging to talk about one flavor. Each cultivar, which is what the different types are called, has its own distinct flavor note and is cultivated for eating, cooking or both. The qualities that my palate prefers in an apple are a crisp bite accompanied by a balance of sweet, sour, and juicy.

Interestingly, as I've learned to listen to my body, I realize that I love fresh, raw apples in the spring and summer but tend to prefer cooked apples in the late fall and winter. Turns out, this is what seasonal eating calls for, especially for my body type. Also for my body type, apples tend to be too sweet and oxidize in my system too fast, so I make sure I eat them with a bit of fat, maybe some nuts or cheese. With cooked apples, I add ghee and spices.

The apple seems to have originated in Asia, although this fact is often forgotten in Western tradition. First reference to cultivation of apples can be found in written manuscripts in Rome, although there is evidence of apples being part of human diet as early as 6500 BCE. Apples are incapable of bearing fruit unless they cross-pollinate. This is where bees come into the picture. They are a major contributor in the success of apple pollination and the variation of crops. So, the next time you chomp into an apple or sip a refreshing glass of apple cider, be sure to offer up some gratitude or a toast to the bees.

From a health perspective, apples are awesome. It's possible an apple a day really could keep the doctor away. Research demonstrates that apples can help balance hormones, improve immune function, regulate blood sugar, flatten your belly and even whiten your teeth. Apples are a great source of fiber, quercetin, vitamin C, potassium and a multitude of other nutrients and phytonutrients.

If you want to know more about the awesome history of the apple, I love Michael Pollan's book, *"The Botany of Desire"*.

DAY 77 – MOLASSES/TREACLE

Molasses and Treacle are pretty much similar products, both are consequences of sugar production, whether cane, beet, or other source. Molasses is what you get after several boiling processes. When I taste Molasses, I think of the black licorice I loved as a kid; which makes sense because traditionally black licorice was made from blackstrap molasses.

As an adult, I'm not quite as into black licorice but I am a huge fan of things like gingerbread and sticky toffee pudding! For me the flavor draw comes from the complexity of sweet, bitter, and almost earthiness. I don't necessarily like cakes and pastries because I'm not a huge fan of the overly sweet. However, if a baked good has molasses it tends to minimize that sweet edge, adding a slightly savory quality and then I can't get enough of it. From a culinary perspective, Molasses is not only for baked goods, it can be found in things like baked beans, sweet and sour sauces, and barbeque.

From a health perspective Molasses is sadly still considered sugar, so limiting it is a good idea. However, it has its good points. It is high in minerals and can even help if you tend to suffer from things like anemia or other hormone imbalances. It is full of antioxidants that can help fight against oxidative stress (I know, it seems counterintuitive that a sugar product could help with oxidative stress). Studies also suggest molasses can be useful in promoting healthy, strong bones, as well as contributing to digestive balance.

I can't recommend high consumption of Molasses or Treacle because it is still at the end of the day a sugar product. However, the occasional use can be beneficial. I have been known to stir a spoonful into hot lemon water or even coffee which makes a nice change. The caveat: Make sure it's unsulfured and organic...otherwise the unnamed chemicals used during processing make any benefits totally null and void.

DAY 78 – ARTICHOKE

The Artichoke is a member of the thistle family. In fact, the part that we are typically used to consuming is the bud of a flower. Artichokes have an interesting taste spectrum. Very young Artichokes are often slightly sweet and almost grassy tasting; while more mature buds can have a bitter back note. If you've never eaten an Artichoke from the bud, I imagine first impression can seem daunting. It is best only to consume the fleshy part of the leaf and the center of the bud, called the heart; although in young plants, the whole leaf can be attempted with better results.

Artichoke contains a chemical compound called cynarin that blocks some of your taste receptors and gives food the impression of sweetness. For this reason, it is sometimes added to drinks or foods as a sweetener, even though technically it isn't really.

From a health perspective Artichoke has quite the impressive resume. Research demonstrates that it stimulates bile production in the liver, a result of the compound silymarin (also found in milk thistle), which helps detox the body. This is also useful for getting rid of indigestion and even hangovers. Artichokes are also high in vitamins and minerals that provide protection against high cholesterol, syndrome x, and bone density issues. Interesting new research suggests the fiber content combined with certain chemical compounds found in the Artichoke leaf can help minimize Gastrointestinal issues, including IBS and Crohn's Disease.

If you don't like eating artichoke, you can find it in tea or liqueur, or you can make a soup out of it. Either way, it's worth expanding your palate's repertoire by including the occasional artichoke.

DAY 79 – PARSLEY (RECIPE)

Parsley is an unassuming little herb that has somehow been relegated to the role of garnish. But don't be fooled and don't leave the garnish because parsley is a queen among herbs. It has been referred to as the "jewel of herbs" and a culmination of all things green. There are several different varieties so the flavor changes with each. The parsley I'm tasting today is a curly-leaf. It's grassy with a hint of bitterness or piquant spiciness. It is also very refreshing and the first nibble was like infusing my tastebuds and mouth with a little bit of sunshine. This makes sense, because Parsley is packed with chlorophyll and vitamin C and many, many other phytonutrients.

From a culinary perspective, curly-leaf has a subtler almost bitter quality as I noted, and flat-leaf is considered more robust and complex. Flat-leaf is typically the kind called for in Mediterranean or Italian cooking. I like adding fresh parsley to all kinds of foods because it seems to perk them up and add an extra dimension of flavor that is bright and interesting. I tend to add it in at the last so the volatile oils are not diminished by heating.

From a medicinal or health perspective, parsley is pretty amazing. In fact, first recorded use of parsley is pharmacological; it didn't seem to work its way into the culinary world until the Romans started using it in various dishes. At least that's the recorded history... I can't imagine someone didn't find it delightful and throw it in a soup just for its flavor some time before the Romans.

Parsley is high in Vitamin C and a great source of Vitamins A and B. It is packed with antioxidants that help decrease the impact of oxidative stress. It also has flavonoids and volatile oils that contribute to things like increasing glutathione (good brain stuff), decreasing cancer and tumor causing agents. In fact, research demonstrates the volatile oil myristicin inhibits the formation and growth of tumors. Parsley is anti-inflammatory, heart healthy and immune boosting. In the world of medical herbalism it is considered a diuretic that helps cleanse and balance intracellular fluids. It is an emmenagogue, which means it stimulates female reproductive hormones (so if you're pregnant, throwing parsley in a juicer is not a good idea). It's also a carminative, meaning it helps with digestive issues (including flatulence), which is why I think it first ended up on plates. Chew on a little parsley after a meal and help everything digest well, and there's a bonus...it freshens your breath.

Ways to get more parsley in your diet? Sprinkle it on your food, makes some parsley pesto, add it to soups, stews, and sauces. Put it on the side of your plate as an after-meal digestive. (:

PARSLEY WALNUT PESTO
1 cup chopped walnuts
1 full bunch of chopped parsley (about 2 cups)

1/2 cup grated pecorino or parmesan cheese
3 garlic cloves, roughly chopped
1/2 tsp salt
1/2 cup olive oil

Put the walnuts, parsley, cheese, garlic, and salt in a food processor and pulse for a few seconds to combine everything (you don't want to puree it). Scrape down the sides of the bowl then pulse again. Drizzle in the olive oil while the machine is running just long enough to incorporate the oil, about 20-30 seconds.
Use immediately and/or store it in the refrigerator and try it out on a variety of dishes.

DAY 80 – NETTLE

That's right, today's flavor is the infamous stinging nettle. I'm sure some are wondering how in the world to taste a stinging nettle without suffering some horrible ramifications. Thankfully, you do not have to fall on it raw with your tongue. Nettles are actually a very delicious and extremely nutritious food. The young nettle leaves have a slight sweet, earthy quality. I'd compare them to another green vegetable if I could but truly, they stand alone (and not because they sting all the other vegetables).

I was first introduced to nettle as a 'food' source many years ago when a friend made a pot of nettle tea to help get over a prolonged bout with the flu. It worked. I'd love to say the nettle tea was delicious but it wasn't. It was earthy, slightly bitter and pretty astringent; adding honey did the trick. I was, afterwards very intrigued to know more about the beneficial qualities of such an ill-reputed plant. My friend then showed me how to cook with nettle and introduce it into my diet in some very delicious ways; nettle soup, nettle leaves in salad, even nettle on pizza. My current favorite nettle use besides tea is cake and pesto. Both are fantastically delicious.

She also taught me how to gather, handle and prepare nettle, which is a requirement if you are going to use nettles and remain on good terms with them. Believe it or not, they won't sting you if you don't offend them. Think about it, when's the last time a stinging nettle came over to your house walked in and stung you? Usually, it happens when you've been aimlessly strolling through the countryside and trod clumsily through their house.

Nettle for dinner is a culinary treat (or breakfast, or tea, or whenever). It's also a health bonus extraordinaire. In fact, what prompted me to choose nettle today, besides sipping nettle tea which I now love, is a piece of research just released demonstrating the beneficial impact of nettle in the fight against cancer. It appears it contains a chemical compound that not only is anti-carcinogenic on its own but also enhances the effectiveness of cancer fighting pharmaceuticals.

Nettle is high in iron, calcium, and vitamins A and C. It is a great source of beneficial fatty acids and it is high in fiber. It's also high in flavonoids and other phytonutrients that help balance Research demonstrates that it is anti-inflammatory and antihistamine. It boosts digestive function, purifies the blood, helps the liver function more efficiently, and has a multitude of other health remedies. Nettle has long been a medicinal intervention in cultures all over the world.

It's also an amazing beauty treatment. Steep nettle leaves for 15-20 minutes and then use it as a hair rinse it makes your hair soft and shiny. You can also use it as a toner on your skin to clear acne and other skin irritations and rashes. If you live in an area where nettle is common, it could be interesting to learn how to harvest it and introduce it to your kitchen.

DAY 81 – KALAMATA OLIVES (RECIPE)

Salty and earthy, with a smooth yet hearty texture, the Kalamata olive is one of my favorite kinds of olive; especially if it is traditionally, rather than conventionally, prepared. Olives, like the apple come in so many varietals it sort of boggles the mind. Kalamata olives are named for their city of origin, Kalamata in Greece.
I love them pitted or with pits and they tend to be a standard in my summertime diet. They are great for a quick and healthful snack and they can bring an interesting twist to many culinary endeavors.

What accounts for the distinct difference in flavor between the Kalamata and other olives? The processing. If you've ever picked an olive straight from the tree and bitten into it, you will know that unprocessed olives can be extraordinarily bitter. This is why they are soaked in brine once picked. Salt cuts bitter and the olive can then be more easily consumed.

The traditional and most tasty preparation for the Kalamata olive is a two-step process. First, it is soaked in brine for a couple of weeks to eliminate the bitter bite, then, they are covered in vinegar (typically red wine vinegar) and olive oil and allowed to ferment for 8 to 10 months; sometimes a slice of lemon can be added to the mix to enhance the flavor complexity. Sadly, conventional methods utilize caustic soda or other chemical compounds to speed up the fermentation process and that doesn't have to be identified on the label. These hidden compounds end up being part of your diet whether you like it or not if you buy conventionally produced olives.

From a health perspective, olives have all the benefits of olive oil plus some added fiber and a few more vitamins and minerals. They are a great snack option if you are trying to eliminate systemic inflammation or are suffering from an inflammation related chronic disease (which is just about all disease). The caveat, you don't need too many of them, you do want to watch your sodium count if you eat a lot of processed foods, and you do want to make sure they are traditionally processed. Kalamata olives imported from Greece are not allowed to be processed any other way, so if you can go for the imported, packed in a jar, you will be all set for a delicious snack that is belly/body/and planet friendly.

Here's a quick and easy tapenade recipe that is delicious folded into pasta, smeared on toast, or as a dip for veggies. Yum...

KALAMATA TAPENADE
3 cloves garlic, peeled
1 c. pitted kalamata olives
2 TBS capers
3 TBS chopped fresh parsley
2 TBS lemon juice
2 TBS olive oil

Salt and pepper to taste

Throw it all in the food processor and pulse until desired consistency.

DAY 82 – CELERY

Celery is one of those plants that inspire me to artistic endeavors. Every time I cut the base from the stalk, I want to use the base to make designs. Celery is crunchy, juicy, slightly bitter, but also slightly salty and sweet; in short, tasty and unique. It's unfortunate that the low fat, low calorie diet fad mindset has relegated celery to a drab diet food instead of the interesting and multifaceted resource that it actually is.

Celery has been a dietary influence in many cultures around the globe; most notably in Egypt and Greece before it became more widely cultivated in the world. From a culinary perspective, celery is an awesome addition to your cooking repertoire. What makes celery so versatile is that every part of it can be used to produce a different influence on a meal. The seeds, stalk, and bulb (known as celeriac) are all great additions and present a variety of creative options for use in the kitchen. My favorite in the winter is mashed celeriac.

From a health perspective, celery is indeed a low calorie, low sugar, low fat, low everything option for snacking. But what it lacks in macronutrients it makes up for in micronutrients. Research is showing that the chemical compounds in celery can decrease systemic inflammation and improve digestive balance. It has been a beneficial addition to diet for people suffering from gastrointestinal inflammation, like IBS and Crohn's Disease; mostly because the polysaccharides found in celery are pectin based rather than starch based. Celery is also packed with Vitamin K and C and other volatile oils that make it a great anti-oxidant. Again, research is showing that it acts as a blood detoxifier and decreases the potential for cytokines responsible for tumors other cancer causing agents.

Lastly, the phenols found in celery appear to cleanse the liver and blood of acrylamides, which are naturally derived toxins found in foods that are fried or cooked at high heat. It's the presence of acrylamide that tips the scales on dark roasted coffee from beneficial to non-beneficial. I don't know if I recommend adding celery seed to your roast but maybe have a celery snack later in the day… can't hurt.

DAY 83 – NUTRITIONAL YEAST (RECIPE)

Yep, nutritional yeast is a flavor. No, it's not the kind of yeast that is used to bake bread or make beer. Nor is it the kind that will wreak havoc on your health.
Chances are you are not familiar with nutritional yeast unless you have ventured deeply into alternative dietary habits. (:

Nutritional yeast tastes very umami. It's salty, cheesy, complex, a little bit pungent, and slightly sweet. In fact, it's often used as a 'cheese' substitute in many raw and vegan recipes. (as if there could ever really be a cheese substitute?!?!) I became a fan of nutritional yeast when I was learning to be a raw food chef (skills that I currently use to enhance my omnivorous diet). Nutritional yeast is indeed a type of yeast, it's made from bacteria that is cultivated and harvested from molasses. It is then dried, which makes it inactive and made into lovely little flakes of yumminess. No really, it's yummy.

Nutritional yeast is a mainstay in vegetarian, vegan and raw food diets because it is a great source of B vitamins, especially vitamin B12, which is very challenging to get if you are avoiding animal products.

The cool thing about nutritional yeast is not only is it great just to have around to sprinkle over foods, like broccoli or popcorn but it also makes a pretty delicious cheese sauce or gravy to sub if you are trying to avoid fattier options.
There was a phase where I sprinkled nutritional yeast on just about everything because it is so deliciously savory. I have since cooled out and use it a few times a week as a nice flavor option to something that might otherwise be a little boring.

From a culinary perspective, nutritional yeast is easy. You can sprinkle it on things like eggs, veggies, pasta, popcorn whatever could benefit from some added cheesy goodness; or you can liquefy it and make it into a cheesy sauce.

From a health perspective, nutritional yeast is packed with nutrients. Interestingly, it is considered a complete protein, just like an animal product, and it provides the full range of B vitamins that animal products provide. It also provides a nice percentage of chromium, selenium and zinc. All of which are antioxidants that contribute to digestive and gastrointestinal health and balance.

EASY VEGAN PEANUT BUTTER CUPS
1 c. melted chocolate (dark or baker's)
4 TBS of peanut butter
1 tsp of nutritional yeast

You can either use a silicon candy mold or a muffin tin. If you use a muffin tin you will want small muffin papers...unless of course you opt for the Peanut Butter Cup sheet pan method. Yum.

Melt the chocolate in a double boiler. While chocolate is melting slightly warm peanut butter, so it's runny and stir in nutritional yeast. Scoop a spoonful of chocolate into the bottom of mold or tin (or another pan) about ¼ inch deep. Let it harden slightly. Then scoop some peanut butter about ¼ inch. Then scoop the chocolate top. Place them all in the refrigerator to harden and then enjoy. Seriously there is no way to mess this recipe up...chocolate and peanut butter.

If you're really feeling adventurous, you can try these:

KALE CHIPS:
1 head curly leaf kale (de-stemmed and tore in bits)
1 cup raw cashews (soaked for 2 hrs)
Juice of one large lemon
1/4 to 1/2 cup nutritional yeast
1 c. carrots grated (the original recipe calls for red bell pepper but I can't eat them)
1/2 tsp of red chili pepper flakes
1/2 tsp sea salt

Puree all ingredients and then pour over pieces of kale in a bowl. Massage them all and transfer to a baking sheet or your dehydrator. If it's a dehydrator set them at 110f (43c) degrees for about 8 hours. If it's your oven keep it below 200f (93c) and turn them occasionally.

DAY 84 – CASHEWS (RECIPES)

Cashews are crunchy, buttery, and slightly sweet. They are probably first in line in my favorite nut category. Since the Cashew tastes sweet and has a good amount of the good fats and starch, it is a good option for snacking. It's also a good mood food.

From a culinary perspective, Cashews are easily added to a variety of dishes increasing the options to savor your meal. They are versatile and a mainstay in the raw, vegan, and vegetarian kitchens. Cashews are also very popular in Indian and Asian cuisine. I use cashews for a variety of crazy things...mostly influenced by my raw food days. I love to shake things up by replacing cream with homemade Cashew milk. I use them as thickeners for soups. They make a fabulous buttery, raw piecrust! They're also great to crumble on top of veggies and toss into a stir-fry.

Even though almonds tend to get the rave reviews for healthy eating options, Cashews offer a more diverse influence on your overall wellbeing. Their abundance in minerals, like copper and magnesium make them especially beneficial for your mental health. In fact, research demonstrates that eating a small handful a day improves your mood and some studies have shown two handfuls a day to be as effective as certain pharmaceuticals. Cashews are high in antioxidants so they help decrease oxidative stress. The copper in Cashews contributes to collagen production, which is what keeps the tissue in your body healthy and plump. It also adds to strong bones and connective tissue. I highly recommend getting some Cashews in your pantry.

HOMEMADE CASHEW MILK

1 c. raw cashews

2 c. water

Soak the cashews in water at least 4 hours, or overnight. Drain the cashews and rinse until the water runs clear.

Place in jar or blender, add 2 more cups water, vanilla, cinnamon, sweetener (optional). Blend in blender or use immersion blender until smooth and creamy.

Try this if you're feeling adventurous:

CASHEW PUMPKIN "CHEESECAKE"

2 cups raw cashews (soaked)
2 cups fresh grated pumpkin
1/2 cup coconut oil
3 TBS lemon juice
6 dates (soaked, drained, then blended til smooth)
1 tsp vanilla
4 tsp cinnamon
1 tsp nutmeg
2 tsp ginger

Soak cashews in water for at least 1 hour, then drain. I usually soak them overnight.

Blend all ingredients until combined and creamy. Pour mixture into small ramekins or a glass, baking dish. Cover tightly and let it set in the freezer for at least 4 hours. This will harden the coconut oil and set the cheesecake. After this time, transfer the cheesecake in the refrigerator for at least one hour before serving. Of course, you can also not freeze it and eat it as a dip! Yum.

If you'd like to add a crust to your cheesecake you can blend two cups of almonds, walnuts, pecans. Add a tablespoon of water if that helps to get things moving. Press the mixture into the bottom of a spring-form pan and pour the other ingredients over the top. Follow the same procedure; freeze for about four hours, and then refrigerate. When opening the spring-form pan, gently insert a knife along the edge of the cheesecake, so that it does not stick to the edge of the pan.

DAY 85 – GHEE

This morning's flavor comes straight from my stovetop. The golden goodness of grass-fed, jersey cow butter is bubbling happily as it is well on its way to becoming delicious ghee. Ghee is sweet, a little savory with a smooth mouthfeel. Although the process for making ghee is like that of making clarified butter, ghee requires a little bit longer, slower, lower heat cooking time. This allows for the removal of even more moisture and enhances the flavor as the milk solids caramelize and rise to the surface.

The tradition of making and utilizing ghee is ancient. In Ayurveda, it is considered a sattvic food, which means it promotes higher consciousness and wellbeing. It is a staple in Indian cooking and Traditional Indian Medicine.

From a culinary perspective, ghee is great, if prepared correctly it will last a very long time in the refrigerator or in cooler temperatures on your countertop. It has a higher heat tolerance once the milk solids are cooked out so it can be used in a variety of cooking endeavors, even those that require high heat. It is also great in baked goods since it delivers a very distinctive sweet, savory almost umami hint of flavor. I use ghee and coconut oil as my main go-to for cooking and baking.

From a medicinal perspective, there is unfortunately very little western research specific to ghee, although there is ample research specific to some of the properties that are found in ghee. For example, ghee contains medium chain fatty acid much like coconut oil; making it a more desirable choice for consumption. Remember that medium chain triglycerides are some of the fat good guys and can do things like help with balanced brain and nervous system function. MCT's in appropriate amounts can contribute to weight loss and cardiovascular health and cellular regeneration. Ghee also contains butyric acid, which helps keep your digestive bacteria happy and healthy; so it is a great option for people trying to manage chronic digestive inflammation and ailments; including IBS and Crohn's Disease.

One more bonus; ghee is typically tolerated well even by people who exhibit milk intolerance or allergy because the milk sugars are cooked out and all that is left is the fat and other nutrients and enzymes. In Ayurveda ghee is often the medium used to deliver medicinal interventions; for example, mixing the appropriate spices with a little ghee to form a "pill" makes them much easier to consume. Then you also have the added bonus of the medicinal properties of the ghee itself.

If you're not up to making a batch of ghee, which does require patience and attention, you can purchase it from most natural or traditional foods markets. Just be sure to get plain old ghee, without the added preservatives that you can't pronounce. I love making ghee because it requires focus. I have to stop and stay present with what I'm doing. In that sense, it is a stress reliever and I feel more connected with my food. I also love that I get the extra deliciousness of the caramelized milk solids on the bottom of the pan, which are a divine sweet treat.

DAY 86 – TURMERIC

Fresh turmeric is a very subtle but complex flavor. Upon first nibble, it is cool and refreshing, quickly followed by a piquant sensation that isn't quite heat but most definitely wakes up my taste buds. It has the qualities of both earthy and effervescent.

Currently, Turmeric has a celebrated place in the super food limelight, which is great, but I highly recommend finding ways to cook with it rather than pop a bunch of supplements. Turmeric is interesting and it imparts not only flavor but also vibrant color. It is used typically in savory dishes but can also be found in some sweets. I grate the fresh root and add it to stir fried vegetables, tonics, teas, soups, and stews. It's a wonderful addition to bone and mineral broths. Get curious and invite turmeric into your kitchen!

From a health perspective, Turmeric has some fantastic qualities. It is in the ginger family and it is one of the most researched herbs with quite a nice repertoire of health benefits. It has been used for centuries in Eastern medicine and over the past decade has been found by western research to reduce systemic inflammation, increase neurological functioning, and it helps decrease oxidative stress. Research has demonstrated that consuming turmeric can help repair your brain and keep it strong and functioning well.

There is also significant research suggesting that regular intake of turmeric can decrease potential for cardiovascular disease. It also demonstrates relief for chronic ailments like arthritis, gastrointestinal inflammation, and cystic fibrosis. As an herbal intervention, you will need to include a warming spice like pepper or ginger for full benefit. Turmeric is also antimicrobial, antibacterial and makes a great balm for the skin, if you don't mind the yellow coloring. (:

DAY 87 – PINE NUTS (RECIPE)

The pine nut is a tiny little unassuming nut; crunchy, slightly sweet, and pungent. The retronasal effect of nibbling a pine nut indeed brings hints of pine and greenery to mind. If you're wondering whether you have ever tasted a pine nut, it is worth remembering if you've ever had pesto. Traditional pesto is a blend of pine nuts, basil, olive oil, garlic, and pecorino cheese. Yum.

In the U.S. Southwest, pine nuts are found in many sweet and savory dishes. It is also dark roasted and served as a coffee. One of my absolute favorite pine nut dishes is a pie made similarly to pecan pie but using instead pine nuts. It is divine. There is something refreshing about the pine nuts that cuts through sweetness of the creamy caramel middle and just makes the whole thing a taste explosion that rivals symphonic immersion. Oh yes, I like pine nut pie very, very much. (:

Pine nuts can also be lightly toasted and tossed in with other dishes as a finishing touch that adds complexity and depth. It's a key ingredient in a variety of global culinary endeavors, such as kibbeh, chestnut/pine nut stuffing, and various traditional Italian dishes.

The use of pine nuts has been recorded in Paleolithic peoples on every continent from Europe to Asia and through the Americas. Like many foods, the pine nut comes with an interesting and complex political history, especially in the U.S. where they were once a staple food for many tribes of Native peoples, several of whom still have treaties insuring harvesting rights each year. (a topic, entirely too complex to go into in this brief post but worth checking out if you are at all curious). It could be nice to keep in mind the depth and breadth of this little nut as you bring them into your kitchen.

From a health perspective, pine nuts are a great source of protein, good fat, and iron. They can give you a boost in energy while helping to reduce oxidative stress with their antioxidant properties. Research demonstrates that the pinolenic acid, a chemical compound found in the pine nut, can help curb appetite by slowing the absorption of food in the gut. (I don't know whether that is a good or bad thing). This little nut (which is actually a seed) is also packed with vitamins A, K, and magnesium, making it a gem in the cardiovascular department.

If you're feeling adventurous, you could try these recipes to give the pine nut a foothold in your kitchen:

PESTO
2 c. packed fresh basil leaves
2 cloves garlic
1/4 c. pine nuts
2/3 c. extra-virgin olive oil, divided
1/2 c. freshly grated Pecorino cheese
Sea salt and pepper to taste

Combine basil, garlic and pine nuts in a food processor and pulse until they are coarsely chopped. Drizzle in the olive oil and keep pulsing until the desired consistency. Mix in the cheese, add salt and pepper to taste and voila'... pesto.

Or you can try making a raw version of cheesecake using pine nuts instead of cashews. It's also very creamy delicious and provides a full palate experience.

PINENUT "CHEESE"CAKE
CRUST
1/2 c. pine nuts

1/2 c. unsweetened, dry coconut

3 dates (soaked and drained)

Pinch Himalayan Salt

Place all ingredients in the food processor. Process until well ground. Press into a baking dish or springform pan.

FILLING

2 c. pine nuts, soaked overnight, drained and rinsed

3/4 c. coconut butter (or coconut oil – the butter gives a richer, creamier texture)

1/2 c. lemon juice (approximately 3 lemons)

1/2 c. of date syrup or 8 dates soaked, drained, and blended

Place pine nuts, coconut butter, lemon juice and dates in high-speed blender or vitamix. Blend until smooth. Pour over crust. Refrigerate until set. Top with flaked coconut, or other fruit, upon serving.

DAY 88 – CAULIFLOWER

Did you know you could use cauliflower to make pizza crust? That's the inspiration for today's flavor, left-over cauliflower pizza for breakfast. Yum. Cauliflower is an interesting vegetable, one that I used to avoid when I was younger. Mostly because my only real experience of cauliflower was either extremely mushy from the frozen succotash blend (ugh, does anyone remember that?) or as an unattractive addition to a veggie platter.

I also quite wrongly assumed that a vegetable devoid of color would also be devoid of nutrient value. I have since learned the error of my ways and while cauliflower is not my favorite raw veggie, which is I think do solely to mouthfeel and texture, it is a definite key ingredient in many culinary endeavors.

Cauliflower has a simple taste, which allows it to enhance the flavors with which it is combined. I frequently use it as a potato substitute, preferring mashed cauliflower than mashed potatoes during the winter months. I also love to coat it in curry and roast it, however, my favorite at the moment, is pizza crust.

Cauliflower is in the brassica family and as such provides all the benefit that kale, broccoli, and brussels sprouts provide. It is extremely high in Vitamin C and folate. It is high in fiber and its many varied phytonutrient properties make it anti-inflammatory, anti-oxidant, and an excellent resource for detoxifying the body. The chemical compound sulforaphane inhibits the growth of bad bacteria in your gut, including h.pylori bacteria, and keeps it from attaching to your intestinal wall.

These days, cauliflower can be found in a variety of colors, which makes it fun to experiment with.

DAY 89 – COLLARD GREENS

Raw collard greens are dense, so they have a good chewing quality. They are only slightly bitter, not anywhere near as bitter as I had been warned in my early years of learning about them. They are refreshing and add a quality of vitality to the food they are wrapped around when eaten raw.

My first introduction to collard greens was while living in Mississippi. Collard greens were a staple vegetable served sautéed or boiled, typically with the addition of ham, onions, and sometimes tomatoes. For the most part they were tasty, having flavor mostly because of the ingredients added, rather than the greens themselves, but I was left thinking they were basically inedible unless cooked in this manner. It wasn't until my stint learning to be a raw food chef, that I learned to use collard greens in place of tortillas and bread to make wraps, burritos, and 'sandwiches'. I quickly developed a love of the Collard Green. They make a perfect wrap for anything edible, making it simple to lower your processed grain intake and bump up your veggie intake quickly and easily.

Of course, collards can also be sautéed, stir-fried, shredded and tossed with any number of dishes and snacks. My latest favorite is a modified BLAST (Bacon, Lettuce, Avocado, Spinach, Tomato) with a touch of mayo; all wrapped snuggly in a collard green. It's messy but delicious!

From a health perspective, Collard Greens are a member of the Brassica family, giving them all the health benefits of cauliflower, cabbage, Brussels sprouts, etc... They have the added bonus of being uniquely beneficial for cancer prevention. Collards have four specific glucosinolates not found in other cruciferous veggies that increase the body's ability to detox and eliminate systemic oxidative stress.

Collards are also packed with vitamins A and K and other minerals that support brain function and nervous system balance. I highly recommend finding ways to slip them into your diet. The only caveat: if you have thyroid issues you will want to be sure cook them rather than eat them raw.

DAY 90 – MANGO (RECIPE)

Juicy, sweet, slightly astringent, and very, very messy; that's a mango. Mango is the flavor for the day even though, technically, eating mango is way out of territory and they're only just beginning their season. So, I eat them as an occasional treat and am grateful they find their way here to the market.

Mangoes are considered a stone fruit, more specifically a clingstone because the fleshy part clings so tightly to the seed. This puts them in the same family in a sense as the olive, date, peach, etc. Unlike the olive or the date, which can be eaten with ease, I have yet to figure out a clean and easy way to divest the mango of its seed. I must admit that's part of what makes it fun to eat if I'm simply eating whole mango. Mangoes are a great addition to any meal if you are trying to bump up the exotic quality. They pair well with meats, veggies, in stir-fries, salads and of course, they make delectable desserts.

From a health perspective mangos are packed with digestive enzymes, vitamins, minerals, fiber, other phytonutrients. They are a great source of Vitamins A, C, E, and B6 and they are full of alpha and beta-carotene. They are also a good source of potassium and copper, making them very beneficial if you struggle with things like anemia or other iron related challenges.

Research demonstrates that mangoes are beneficial in preventing age related macular degeneration and other eye ailments. They have pantothenic acid which is just one of the chemical compounds found in mango that contributes to brain health. The digestive enzymes found in mango help the beneficial bacteria in your gut grow stronger and increase gastrointestinal health from throat to colon. Research is also suggesting they are beneficial in preventing a variety of cancers such as prostate and colon. Oh, and they also help regulate blood sugar. The mango is a delicious and beneficial food, however, a little bit can go a long way since they are also higher on the glycemic index/load scale... but a treat now and then will do your body some good.

Gnawing mango right off the seed is my favorite way to eat one, however, my second favorite is in this Black Bean, Avocado and Mango salad. This trio makes an amazing nutrient power combination.

BAM SALAD
1 ripe mangoes, peeled and cut into cubes
1 c. black beans (cooked)
1 medium avocado (cut into cubes)
1 tsp of cilantro, chopped fine (optional)
1 lime
dash of cayenne
dash of olive oil (optional)

Peel and cut the mango into cubes and place in a bowl. Add the cooked, chilled, black beans and the cubed avocado. Squeeze the lime over the fruit, and add cilantro and a dash of olive oil, toss it all together so everything is coated. Sprinkle a dash of cayenne and you have a nutrient dense and amazingly delicious salad that can almost be a meal in itself. Feel free to double up the recipe!

CHAPTER 4 - APRIL

DAY 91 – MINT

Inhaling fresh mint is uplifting to the soul. Nibbling the sweet, aromatic fresh leaves is refreshing and revitalizing. The mouthfeel is at first warm but then finishing with a cool sensation from the volatile oils. There are many, many varieties of mint and its use is recorded in cultures around the world. It appears that initially it was a tonic or medicinal herb and then worked its way into the culinary world. From this perspective, fresh mint is preferred so that the volatile oils are bright and intact. I love throwing fresh mint on salads and in other veggies just to give an extra layer to the flavors.

Mint is versatile and can be enjoyed in both savory and sweet dishes. It's definitely worth getting to know the different varieties of mint; such as chocolate mint; which tastes exactly how it sounds chocolate and mint combined in one nibble. Peppermint, Wintermint, and Apple mint are other interesting variations. The choices are endless and each one has its own delicious quality.

From a medicinal perspective, mint is an excellent digestive tonic; useful for nausea and stomachache. Research is demonstrating that it is highly effective in calming the gastrointestinal tract in cases of Irritable Bowel or Crohn's Disease. Studies also demonstrate that inhaling mint enhances cognitive function and elevates mood. It also helps stimulate memory.

Sipping mint tea and inhaling the aroma can be a great way to boost your energy and focus when you hit those afternoon slumps. This happens because the olfactory system plugs directly into the limbic system, which is responsible for emotional responses and memory. Inhaling and sipping creates a nice retronasal effect; while also calming the nerves and soothing digestion.

Mint is also full of antioxidants and other phytonutrients that help alleviate oxidative stress and systemic inflammation. I give a resounding vote for inviting a little uplifting mint into your life.

DAY 92 – DILL

Today's flavor comes from a sparkling conversation over lunch; dill seems to be an herb that people either love or hate, there's not much in between. I find it slightly sweet with a hint of earthy grassiness, as well as impressions of sour. Fresh dill can be quite refreshing and add a complexity to various culinary endeavors. Dill is also, of course, a main flavor component in pickles and pickled foods. It's nice to sprinkle over fish or egg dishes.

From a health perspective, dill is similar to parsley with its chemo-protective qualities. The volatile oils contain chemical compounds that decrease the carcinogenic impact of toxins. Dill is also anti-bacterial, which is potentially one reason it is used so widely in 'pickling' vegetables. It helps neutralize the bacteria count.
Dill is nutrient dense and has vitamins and minerals that help increase things like bone density, cardiovascular health and gastrointestinal health.

DAY 93 – APPLE CIDER VINEGAR

Apple Cider Vinegar tastes, well...vinegary. It is sour, tart, astringent, and when diluted a little bit sweet. Apple Cider Vinegar is made through a fermentation process. It becomes vinegar rather than alcohol because the fermentation process is allowed to continue until ultimately all of the alcohol oxidizes away and you're left with vinegar. This same process happens to grapes and other ingredients that can be fermented into alcohols; if you leave them to ferment long enough, they will ultimately develop into a type of vinegar.

From a culinary perspective, apple cider vinegar is an interesting ingredient. I think it has a much better, more complex flavor than white vinegar so I tend to swap out and use the ACV wherever a recipe calls for white. It is also a great addition to slow cooked meats. The acetic acid, which is a key component of ACV helps break down the protein molecules in the meat making it tenderer and enhancing the flavor spectrum. ACV is also great for preserving different and various vegetables since it is a preservative.

The main preservative component, which is also great for annihilating bad bacteria, is Acetic Acid. ACV can be used in baking as an egg substitute, just use a tablespoon of ACV wherever you would have used one egg. I love using ACV in salads and sauces, especially raw food dishes. I also love to just sip on it, adding a tablespoon of it to warm water. It works wonders, which brings us to the health benefits of ACV.

The acetic and malic acids in Apple Cider Vinegar make it antimicrobial and antibiotic. In fact, its first recorded use is in Greece. Hippocrates prescribed it for a wide variety of ailments, including colds and flu, digestive issues, and even in wound care. Roman soldiers and Japanese samurai both recorded using ACV as an energizing tonic, mixing it with honey and sipping on it throughout the day. It was also added to water to kill any potentially harmful bacteria.

Today recommendations for sipping on apple cider vinegar or adding it to food are plentiful. Even better, it also works outside of your body, on your skin, hair and even as a deodorant. Sipping ACV balances the ph in your body and fights against bacteria. It can be helpful against urinary tract infections, foodborne bacteria, candida, and e.coli. It also is helpful for balancing blood sugar, satisfying appetite and research suggests that 1-2 tbsps a day for at least 12 weeks can aid in weight loss.
I sip a cup of ACV almost daily as a refreshing tea like drink. I also use it on my hair as a final rinse, which makes it soft and shiny, as well as using it on my skin as a toner. It's all around great stuff.

The caveat: make sure you are drinking unpasteurized real deal Apple Cider Vinegar that has been fermented the traditional and time honored way. Otherwise, you are just going to be drinking synthetic additives and colorings. You can tell it is unpasteurized because it will still have the "mother" floating around in the bottle. The mother is the actual, initial bacterial host, which is way awesome.

DAY 94 - SMOKED MACKEREL

Another flavor from my breakfast bowl; oak barrel smoked mackerel, small batch, sustainable, artisan. It tastes salty, smoky, earthy, pungent but most of all fishy. Smoked mackerel, kippers, sardines, they're all foods that I really want to love or at the very least like because they're so darn good for you. Unfortunately, it's a tough one.
Today's smoked mackerel is a little more palatable because it's traditionally smoked, which gives it a much better texture, in my opinion and it feels good to eat something that is sustainably and consciously made. I've paired this mackerel with some eggs and fresh spinach, which makes a nice combination.

Mackerel is a cold water, oily fish that is packed with Omega 3 fatty acid. Omega 3 fatty acids are highly beneficial for your brain and body.

They help maintain cardiovascular health and increase cognitive function. They decrease systemic inflammation and oxidative stress. Research demonstrates Omega 3's are also a beneficial addition to your diet if you are suffering from gastrointestinal issues, like IBS or Crohn's Disease.

Studies suggests that the standard western diet is deficient in Omega 3's and many people can benefit from increasing their intake. I'm always a proponent of getting what you need from your food rather than from supplements and smoked mackerel is one way to do that. Three servings of cold water fish high in Omega 3's a week is a good plan.

So, what's the catch? (pun intended). Well, you want to be sure you're eating fish that is wild and sustainably caught. Farmed fish are much higher in Persistent Organic Pollutants (POPS) and they are often quite stressed out, requiring a variety of pharmaceutical interventions to keep them "healthy". These two factors change the nutrient potential of fish and end up adding to systemic inflammation and other health issues rather than helping. Keep in mind also, the larger the fish the higher the toxin potential. These smaller in size, wild caught mackerel are a good option for your health and the health of the planet.

DAY 95 – DATES

Dates are sweet and delicious. They have a wonderful texture and almost creamy mouthfeel. I love them because although they are sweet, they aren't over the top like many sugary foods. Dates are an amazing staple ingredient in a variety of global cuisines like Middle Eastern and they're highly useful in the raw foodie world. I use dates as a sweetener and as a binding ingredient for sweet treats and other culinary experiments.

For example, soaked dates and nuts blended together make an awesome quick and easy 'pie crust' that doesn't need to be baked or messed with, simply blend until crumbly, press them into the pan and pour your ingredients over the top.

From a health perspective, dates are awesome, even though they are higher in sugar content. They are jam packed with nutrients like potassium and manganese, copper, and antioxidants like lutein. They are a good source for vitamin A, B, and K, as well as a great source of fiber. Dates also contain tannins, which make them anti-inflammatory.

Research shows that dates can help regulate heart rate and other cardiovascular irregularities. They are a great source of iron so they increase the body's ability to transport iron and increase the oxygen carrying capacity of red blood cells. The potassium in dates is also considered an aphrodisiac and research suggests that dates can help with a variety of sexual and reproductive issues in both men and women.

Dates tend to be my main source of sugar when I happen to include something sweet in my diet. I soak them and make date syrup out of them which is a main ingredient in many Middle Eastern recipes; and I also add them to various recipes as a sugar replacement, not to mention just nibbling on them whole when I want a little boost of energy or focus.

DAY 96 –WHORTLEBERRY

The whortleberry is also known as a bilberry or the European blueberry. It is a small berry often confused with the American blueberry although there are distinct differences. The berries I had to day were in a lovely whortleberry jam. Small and packed with flavor both sweet and tart, they added well to a bowl of yogurt with pecans. Whortleberries have a more intense flavor than the cultivated blueberry and a deeper color with a tougher, more compact fruit body. They also grow on plants lower to the ground as individual fruits rather than in clumps on taller bushes like their counterpart, the blueberry. Whortleberries are sometimes referred to as huckleberries depending on what country you're in.

Clearly, they do well in jams and other sweet dishes but also could do well in a savory dish that needed to soften a pungent edge, such as wild game or fowl. I have just found a recipe for whortleberry pie and meadowsweet custard, which I absolutely will be trying when they are both in season. In the meantime, I'll stick with having the jam in my yogurt and on the occasional slice of toast or piece of venison.

From a health perspective, whortleberries are amazing; in fact, it appears that first recorded use of them was as a medicinal intervention for gastrointestinal issues. They are astringent in nature even though sweet and tasty. The bilberry has many of the same health benefits of the blueberry, including the incredibly high antioxidant properties (the highest of any other berry or fruit). They are packed with vitamin C and E. They are a great source of resveratrol, the nutrient found in red wine that packs a healthful punch.

One other amazing benefit of bilberries is their ability to decrease the destruction of connective tissue by neutralizing the enzymes that do the most damage. Additionally, research suggests they are effective against colon cancer and other gastrointestinal cancers as well as effective against urinary tract issues. Much like cranberries. Studies also show that a cup of bilberries a day can reduce blood pressure and decrease the potential for cardiovascular disease along with all the other amazing things that they do for your health. It's safe to say that whortleberries are a great addition to the superfood list.

DAY 97 – PEANUT BUTTER (RECIPE)

"If someone tells you that you are putting too much peanut butter on your bread, stop talking to them. You don't need that kind of negativity in your life"... (:

Today's flavor comes straight from my sourdough sprouted seed and rye toast. Peanut Butter is a fiesta of flavors and mouthfeels; creamy, crunchy, salty, sweet, even umami if the peanuts are roasted first. This particular peanut butter is made from organic roasted peanuts. It's crunchy with a touch of sea salt. There was a time when I dare say peanut butter was a staple ingredient in many homes across the globe. However, in recent years, especially in the health food world, the poor peanut has become very much maligned. In some ways, the bad reputation has been incurred not through any fault of the poor little peanut rather through growing, producing and 'manufacturing' it in ways that are unhealthy.

By itself, the peanut is actually a good resource for nutritional health. They are a great source of protein and fiber, as well as other phytonutrients like, biotin, manganese and copper. They are also packed with antioxidants; in fact, the peanut skin rivals grapes for their resveratrol content and even beats the carrot, beet, and apple when it comes to antioxidant content.

What's more? When you roast them, it increases the bio-availability of these antioxidants by 22%. Bio-availability means amount that your body can assimilate. Sometimes nutrients are in a certain food but we aren't able to digest and assimilate them, which makes them less beneficial; not so with the peanut, especially once roasted. I put peanut butter in yogurt and eat it on apples. Of course, there is always peanut butter fudge (raw is delightful) and peanut butter cookies and the amazing peanut butter sandwich. Peanut soup is beyond delicious and adding a handful of peanuts to stir-fry can really bump it up a notch.

So why the bad reputation? Well, by itself the peanut is great. However, whether it will be healthy or harmful all depends on how it is grown and produced. Unfortunately, in the United States, peanuts are quite often rotated with tobacco crops to improve soil health. The problem with that? There is no real regulation on what pesticides, herbicides and other toxins can be used on the tobacco since it is not technically a food. So, while the peanuts are 'cleaning' and nourishing the soil they are soaking up and suffering the consequences of the soil toxins from the previous tobacco harvest. Yuck.

Buying organic peanuts can eliminate that issue. The second challenge for peanuts? They can easily develop a mold in the Aflatoxin family that can cause some issues. Aflatoxins are super high carcinogen and can wreak havoc on the respiratory and nervous system in high enough amounts. The USDA heavily regulates peanuts produced in the U.S. to protect against Aflatoxic contamination. Downside? Most of the world's peanuts are produced in China where the regulations are much looser.

Other issues with peanuts? Of course, there is also the peanut allergy, which is indeed a problem, so obviously avoid them if you're allergic. Then there is the next issue of processing. For whatever reason, (I'm guessing to get more bang for your buck) many manufacturers started adding extra ingredients like hydrogenated oils, fats and sugars to their peanut butter and it's incredibly challenging to get just plain old roasted peanut butter without any other additives. Even peanuts in a jar for just eating as a snack are roasted in oil or other flavorings that are better left unconsumed. If you've been innocently buying peanut butter, even organic, without reading the label, I highly recommend you get out your magnifying glass and read the fine print ingredients. Chances are there are things in there you would rather not be eating.

The bottom line is; if you want all the good stuff that peanuts and peanut butter can add to your life then go the minimalist route and buy organic, peanut only, peanut butter. Your body and belly will be happier for it.

PEANUT BUTTER FUDGE:
1 c. organic peanut butter (creamy or crunchy will work)
1/4 c. coconut oil or butter, melted
2 TBS raw honey (you can also use a few dates or date sugar instead,

this will also make them thicker, or you can simply leave the sugar out)

1/4 tsp. sea salt

1/2 tsp. vanilla

Combine all ingredients in food processor. Pour mixture into a lightly oiled 5" x 7" pan. Cover and freeze until set, approximately 1 hour. Cut into 24 1-inch squares and store in an airtight container in the freezer.

DAY 98 – SESAME SEEDS (RECIPE)

Sesame seeds are tasty; nutty, crunchy, chewy, and umami if they have been roasted. They are tiny, delicate and one of the oldest documented condiments; with record of their use as oil seeds as far back as 4,000 B.C.

The tiny but popular sesame seed is a common and often staple ingredient in cuisines around the world. Foods like Tahini, Halva, and Til-Patti are made entirely from sesame seeds, while other foods use them as additions to create complexity or appearance. Sesame oil is one of the most commonly used oils in the world for cooking and in some traditions, it is used medicinally. I use sesame oil and toasted sesame oil, which has a distinct taste, for a variety of cooking endeavors. I also use sesame oil as a massage oil and wintertime hair treatment.

From a health perspective, sesame seeds are an excellent source of minerals like copper, manganese, zinc and calcium. They are also a good source of Omega 3 and 6 fatty acids, which contribute to heart health and lowering cholesterol. Research suggests that including sesame seeds in your diet can help fight against oxidative stress by eliminating free radicals. They can help rebuild connective tissue and collagen as well as aid in bone density and strength. Sesame seeds are also a good source of tryptophan, which helps balance mood and decreases anxiety.

In Ayurveda, sesame seeds are considered warming and lubricating. To massage with the oil or include seeds in the diet can help all three doshas come back into balance.

For a sweet and healthy treat you can give these a try, they're also awesome for energy so the next time you hit that long bike ride or hike, throw a few of these in your bag.

PISTACHIO SESAME BALLS

1/2 c. organic almond butter

1/2 c. organic pistachios

1/2 c. organic sesame seeds
6 organic Medjool dates (pitted)
1 TBS organic coconut oil

Pulse all ingredients in food processor until well blended. Roll into balls and refrigerate. Eat, enjoy, repeat...

DAY 99 – CURRANTS

Currants are chewy and slightly sweet with a hint of sour. They are often mistaken for raisins and, although they are also a type of dried grape, they are different from the typical raisin. Today's flavor comes straight from the middle of my Welsh Cake in the courtyard of Llanthony Priory nestled in the Black Mountains of Wales. Welsh Cakes are reminiscent of a cross between a silver dollar pancake and a Christmas sugar cookie. This Welsh Cake is deliciously dotted with currants to temper the sweetness of the sugar and butter base.

What makes a currant different from a typical raisin? Raisins are dried white grapes while currants originally from dried seedless red grapes. Currants originated from the Corinth region in Greece, hence the name "currant". The first recorded reference to currants is found in writings from 75 A.D. Currants have a more intense flavor than the average raisin and pack quite a nutritional punch as well. They are amazing additions to baked goods and salads but also add well to savory dishes.

From a health perspective, currants are little powerhouses of goodness. They are packed with Vitamins and minerals, most notably Vitamin C and A, as well as Copper, Manganese and Iron. They are also an awesome resource for antioxidants; polyphenols and anthocyanins that help in the fight against oxidative stress and systemic inflammation.

Because the currant is dried in relatively low humidity many of the benefits of the red grape are still available in the dried fruit. Research has shown that consuming just two tablespoons of currants a day helped regulate blood pressure without increasing blood glucose levels in the way that regular raisins do.

All in all, I think currants are delicious and a nice addition to your dietary repertoire. Maybe they don't need to be added as part of sugary, buttery, delicious goodness of a Welsh Cake but I'm sure you can find places to toss them in.

DAY 100 – BROCCOLI

Oh, poor broccoli! No other vegetable has been so scorned or revered all at the same time by the same media. People seem to either love it or hate it. I am one who loves it. I especially love fresh, organic broccoli. I don't care what anyone says, there is a distinct taste and flavor difference between organic or sustainably grown broccoli and conventionally grown.

Young fresh broccoli has a crispy, crunchy, earthy flavor, with faint hints of sweet. My favorite way to eat broccoli is to quickly blanch it in boiling water and then sauté in coconut oil with garlic....very delicious. Of course, broccoli is such a mainstream vegetable there are a multitude of ways to prepare it. You can try making it into soup, tossing it as stir-fry, even baking it into a quiche.

From a health perspective, broccoli has the reputation as healthy for a good reason. It is a cruciferous vegetable, which means it has all the benefits of its kin; brussels sprouts, kale, and others. Research demonstrates that the flavonoids in broccoli increase colon health and decrease the potential for colon cancer (and other cancers). Broccoli is also high in vitamin C, K, an A. It is beneficial for cardiovascular health and helps lower blood pressure.

Studies suggest that sulforaphane, a chemical compound found in broccoli, can also help repair and prevent damage to small blood vessels caused by diabetes. Broccoli has the amazing ability, due to a unique trio of phytonutrients, to detoxify the body on a cellular level. Given all the amazing benefits of broccoli, it's worth giving it a chance...just don't overcook it! (:

DAY 101 - BRINKWORTH BLUE

Today's flavor comes straight from the Stroud Farmer's Market and Hill End Farm in Brinkworth. Creamy, pungent, earthy and slight hit of sweet that comes from the cream, Brinkworth Blue cheese is amazingly delicious. It happens to go amazingly well with a slice of 9 seed bread from the Artisan Bakery.

Brinkworth Blue Cheese is handmade on a family farm in Brinkworth, Wiltshire, U.K. It's described as a medium strength, creamy blue cheese from Friesian cows. (I am now on a mission to find a blue from a Jersey or Guernsey to see if I can tell the difference).

Blue cheese is created by adding the mold *Penicillium* to fermenting cheese so that it creates a blue, green or gray vein of mold through the cheese. Sounds a bit off putting when you read about it but trust me, it's absolutely delicious on your plate. I love blue cheese on its own or as a side with a nice savory game, like venison or wild boar. It also is amazing with bolder vegetables, like broccoli or kale.

From a health perspective, blue cheese is a very heart healthy food. Research demonstrates that blue cheese in particular, has an anti-inflammatory impact, so it helps relieve oxidative stress, systemic inflammation and increases cardiovascular health. Side note and total bonus: The research also indicates that pairing blue cheese with a good red wine increases the heart healthy potential and the yum factor exponentially. I'm sure it's all about moderation but really, could there be a better pairing for your health? (:

Chances of finding a Brinkworth Blue in the area outside of Wiltshire, U.K. are slim but I would venture to guess if you wanted to go on an adventure in your area you would more than likely find a comparable blue that would excite your palate and enhance your overall well-being.

DAY 102 – PARSNIPS (RECIPE)

Parsnips are sweet and crunchy, with an interesting back note of flavor that is ever so slightly menthol or minty, which makes them taste a little more refreshing and vibrant than a carrot in my opinion. Today's flavor comes straight from a traditional Sunday roast done exceptionally well by Graham Thomson at the Seven Stars Inn in Bottlesford, Wiltshire, UK.

Roasted parsnips are a traditional ingredient on the Sunday roast menu all across the U.K.but that's not all that makes them notable. Parsnips can enhance any number of culinary endeavors both savory and sweet. In fact, one of their earliest recorded uses is as a sweetener and an aphrodisiac in Roman times. Use of the parsnip is also recorded in Traditional Chinese Medicine and is noted for its sweet, bitter and warming qualities.

From a health perspective, parsnips are a fantastic way to get your vitamins and minerals. They have a significant amount of potassium, iron, copper, and manganese, as well as being rich in Vitamin C, B, K, and E. They have similar properties to their close relatives the carrot and turnip, which include phytonutrients that are beneficial in decreasing systemic inflammation and oxidative stress. They also contain flavonoids that are anti-fungal.

Research demonstrates that the chemical compounds found in the parsnip help maintain colon health and decrease the potential for colon cancers, while also maintaining healthy blood cells and decreasing the potential for leukemia. Parsnips are high in fiber and although they are sweeter than carrots once cooked they are still on the lower side of the glycemic index.

Here's a delicious sounding maple and parsnip cake recipe from Catherine Berwick. I haven't tried it yet, but you can bet as soon as I get my hands on some fresh maple syrup, I will be whipping this up.

PARSNIP AND MAPLE SYRUP CAKE
175g butter, plus extra for greasing
250g demerara sugar
100ml maple syrup
3 large eggs
250g self-raising flour
2 tsp baking powder
2 tsp mixed spice
250g parsnips, peeled and grated
1 medium eating apple,
peeled, cored and grated
50g pecans, roughly chopped
zest and juice 1 small orange
icing sugar, to serve
For the filling
250g tub mascarpone

3-4 tbsp maple syrup

Heat oven to 180C/160C fan/gas 4. Grease 2 x 20cm sandwich
tins and line the bases with baking parchment. Melt butter, sugar and
maple syrup in a pan over gentle heat, then cool slightly. Whisk the
eggs into this mixture, then stir in the flour, baking powder and mixed
spice, followed by the grated parsnip, apple, chopped pecans, orange
zest and juice. Divide between the tins, then bake for 25-30 mins until
the tops spring back when pressed lightly.

Cool the cakes slightly in the tins before turning out onto wire
racks to cool completely. Just before serving, mix together the
mascarpone and maple syrup. Spread over one cake and sandwich
with the other. Dust with icing sugar just before serving

DAY 103 – PEA SPROUTS

Pea Sprouts, sometimes referred to as pea shoots, are crisp and vibrant
green. They have a hint of summer's fresh mown grass and they are earthy
and slightly sweet as a back note. Delicious and refreshing.
Today's flavor comes straight from the plate in the Greenbank Hotel,
Falmouth, Cornwall, where Kenneth Graham wrote much of Wind in the
Willows. The setting is sublime, staring out into the harbor, savoring my
meal and imagining the creative minds who have graced this location.

Fresh pea sprouts are a great addition to any meal that is in need of the
green vitality of nature. They are an interesting addition to sweet and
savory dishes alike.
Toss them on a salad, throw them in a stir-fry, even add them to dessert.
Believe it or not, pea sprouts on a custard are amazing.

From a health perspective, pea sprouts are packed with Vitamin A and
Vitamin C. As a micro-green they are also filled with phytonutrients and
antioxidants. Research shows that they have 7 times the amount of
Vitamin C and A as a cup of blueberries and are an amazing addition to
your heart health repertoire. Pea sprouts are also a great anti-inflammatory
and detoxifier at the cellular level. Research demonstrates that pea sprouts
are also a great intervention for insulin resistance and help with glucose
balance in the fight against diabetes.

And now back to Toad, Badger, Mole, and of course, Ratty. (:

DAY 104 – SWEDE/RUTABAGA

Earthy, pungent and slightly astringent, the Swede, is also knows as a yellow turnip or even in some places as a rutabaga, or so I'm lead to believe. The Swede is a large yellow turnip, easily distinguishable from the smaller white turnip which is never confused with anything other than itself, while the large yellow swede/turnip/rutabaga can challenge even the most pleasant of foodie traditionalists to a dual of identification. For the purposes of this short flavor description, I will stick with the Swede and hope for the best (although, quite honestly rutabaga is much more fun to say...try it)

The Swede is a key ingredient in the traditional Cornish Pasty and you can find out more about that over the next day or two when we blog about our pasty adventures in Cornwall. In the meantime, suffices to say, the swede is a starchy member of the brassica family. It is delicious roasted, sautéed, stewed, and even pureed.

From a health perspective, swedes are high in Vitamin C and B6 as well as many minerals, antioxidants and phytonutrients. Swedes are a great resource for manganese, potassium, and iron.

Research demonstrates that the swede is helpful in reducing the potential for colon and prostate cancers and inhibits tumor growth and proliferation. The swede helps balance the digestive system and certain chemical compounds inhibit bad bacterial growth, studies show it inhibits the growth of h.pylori bacteria and helps heal stomach ulcers. The swede is also a high fiber, lower starch food that helps to balance blood sugar and manage insulin release and uptake. Make friends with a swede and invite it to lunch. You won't be sorry. (:

DAY 105 – STRAWBERRIES (DOMESTIC)

Luscious, sweet and juicy. I realize it's too early for strawberries and I'd prefer to stay in season but I enjoyed some strawberries today that were just too delicious to ignore. Maybe it's because spring was really setting in and the day was sunny and warm, filled with birdsong and busy bees; either way, these strawberries were divine.

Strawberries, believe it or not, aren't technically a berry. They are considered an "aggregate fruit" which is a little complicated to explain in this short post, but doesn't take away from their flavor potential one iota. The strawberry is a sort of commonplace and well-known addition found in many kitchens. It could be easy to take it for granted if one wasn't paying attention because it truly is an amazing resource for your health and your palate.

I find that wild strawberries taste the most delicious. They are tiny and packed with flavor. It's also my experience that the larger the strawberry the more bland the taste; the large ones typically being the ones that are grown out of season and conventionally hybridized. From a flavor and nutrient perspective, smaller strawberries in season are the way to go whenever possible.

Also, keep in mind that strawberries are one of the foods that you want to be sure are organic. Conventional strawberries are grown with an inordinate amount of pesticides that are better left out of your house and out of your body.

From a health perspective, strawberries are jam packed with vitamin C, A, and E. They are also an amazing source of antioxidants and phytonutrients that help with balancing blood sugar, inhibiting oxidative stress, and decreasing systemic inflammation. There is some pretty cool research out there demonstrating that strawberries are a great source of copper and help with red blood cell health.

My favorite way to eat strawberries is fresh and full, preferably right from the plant.... and then dipped in nocciolata (the healthier and much more delicious version of nutella).

DAY 106 – WILD GARLIC

Piquant, pungent and ever so slightly sweet; the small bulbs of wild garlic are deliciously delicate. Today's flavor comes straight from the forest floor, nestled among the first bluebells of spring. The aroma of garlic fills the dell as the sun pokes through the budded branches and warms their palm like leaves.

Wild garlic, also known as ramson, is different from the typical conventional garlic we can find in the store. It is slightly sweeter, with a light flavor and the leaves and stems are edible as well. Today's garlic was foraged to accompany a slow baked, locally sourced chicken and wild nettle soup (foraged carefully with the garlic and some dandelion).

From a health perspective, wild garlic has all the amazing qualities of typical garlic with the added benefit of fresh forest air and a lovely walk in the woods. Garlic is antifungal, antibacterial, and antimicrobial.

Research also demonstrates that garlic is highly beneficial in lowering blood pressure and reducing the risk of cardiovascular disease. Garlic is also an immune booster and is excellent for fighting flus and viruses. Wild garlic is beneficial for healthy digestion and helps stimulate production of health flora and fauna in the gut while eliminating the baddies, including parasites.

Research suggests that garlic is also useful in preventing a variety of cancers and aids in decreasing oxidative stress as well as systemic inflammation. Wandering the woods for wild garlic is a bonus and a definite treat, if you don't have woods near you, it could be worth checking at your local farmer's market or asking your natural food grocer if they can get their hands on it for you. You won't be sorry. (unless of course you've accidentally picked lily of the valley, which is quite toxic...doh!)

DAY 107 – PUMPKIN SEEDS

Crunchy, chewy, nutty (even though they are seeds) and slightly sweet if they are fresh; pumpkin seeds are packed full of goodness. Pumpkin seeds, also called a pepita, are a delicious addition to your palate's repertoire. They are versatile and can be easily added to any number of dishes, both sweet and savory to enhance flavor and nutritional value. I love to toast them and toss them in yogurt, on sautéed greens, or even pop them in sweet treats and baked goods.

Pumpkin seeds come from the inside of a pumpkin or other closely related squash. They can be toasted in the shell and eaten with shell intact, which increases their zinc content. Or they can be shelled and eaten just as the inner seed. Either way, they are delicious and nutritious.

From a health perspective, the pumpkin seed is a powerhouse of nutrient density. It is an awesome resource for magnesium, copper, zinc, and iron. They are also full of antioxidants two of which are unique to the pumpkin seed and are effective in reducing the potential for prostate cancer. The simple little pumpkin seed is antimicrobial, antiviral, and antifungal, with exciting new research demonstrating the impact of its antimicrobial effects on the enhancing immune response. The phytonutrients in the pumpkin seed also decrease oxidative stress and systemic inflammation while improving insulin regulation for individuals with insulin resistance syndrome and diabetes.

They are also very low on the allergen list with minimal oxalates and other things that can make seeds a sensitive issue. All of that adds up to a yummy and nutritious snack option and palate pleasing culinary treat.

DAY 108 – COTSWOLD BRIE

Creamy, salty, sweet, and slightly pungent; Simon Weaver's organic Cotswold Brie is scrumptious. It pairs well with an organic braeburn apple and some artisan spelt flatbread. Today's flavor comes straight from my snack bag filled with goodies from Purton Farm Shop, while I wait for my plane.

Simon Weaver's Cotswold Brie comes from the milk produced by Kirkham Farms Fresian cows in the County of Gloucestershire in the UK. The cows spend their days ranging the landscape feeding on organic grassland and enjoying the fresh air. The cheese is fresh, simple, delicious with just enough complexity. Simon Weaver reminds us that flavor is influenced by season and terroir so nuances will change from time to time.

This cheese is perfect for the occasion. In general, brie is a soft white cheese made from cow's milk (unless otherwise noted). It gets its name from the region in France where it originated. The SW Cotswold Brie is artisan style made with simple ingredients and old world craftsmanship. Brie is a good source of protein and vitamins and minerals. Eating the rind as well as the inside creamy stuff gives you a good dose of Vitamin B1, B12, and B7 as well as some zinc to help boost immune function. There's also some Vitamin A, D, and K2 which is a very important nutrient for heart health and bone density. The bacteria in Brie are a healthy addition to your digestive flora and fauna and contribute to gut balance. So, other than the obvious reasons like allergy, adding some delicious Brie to your dietary repertoire could be good and good for you. Today it was a lovely and welcome addition to my airport picnic.

DAY 109 – RHUBARB (RECIPE)

Fresh rhubarb is tart, juicy and very astringent. It's crispy and crunchy like celery and has a slight berry or pomegranate taste to it. The fresh rhubarb caught my eye while stocking up on veggies for the week. (Strawberries and rhubarb...guess what is on the menu for tomorrow...pie anyone???). Rhubarb is an interesting veggie, even though it was re-categorized as a fruit in 1947 by New York State. The stems can be eaten raw although cooking them makes them slightly more palatable. Raw they make a great addition to salads or other fresh fruit or veggie conglomerations. They can also be tossed into stir-fries or even pureed and added to mashes. Their biggest claim to fame is as pie filling or jams. Strawberry rhubarb pie is a nationwide summertime favorite.

From a health perspective, rhubarb is good and good for you. Just don't eat the leaves since they are toxic. The stalks are where all the good stuff is hanging out. They contain nutrients like vitamins B, A, and K. The red in the stalk means higher amount of vitamin A and also beta-carotenes and zeaxanthine which are great for bone strength, oxidative stress and systemic inflammation. Research demonstrates that the chemical compounds in rhubarb are beneficial for slowing the progression of Alzheimer's Disease. Early recorded use of rhubarb is for gastrointestinal issues. Rhubarb helps balance digestive flora and fauna and also soothes intestinal distress. In Chinese Medicine, rhubarb is a good food to help rebuild food intake after long illness.

RHUBARB SALAD WITH GOAT CHEESE
3/4 pound rhubarb, cut into 3/4-inch pieces
1/4 c. honey
1/2 c. walnut halves
2 TBS olive oil
2 TBS balsamic vinegar (preferably white)
Coarse salt and ground pepper
4 bunches arugula (about 1 pound total), tough ends removed
1 fennel bulb, cored and thinly sliced crosswise
1/2 c. fresh goat cheese, crumbled
Preheat oven to 450 degrees, with racks in upper and lower thirds. On a rimmed baking sheet, toss rhubarb with honey. Roast on upper rack until beginning to soften, about 5 minutes. Let cool on baking sheet. On another rimmed baking sheet, toast walnuts on lower rack until fragrant, 5 minutes. Let cool, then chop.
In a large bowl, whisk together oil and vinegar and season with salt and pepper. Add arugula and fennel and toss to combine. Top with rhubarb, walnuts, and goat cheese.

DAY 110– JUNIPER BERRIES

Clean, refreshing, piney and sometimes very bitter; juniper berries are an interesting component to your flavor repertoire. Juniper berries are not actually berries, they are more closely related to a pine cone. If you look at a juniper berry closely you will see that it has very fleshy, densely compact scales, which give it the appearance of being a smooth berry. Juniper berry's initial claim to fame in the U.S. was as a medicinal intervention. It was used as a diuretic and an appetite suppressant by certain Native American tribes.

From a culinary perspective, the juniper berry enhances the complexity in broths and stews. It is a popular ingredient in many European cuisines. Its piney resin aids in the preservation of meat, which is why it is a main additive in traditional corned beef. (It must have some pretty amazing preservation qualities because it is also recorded as a prominent ingredient of the Egyptian embalming formula in the time of Pharaohs). It is typically used in savory dishes but it also can be an interesting ingredient in sweet dishes. Lastly, Juniper is a main ingredient in gin...only sayin.

From a health perspective, juniper berries are antifungal, antimicrobial, and anti-viral. There's a reason pine cleaners are pine based, this is due to the pinene, which is a great chemical compound that also acts as an antioxidant. Juniper is also as mentioned, a diuretic, which also tones and detoxes the liver.

Research suggests that it balances digestion, stimulating appetite if need be but also decreasing appetite when necessary. Juniper berries are useful, according to research, for eliminating urinary tract infections or other kidney and bladder related issues. Even better they are jam packed with antioxidants that help fight free radicals and oxidative stress.

DAY 111 – YUCCA

The fruit of a Mojave Yucca, also called a Spanish Bayonet, is interesting to say the least. The taste is chalky, bitter, yet also juicy and slightly refreshing, reminding me of, believe it or not, watermelon rind. The Yucca is often thought of as a cactus, however, it is actually in the evergreen family. The Yucca Schidigera, which is today's flavor, comes straight from a Yucca forest in the desert outside of Las Vegas. This particular type of Yucca is found only in certain regions of the Mojave, Sonoran, and Chihuahuan Deserts of the southwest.

The Yucca is actually a pretty versatile plant from both a culinary and a medicinal perspective. In Southwest and Native American cuisine yucca finds its way on the plate from the root, the stalk, the seed, and the fruit of the tree. The fruit can be eaten raw, or it can be baked, sautéed, or roasted. It can also be mashed or pureed. The stalk is also good to eat and can be roasted whole and then peeled and diced into cubes which can then be eaten or added to soups and stews. The seeds can be roasted and ground into flour and then used to make tortillas or flat breads. The roots are better used medicinally as they tend to be bitter and contain saponins.

From a health perspective Yucca is pretty amazing. It contains quite a few polyphenols, the most popular of which is resveratrol, the same chemical compound found in red wine and various other fruits and berries. In Native tradition, Yucca has been used for arthritis, inflammation, and digestive issues. It is also used to treat skin conditions like rashes and sores. In the U.S. the National Institute of Health has conducted research on the polyphenols found in the yucca tree and have so far found that yucca seems to have anti-arthritic and anti-inflammatory properties. Studies also show beneficial impact on high cholesterol, diabetes, and poor circulation.

The saponins in the Yucca plant also make it a great soap, and it has been used traditionally as shampoo and skin cleaner by the various tribes native to the Mojave desert... I'm tempted to try this one. I'm always on the lookout for fun and interesting ways to make natural products for hair and skin.

So, as you can see, if you ever find yourself wandering through the Southwest deserts, you may want to keep an eye out for the "Spanish Bayonet" so you can have some yummy food, keep your cholesterol in check and make your hair all clean and shiny. (:

DAY 112 – KUMQUAT (RECIPE)

Tangy, sour, sweet, and slightly bitter depending on how ripe; the kumquat is a tiny powerhouse of citrusy goodness. Today's flavor comes straight from the dwarf kumquat tree on my patio. Kumquats are warm climate fruits that look like tiny little oranges.

Kumquats are meant to be eaten with the skin, the skin in fact being sweeter sometimes than the inside fruit. Kumquats are also in the evergreen family, found mostly in Southeast Asia, although their popularity is growing and bringing them to other climates. They look like a very tiny tangerine, approximately the same size as an olive. They taste very citrusy, with the interesting difference that the skin is typically much sweeter than the inside fruit and adds a woody complexity to their taste spectrum.

Because kumquats are part of the citrus family, they can be used in the same way that most citrus is. They do well in marmalades, jams, jellies, dried fruit, or preserved and added to sweet or savory dishes and beverages. In Asian culture, the kumquat is also preserved in brine and then used as a health remedy.

From a health perspective, Kumquats are full of nutrients. They are a great resource of bioflavonoids and phytonutrients that help manage blood sugar, immune function, cardiovascular health and systemic inflammation. Research suggests that the kumquat is beneficial for digestive balance as well. Just 8 kumquats provide sufficient fiber and phytonutrient benefit to exceed the suggested daily balance. Because they are citrus they are also packed with volatile oils that stimulate the olfactory response to balance mood and increase serotonin production. Research has also demonstrated that the kumquat can be a beneficial addition to your diet if you are trying to get rid of gallstones or liver inflammation.

KUMQUAT TAGINE
1 tablespoon extra-virgin olive oil
2 onions, thinly sliced
4 cloves garlic, slivered
1 tablespoon minced fresh ginger
2 pounds boneless, skinless chicken thighs, trimmed of fat, cut into 2-inch pieces, (any kind of meat can be used or veggie sub)
1 teaspoon ground coriander
1 teaspoon ground cumin
3/4 teaspoon ground cinnamon
1/2 teaspoon salt
1/2 teaspoon freshly ground pepper
1/8 teaspoon ground cloves
2 cups of broth
2 cups of kumquats, roughly chopped
2 cups of chickpeas, rinsed
1 1/2 tablespoons honey

Preheat oven to 375°F. Heat oil in an ovenproof casserole or Dutch oven over medium heat. Add onions; cook, stirring often, until softened, about 4 minutes. Add garlic and ginger; cook for 1 minute, stirring constantly.

Add chicken; cook, stirring often, for 8 minutes. Stir in coriander, cumin, cinnamon, salt, pepper and cloves; cook until aromatic, about 20 seconds. Stir in broth, kumquats, chickpeas and honey. Bring to a simmer.
Cover the pan and transfer to the oven. Bake, stirring occasionally, until the chicken is cooked through and the broth is bubbling and somewhat reduced, about 1 hour.

DAY 113 – OKRA

From a texture perspective, my first experience with Okra was unfortunate, to say the least. However, I persevered and tried it again to find that it is quite delicious both raw and when prepared correctly. Young okra has the best flavor and texture and can be eaten raw, diced and sliced, and added to things that could benefit from fresh crunchy crispness.

It is really tasty when it is pickled, fried, or grilled. Otherwise, southern cooking it is traditionally added to stews, gumbos or soups. One feature of okra that makes it tricky to cook with (or maybe desirable to cook with depending on the dish) is that during the cooking process it becomes gelatinous or gummy in texture. It acts as a thickening agent in soups and stews because of the gelatinous quality. Okra is popular in southern cuisine and in other cuisines around the world. The first recorded use of Okra is in Egyptian cuisine although it actually seems to have originated in what is now modern day Ethiopia. One other interesting tidbit about Okra is that the seeds were roasted and used in place of coffee during the war. I am curious to try that and see what okra seed beverage tastes like. I'll keep you posted.

From a health perspective, Okra is really amazing. It is low calorie, high fiber and high nutrient density. It is packed with antioxidants, helping decrease oxidative stress and systemic inflammation. It is high in Vitamin C, A, and K making it a great resource for cardiovascular health, immune function and skin and bones. Okra also supports digestive balance and helps heal the gastrointestinal tract by coating it in mucilage and encouraging beneficial flora to grow. Research also suggests that Okra can help with kidney disease, particularly kidney damage related to diabetes.

Lastly, Okra has the dubious reputation of being a natural Viagra since it seems to open the arteries in the same way that Viagra does, giving it the nickname "the love veggie" in some foodie circles.

All in all, I think Okra is worth a try... don't be scared of it. It could be interesting to try it raw first and then ease into cooking it. Find ways to appreciate the potentially slimy aspect or use it as a thickening agent. Just an aside, you can also use it on your hair to create body and shine and your skin to boost collagen.

DAY 114 – PINEAPPLE

Refreshing, juicy, and tangy with just enough sweetness to compliment the tanginess and feel completely satisfying; today's flavor inspiration comes from my afternoon snack. The pineapple is really quite a bizarre fruit, in fact, technically, it's not a fruit at all. Rather, it is the culmination of berries that have grown together into one large organism around the stock and continued to grow out the top, which is why there are the green shoots on the top of a pineapple. Who knew???

From a culinary perspective, pineapple is really quite versatile, transforming both sweet and savory dishes alike into complex and delicious offerings with an exotic flair. Pineapple is found in cuisines around the world and is one of the most economically popular fruits found around the world. Unfortunately, conventional pineapple plantations are also highly industrialized and use massive amounts of organophosphates that are highly damaging to the environment and us. So, if you are going to buy pineapple try to go for organic and maybe keep it as a treat instead of a daily mainstay.

The enzymes in pineapple make it a great addition to meat dishes because they help tenderize, also when cooked, the sugars in pineapple become even sweeter and more intense without breaking down into quite the glycemic load that other fruits can. Pineapple is delicious raw, grilled, baked, roasted, really any way possible from a culinary perspective.

On the medicinal side, Pineapple has quite a nice repertoire for wellness. It contains bromelain, which is an enzyme that is an amazing anti-inflammatory, anti-cancer, anti-clotting agent. Bromelain also is a digestive aid, helping foods break down and nutrients to assimilate. It is great for respiratory issues and can help clear the lungs for people suffering from asthma, bronchitis, or other respiratory ailments. It is high in fiber, which is always a good thing and it helps repair intestinal inflammation.

Pineapple is also a super resource for minerals like copper, potassium, and manganese; which help with cardiovascular issues, as well as the reduction of oxidative stress. Pineapples are also high in Vitamins C and A and help replenish collagen and strengthen muscles and bones. There are actually quite a few studies out there demonstrating the benefits of eating pineapple. Some of the research shows that eating pineapple can help with things like macular degeneration, diabetes, and prostate cancer.

Incidentally, pineapple did not originate in Hawaii and the largest current day supplier is actually Costa Rica and other Central American countries. It seems that pineapple originated in South America somewhere between Paraquay and Brazil and has since then been cultivated in warm climates all around the world.

DAY 115 – MATCHA

Earth in a glass; Matcha is pungent, earthy, with hints of sweet and bitter depending on the grade and the way it is prepared. Today's flavor comes from my breakfast concoction. Matcha is the end result of finely powdering young, shade grown green tea leaves that have been de-stemmed and de-veined. Because the leaves are shade grown, they are higher in chlorophyll, theanine, and other phytonutrients contributing to their healthful properties.

Matcha is the powdered tea that is used in Japanese tea ceremonies and also in a variety of Japanese desserts and noodles. Although it originates in Japan, it is making its way into cuisine around the world; puddings, ice creams, baked goods, smoothies. Today's inspiration came after I added Matcha to my blended concoction of strawberries, spinach, avocado, and mache'. Potentially it's the makings of a smoothie, except the use of just enough room temperature water, makes it more like a delicious raw soup. Matcha has gained wild popularity in the health and fitness world partly because of its potential for increasing mental focus, clarity and energy without the negative repercussions that can be experienced with caffeine.

Whilst I love matcha and think that it is indeed a healthy addition to one's dietary repertoire, I also feel that it's a bit unfortunate that the globalization of it has created a demand that causes production devoid of any of its sacred or special preparation.

Historically and traditionally, Matcha takes almost a month to prepare from pre-harvest to finish. A couple of weeks before harvest, the best bushes are covered and protected from direct sunlight, then at harvest only the best leaves are handpicked and laid out flat to dry. Once they are dry, the stems and veins are removed and the dry leaves are then stone ground by hand to produce a fine powder. The powder can then be consumed in its entirety rather than removing the leaves as you would typically do after steeping a cup of tea. So, if you end up sipping on some Matcha maybe just spare a thought to how, when, where, and why it ended up in your cup.

From a health perspective, Matcha is a wealth of nutrients. Because the whole leaf is consumed, all the nutrients are consumed as well. It is a rich source of Vitamins A, B, C, E, and K. Green tealeaves are full of antioxidants that offer protection against a multitude of cancers. Research suggests that consuming matcha can help with cardiovascular disease, as well as, reduce high cholesterol, high blood pressure and decrease oxidative stress. It also helps stabilize blood sugar, decreasing the potential for diabetes or insulin resistance.

EGCG is one of the most studied components of green tea and the one that seems to be the most celebrated. EGCG is a polyphenol that research suggests can significantly decrease illnesses like cancer, endometriosis, chronic fatigue syndrome, and neuro-degeneration, including AIDS related dementia. It is the combination of EGCG and L-theanine that increases and maintains thermogenesis and metabolic processing.

DAY 116 – BARLEY

Chewy, nutty, and slightly sweet; barley is a cereal grain with a very interesting history. It is one of the first cultivated grains in human history and is still in many cultures a staple ingredient in daily diet. While economically, wheat seems to take the forefront in cultivation and consumption, barley is apparently the superior grain in many ways.

Many historical publications on agriculture and early man would have us believe that grain came into the human diet in the shape of bread, making for a more readily available food source. However, there is now new evidence and new interpretation of data that suggests it was beer or similarly fermented beverage that actually came first. Bread was prepared as a way of making the ingredients for beer more travel ready...not necessarily to be consumed as part of a meal. Gastronomical Anthropologists suggest that the consumption of beer by ancient agricultural peoples was not necessarily for the intoxication factor; rather it was more because the fermentation process made for safer and healthier beverages.

Livestock and agricultural practices potentially contaminated communal drinking water and fermenting increased the health of the gut and decreased the impact of bad bacteria. It is thought the early daily beer was actually more like the current day health drink "Rejuvelac" which is basically fermented barley water. Ceremonial drinks were left to ferment longer, which then gave them a higher alcohol content. The fermentation process also increases the bioavailability of the nutrients in the grain, specifically B vitamins and decreases the toxic impact of phytic acid found in the grain shell.

Even though conventional barley has been hybridized to have less of the toxic impact, it still contains enough to be a digestive irritant; you should always soak whole grains if you are choosing to eat them. I soak barley occasionally and make my own rejuvelac, which is especially refreshing in the summer months. I also, use the soaked grains to add to salads, soups, stews, stir-fries. They are probably one of my favorite grains because I find them so chewy and fun to eat.

From a nutritional perspective, I'm sure you know there are a million opinions about the consumption of grain, including barley. Dietary information is so conflicting; should we eat them, should we not eat them? Unfortunately, there is no easy answer to that question...from my perspective it depends on many things like body-type, ethnicity, genetic predisposition, metabolic processing, etc, etc... the best you can do is pay attention to your own body and learn how you respond to the consumption of grains. Do they provide energy? Do they make you feel sluggish? Do they impact your mood? These are things you can pay attention to in order to help learn whether they are good for you to consume or not.

Just from a straight nutritional profile, when eaten as a whole grain, barley is a great source of fiber and nutrients. In fact, the only way I would ever suggest eating it is in its whole grain state. It is high in manganese and B vitamins. Research suggests that Barley can be useful in balancing cholesterol and helpful in fighting diabetes and insulin resistance. Barley is also a good source of Selenium, which helps prevent Colon cancer and other gastrointestinal ailments.

DAY 117 – MOURVEDRE

Tannic, astringent, blackberry, and slightly pungent; Mourvedre is a particular varietal of wine grape. It is a dark and jammy grape, grown in warm Mediterranean climates. This particular grape originated in Spain and has worked its way into France, Australia, some areas in Central and South America and the U.S. It is said this particular grape is not for the vintner who is faint of heart; it likes its face in the sun and its feet in the water. Which basically means it requires full sun and moist soil to thrive. The Mourvedre grape is one of my favorite varieties and I'm glad it's making a comeback onto the wine scene.

From a food perspective, this grape is typically combined with Grenache and Syrah grapes into what is is called a GSM (Grenache, Syrah, Mourvedre) blend that seduces the palate with its spicy and slightly heavy, heady influence. It pairs really well with wild game and heartier meats, like grass fed or pasture raised and aged beef, or pork/boar that has spent an ample amount of time foraging. Not to worry if you are vegetarian, Mourvedre grapes pair well with heartier stews or pungent, earthy veggie combinations.

From a health perspective, Mourvedre grapes are a rich source of antioxidants and other phytonutrients. Resveratrol is among the most popular, being in the limelight of pop culture health and fitness. Research suggests that resveratrol decreases incidence and potential of cardiovascular disease as well as balancing cholesterol and reducing the formation of blood clots. Resveratrol also protects against cell damage and mental decline. The ellargic acid found in red grapes also contributes to metabolic stimulation and increases the body's fat burning potential, mostly by decreasing the body's ability to produce new fat cells and delaying the growth of fat cells already present.

Of course, all this good stuff about red wine is dependent on moderation and type of wine. So, if you're going to have a glass, make it just a glass or two tops, and make sure it is a consciously produced wine. Old world wines from France, Italy, and Spain tend to have more stringent fermentation guidelines, otherwise, I say go for the organic, or better yet the sustainable and/or biodynamic wines. This is especially true for the

Mourvedre grape, which was almost eliminated in the late 1800's due to a mildew invasion that moved through vineyards all across the globe. It's one reason these particular grapes can be recipients of higher doses of pesticides/herbicides, so it's best to be mindful and choose a vineyard that produces consciously.

Of course, wine isn't the only thing that can be made out of a Mourvedre grape. It can also make a pretty delicious jam.

DAY 118 – TANGERINE

Tangy, sweet, refreshing, sour, and astringent; the tangerine is a refreshing relative of the mandarin orange. Or at least some horticulture classification systems agree that they are related. Others do not and insist that the tangerine is its own species of citrus originating in the area of Tangiers, hence the name Tangerine. Hopefully, the Tangerine does not have an identity crisis despite this variation in classification because Tangerines are really quite delicious and good for you.

There is something about the Tangerine that inspires creative endeavors... there is a book titled Tangerine, and a song about Tangerine, and a musical group named Tangerine Dream. What is it about the exotic Tangerine that we seem to love so much? Tangerines are small and aromatic, making them great additions to salads and veggies. They are also awesome in stir -fry or with savory meals, like a marinated braised pork loin. Or, if you are inspired by the romantic food writings of M.F.K. Fisher you can warm them on a radiator allowing their plump, juicy goodness to inspire your creative airs.

> " It was then that I discovered little dried sections of tangerine.
> My pleasure in them is subtle and voluptuous and quite
> inexplicable. I can only write how they are prepared.
>
> In the morning, in the soft sultry chamber, sit in the window
> peeling tangerines, three or four. Peel them gently; do not
> bruise them, as you watch soldiers pour past and past the
> corner and over the canal towards the watched Rhine.
> Separate each plump little pregnant crescent. If you find the
> Kiss, the secret section, save it for later..." ~ MFK Fisher

From a health perspective, like all citrus, the tangerine is an excellent resource for Vitamin C and fiber. The volatile oils, like thymol and limonene, add an extra element of health with their ability to aid in digestive issues and promote cell regeneration, and even act as a natural pesticide. Tangerines are also packed with minerals like potassium, magnesium and manganese. Research demonstrates that including citrus, like tangerine, in your diet can help with oxidative stress, systemic inflammation, cardiovascular issues, high blood pressure, and gastrointestinal ailments. It also acts as a fortifying agent for blood and cellular structure, increasing the growth and repair of healthy red cells.

I like to use tangerines as dressing for fresh veggies and salads; squeezing the juice of a tangerine with my bare hands into the bowl and mixing and massaging thoroughly. This not only adds amazing, refreshing flavor, but also preserves the fruit or veggie until ready to eat. Don't forget to lick the juice from your fingers and inhale the tantalizing scent of tangerine as you reflect on their many treasures and gifts to our dietary repertoire.

DAY 119 – HYSSOP

Zesty, pungent, and slightly sweet with the smallest back note of bitter; that's how Hyssop tastes to me. Today's flavor comes straight from Israel, a gift from my very cool brother. I had never tried hyssop as an isolated herb before today although I have had it in Za'atar; a spice combination I love. Hyssop really has quite a lovely flavor. It is in the mint family, so possesses a similar zesty volatile quality. Hyssop also contains a pretty significant amount of tannins so less is more when using it in food. Hyssop originates in Southern Europe and the Middle East. Variations of the original herb have found their way into other countries, including the U.S., however, the variety most often found outside of the original regions is typically not the originally noted variety...lacking both flavor and medicinal quality.

From a culinary perspective, hyssop finds its way into many spice blends in Middle Eastern and Mediterranean cooking. Because of its more pronounced flavor, a little bit goes a long way. Used sparingly it can be versatile and enhance both savory and sweet dishes. In Panama, hyssop is fed to live fish to infuse them with the flavor. Apparently, it is especially delicious with mushrooms and lentils (: And it adds an interesting twist to fruit dishes. One recipe I encountered suggested sprinkling hyssop underneath the crust of peach cobbler to add a pleasant flavor surprise. Hyssop is also a key ingredient in liqueurs like Absinthe and Benedictine.

Medicinally, hyssop has a very long history as a remedy for health. There are references in the bible and other religious text as well as medieval herbal compendiums. Historically, it has been used for coughs and asthmatic conditions, as an expectorant and decongestant. It has been recommended for digestive ailments and expelling worms. It repels moths and other insects and when applied directly to the skin can aid in reducing skin irritation, including rashes, bites, and fever blisters.

Research demonstrates that hyssop is a rich source of polyphenols and actually has many properties similar to oregano oil. It acts as an antiviral, antibacterial, and antifungal remedy. It aids in gastrointestinal issues and in cases of Urinary tract infection helps fight bad bacteria and restore balance.

Hyssop is also a nervous system stimulant, so caution against using too much as it can apparently induce increased nervous system activity, including seizures.
All in all, I find hyssop to be a fascinating herb and I will continue finding ways to make it a regular in my kitchen.

DAY 120 – BELGIAN ENDIVE

Refreshing, crisp and slightly bitter; Belgian endive is a member of the chicory family. In the U.S. we typically refer to Belgian endive as just endive. I find it a delicious and fascinating vegetable to enjoy in a variety of ways. I like to prepare them like little boats, filling them with delicious goodies. Today's endives were filled with pecans, goat cheese, and a hint of lavender.

Belgian endive has been around for thousands of years, cultivated by Egyptians, Greeks, Romans and has been a mainstay in many cultures. They are versatile, not only good eaten raw, but also baked, stir fried, and sautéed. Another delicious way to prepare them is to caramelize them with apples and walnuts, oh yes.... quite scrumptious.

From a medicinal perspective, Belgian endive is a bitter so it is great for stimulating a balanced digestive process. It is a good source of vitamins and minerals, mainly Vitamin A, C, K and E, as well as potassium and calcium. Endive is high in fiber and low in calorie.

Research suggests that the antioxidants in endive act as anti-inflammatory compounds as well as increasing the body's ability to repair damage to the cells. It is beneficial for cardiovascular health and aids in decreasing "bad" cholesterol. Studies have shown that including endive in your dietary repertoire can boost immune function, strengthen bones, and increase gastrointestinal health. It also appears that eating endive can help dissolve kidney stones and cleanse the liver and gall bladder. Endive is a pretty easy food to include in your diet, not to mention being delicious and fun to arrange in beautiful patterns. I say, give it a try.

Chichorium Endivia

CHAPTER 5- MAY

DAY 121 – HOPS

Humulus Lupulus

As an isolated flavor hops are slightly bitter and pungent, with a little bit of a cloying earthiness. Not nearly as bad as it sounds, they are an interesting addition to food and drink. There are many varieties of the hop plant and it is the flower that is used in the culinary, medicinal, and brewing world. Traditionally, historical writings suggest that hops were used first and foremost as a medicinal intervention and then became part of a beer brewing process. Slowly hops began making there way into the culinary world and can be an engaging herb to bring into the kitchen for a little experimenting.

Chefs recommend choosing the varieties higher in acid and bitter components for sweeter dishes and the subtler, more floral varieties for heartier savory. You can use them anywhere you use herbs like oregano, tarragon, or other earthy herbs like marjoram. Sprinkling them on, mixing them in, sautéing them, however you would use these other herbs, hops can go right along side. A word of caution; a little bit of hops goes a long way.

From a medicinal perspective, hops are used as a natural remedy for anxiety, restlessness and insomnia. Research has also demonstrated that hops can be a useful intervention for attention deficit disorder and restless leg syndrome. Because it is a bitter, hops is beneficial for stimulating the digestive process. Hops has antibacterial, antifungal qualities, which is one reason it is beneficial in the beer brewing process; but this also makes it an interesting candidate for cancer research. Studies are showing that hops is a beneficial addition to your dietary repertoire to help stave off various types of cancer.

Today's flavor inspiration comes from a cup of tea, rather than a bottle of beer, which is one of the other main ways hops are consumed. It can also be put inside your pillowcase to help encourage restful sleep.

I think hops are a beautiful herb, reminding of little bells or rattles. It is worth perhaps finding the isolated herb and giving it a try, even in the kitchen as a culinary experiment. Another word of caution, hops as an isolated herb has a very strong smell...not the best, but once cooked, calms down into an earthy, almost tangy aroma.

DAY 122 – DRUNKEN GOAT (CHEESE, THAT IS...)

Creamy, savory, earthy/goaty, with a slightly bitter and sweet finish, that describes the flavor of Mitica Drunken Goat cheese from my perspective. It's called Drunken Goat because it's final fermentation stages occur while it is soaking in red wine. The rind takes on the color, scent and a very slight flavor of the wine, while the inside remains white and creamy finishes it. This particular cheese originates in Spain and is a semi-firm. The extended aging period makes it less goaty than fresh goat cheese so it is an easy cheese to enjoy even if you don't typically enjoy goat cheese.

This cheese pairs well with fruits and more mild veggies. My favorite way to eat it is with granny smith apples and sliced fresh fennel...super delicious. Walnuts seem to compliment its flavor really well also. I like it because it is not too heavy or cloying as some creamy cheeses can be.

From a culinary perspective, Drunken Goat is lovely on a tapas plate, as appetizers, or dessert. It's also delicious as an addition to sandwiches (favorite veggie sandwich is walnut sourdough bread, drunken goat cheese, thinly sliced apples, thinly sliced fennel, arugula, cranberry or pesto aioli...totally scrumptious!).

From a health perspective, goat cheese is great. It is higher in calcium and Vitamins A, B and D than cow's milk. It is also lower in cholesterol and fat. For people who are lactose intolerant goat cheese is a great option because it is easier to digest than cow's milk. This is because goat cheese has less lactose, which also has a different chemical structure. The fat in goat's milk is often more efficiently digested because the globules are smaller and typically, there are more short and medium chain fatty acids making it easier on the stomach. Goat's milk also has a slightly different protein structure, which can make it less triggering for people with milk allergies.

Goat cheese is also a great source of selenium, potassium, and copper all of which are fundamental ingredients for nervous system health as well as strong bones and beautiful skin.

DAY 123 – CHIVES

Pungent, zesty, earthy, sometimes slightly warming and even sweet; chives are part of the allium family. They are related to onions and garlic. For such a small herb they have a powerful flavor, delivering many of the characteristics of onion or garlic but in a much softer, more complex way. The use of chives, both culinary and medicinal, has been part of recorded history for over 5,000 years. They are best fresh and raw, although having some dried chives in your herbal arsenal can be quite useful. Chives are delicate, despite their strongish flavor, so it's a good idea to sprinkle them on, and in, things as a finishing touch, rather than cooking with them. That way you get the full benefit of their flavor and their healthy goodness.

Some interesting uses for chives besides on your plate? They can be planted around the edges or sporadically throughout other plants to help deter insect pests, and yet, when they flower the bees love them, so you get a double delight if you cultivate them in your garden. Like their counterparts, the onion and garlic, chives are also antifungal, antimicrobial, and antibacterial. The juice from a chive can be used as an insect repellent and as an agent against fungal infections.

From a medicinal perspective, chives have many of the same properties of other Allium family members, just in a lighter dose. Chives are a good source of Vitamin A and K, and a multitude of minerals like potassium, magnesium and copper. They have anti-inflammatory properties and can also help alleviate pain and irritation if used topically. Apparently, Romans used the juice of chives to treat sunburn and chewed on raw chive stems to heal sore throats. I wonder if just sprinkling them over a nice plate of scrambled eggs is good enough???

DAY 124 – MARJORAM

Marjoram is part of the mint family. It has a flavor that is pungent and woody, with a hint of earthy spiciness. It is a bright and refreshing herb, with a citrusy quality that is almost sweet but not quite. There seems to be confusion whether marjoram and oregano are interchangeable and ultimately the same thing; and while they are very similar they are indeed not the same. Marjoram is a softer herb, with a mellower and sweeter flavor than oregano, although truthfully both herbs have many varieties so comparisons are challenging. Personally, I enjoy the lighter quality of marjoram a bit more than I like the deep earthiness of oregano.

From a culinary perspective, Marjoram like it's aromatic counterparts is good to experiment with in the kitchen. It can enhance both sweet and savory dishes, whether adding as a integral ingredient or simply sprinkling fresh herb over the top of something. Marjoram and rosemary pair very nicely together, so there's a hint for use.

Medicinally, marjoram has a well-respected history that goes back to ancient Egypt, Greece and surrounding areas. Symbolically, marjoram was considered a gift from Aphrodite and was used to ensure happiness, health, and harmony. As a remedy it has many cited interventions for things like digestive issues, colds and flu, and skin problems. Research demonstrates that Marjoram contains similar volatile oils to other members of the mint family and acts as a great antimicrobial, antiviral, antifungal, and antiseptic compound. Sipping Marjoram tea can help aid gastrointestinal issues as well as combat stomach and intestinal bugs that may be causing distress. Studies show that Marjoram is also packed with vitamins, minerals and antioxidants that help decrease systemic inflammation, increase cardiovascular health, and improve your mood.

DAY 125 – MACHE (LAMB'S LETTUCE)

Mache, also known as lamb's lettuce (which is the name I prefer) or corn salad, is a lovely little green, subtle in flavor yet distinct. It is earthy, sweet, slightly nutty, and the tiniest bit astringent, which makes it a great compliment to many dishes. It has quickly become one of my favorite greens and it finds its way into a variety of meals on a daily basis.

I was first attracted to lamb's lettuce because of the way it looked and its delicate name. It is a small rosette of bright green leaves, often with a little bit of root still intact, giving it that freshly foraged look. While its leaves look delicate and give the impression of young and fragile, lamb's lettuce is a relatively hardy green that is packed with nutrients.

Being utterly smitten with everything about this green, I wanted to know more. Upon deeper investigation, I discovered that Mache has quite a nostalgic following and sparks intense discussion about seasonal eating, harvesting, and even cultivation for specific nuances of flavor. I'm even more fascinated by this amazing little salad plant now.

Lamb's lettuce is a member of the honeysuckle family, believe it or not and as mentioned, it is packed with nutrients. It has three times the vitamin

C than its green lettuce-y counterparts and 14 times the Vitamin?. It's also full of vitamin B and minerals like Copper, Potassium, and Iron.

Other fun tidbits about Lamb's lettuce??? This wild green goes by quite a few alternate names and is spread across multiple countries and continents. In Germany, it is also referred to as Rapunzel because it is featured in the Grimm's fairy tale of the same name as the delicacy stolen from the witch's garden. First recorded cultivation of lamb's lettuce in the U.S. was by Thomas Jefferson in his Monticello gardens.

DAY 126 – SWISS CHARD

Bitter, astringent, chalky, but surprisingly delicious; Swiss Chard is actually a close relative of the beetroot. As wild vegetation, chard was called sea beet, in its cultivated form it has interesting names like Perpetual Spinach, Seakale Beet, Crab Beet. More commonly Chard is called Swiss Chard, however, the reason for the prename "Swiss" is unclear. Chard is not native to Switzerland; rather it is thought to have originated in more Mediterranean climates. It is a popular vegetable in Mediterranean cuisine and has been growing in popularity in Europe and the U.S.

Chard is not technically a bitter, however it does contain a substantial amount of oxalates, which is what gives it the harsher perception of bitter flavor and astringent quality if eaten raw. Cooking chard eliminates this issue and it becomes a lovely addition to savory dishes. One of my favorite ways to prepare Swiss Chard is as breakfast option, topping cooked chard with two nicely poached eggs. Chop the chard stems finely, sauté them with garlic and then, once the stems are tender, fold in the larger leaves that have been julienned. Once it's all nice and soft, serve it up on a plate, top with lovely poached eggs and voila... yumminess. You can also add chard to soups, stews, and other culinary endeavors.

Chard comes in a rainbow of colors, which makes it a fun and highly nutritious addition to your dietary repertoire. It is an amazing source of Vitamins A, K, and C, in many cases, a single serving putting you well up on the traditional required daily (which is only a minimum but at least it's a start). It also has many of the special nutrients found in beets and spinach; making it a great resource for eliminating systemic inflammation.

Chard leaf also contains a nifty little chemical compound specific to it only called syringic acid. Research demonstrates that this compound plays a significant role in managing blood glucose levels. All in all, it could be a good idea to add some cultivated Sea Beet (aka Chard) to your frequently consumed veggie list. (:

If you have a garden, Chard is an awesome functional and ornamental addition. It can turn your landscape or container garden into deliciously edible art.

DAY 127 – JASMINE

Subtle sweetness with the tiniest hint of earth; jasmine is an exotic addition to a culinary experience. Pink and white jasmine (not to be confused with star jasmine which is much less fragrant) are two of my favorite scents in the flower world. These are also the typical flowers used in the culinary world. My first introduction to jasmine in a food was as a traditional jasmine tea, which when prepared as the real deal is a subtle and delightful experience. My next introduction to culinary jasmine was in a shortbread cookie... oh yes, there is something about the subtle sweet flavor of flowers mixed with the buttery crispness of shortbread.

In the world of molecular gastronomy jasmine has the same molecular structure as pork, so it is a suggested pairing and there is also a comparable molecular structure to ginger, so apparently ginger and jasmine compliment well. Molecular gastronomy is based on the idea that foods with similar molecular structure will create "food harmony" for your palate. An interesting endeavor, however, I fear it has turned many a kitchen into a chemistry lab rather than a place of nourishment and lovingly prepared offerings...but I digress.

Jasmine is an edible flower that can be eaten raw, infused for the subtle flavor, or added straight to both savory and sweet dishes. If you haven't tried incorporating edible flowers into your culinary repertoire, I highly recommend it.

In the case of the lovely jasmine, it is not only a subtle and exotic addition it also has its own arsenal of health properties.

From an aromatherapy perspective jasmine is noted for being antidepressant and aphrodisiac. It also can have a sedative effect for people suffering from anxiety. Jasmine is also antiviral, antifungal, and antiseptic, so it makes a great intervention for skin issues including as a wound cleaner. Research demonstrates its germicidal properties act as an inhibitor for tetanus. When inhaled it can aid in the healing of respiratory infections and helps with coughs from cold and flu. The essential oil of jasmine can help reduce scarring and can help clear up eczema and psoriasis. Jasmine is also a wonderful intervention for hormonal balance, regulating symptoms of PMS and other issues created by imbalance or stress. Who knew that lovely, unassuming little white flower had so much power?!?!

DAY 128 – LEMON BALM (RECIPE)

Refreshing, uplifting, zesty, slightly sweet; lemon balm is an herb that has the ability to improve your mood just by its smell. Nibbling the leaves takes you a refreshing step further into a subtle yet satisfying citrus-y flavor. Lemon Balm is also called Balm Mint. It imparts a subtle lemon flavor and from a culinary perspective is a nice addition to dishes both sweet and savory that might benefit from slightly lemony, sweet, and refreshing flavor notes. Because it contains an interesting spectrum of chemical compounds, such as rosmarinic acid, the Journal of Meat Science (yeah, I know, who knew there was a peer reviewed journal dedicated to meat) suggests that lemon balm also has the potential to be a food preservative; making it a healthier option.

For a great refreshing addition to a meal you could try making this LEMON BALM PESTO:

Just blend up all the ingredients and you're ready to go:
2 cups fresh lemon balm
½ cup extra-virgin olive oil
3-4 cloves garlic

For all its subtle flavor, lemon balm packs many other healthful properties. Its scent alone is a mood booster and improves mental focus. Sipping it as tea, which is actually my favorite way to enjoy it, is refreshing and can help manage stress by acting as a mild sedative. Lemon Balm also has amazing antiviral, antifungal, antibacterial qualities. Research demonstrates it is highly effective in exerting a direct inhibitory effect on systemic viruses like the herpes virus.

It also has exhibited promising success in the treatment of Grave's disease and instances of hyperthyroidism. Whether eating it in foods, sipping as a tea, or supplementing it in other ways, lemon balm can play a strong role in helping to decrease oxidative stress and repair DNA damage within cell plasma. Topically, lemon balm helps protect and repair damage to the dermal layer and it also acts as a fantastic insect repellent. Keep a jar of lemon balm salve handy for minor skin irritations and issues including relieving the irritation of pesky bug bites.

Word of caution: if you are taking medication for underactive thyroid, it is possible that lemon balm can inhibit the uptake and assimilation.

DAY 129 – LEMON VERBENA

Lemon Verbena smells lemony and uplifting which makes it quite refreshing. Its taste is subtly sweet and actually more like lemongrass than lemon. It has similar grassy notes. While I don't mean to be on a lemon streak, it seems like lemony and citrusy flavors seem to be making their way to my plate. It must be spring.

Lemon Verbena is a native of South America and really more popular in the herbal world than in the mainstream culinary world. When I think about Lemon Verbena, I always think about Laura Ingalls Wilder and Little House on the Prairie. Laura was enamored of her teacher's Lemon Verbena perfume. I can see why, it is an herb that delights the senses.

From a culinary perspective Lemon Verbena can be used in many of the same ways that lemongrass or other lemon-flavored ingredients can be used. It is a delicious addition sprinkled over foods ready to serve, or as an ingredient in sorbets or other simple palate cleansing desserts. It's also delicious as a tea.

Medicinally, research has been done on the antioxidant quality of lemon verbena with good results. The chemical compounds in this herb help eliminate free radicals and decrease oxidative stress while also helping cells to repair. One study conducted on runners with muscular tissue damage, demonstrated that the chemical compounds in lemon verbena helped the tissue repair quickly without interfering with the adaptive response to exercise. Another study focusing on overall aerobic performance found that lemon verbena supplementation helped decrease systemic inflammation and neutralize post-exercise cytokine response.

Other research published by the Journal of Ethnopharmacology suggests that the antifungal, antimicrobial, antibacterial qualities of Lemon Verbena are very helpful in the elimination of candida albicans.

I have a small lemon verbena plant in my very tiny balcony garden and it is refreshing just to enjoy a little nibble of the leaves every now and then.

DAY 130 – FLAX SEEDS (RECIPE)

Flax seeds taste nutty with a hint of grassiness or a quality of earth when they are fresh. They have the added bonus of being fun to eat because they are so small and chewy. Flax seeds have gotten quite a boost in popularity in recent years because of their reputation for being high in Omega 3 Fatty Acids. Although it may seem to some that flax is a relative newcomer on the scene of food and health, it is in fact, very old. Flax also goes by the name linseed and has been popular in cultures all over the world for thousands of years. Flax is still today cultivated as fiber, food, and medicine giving it some major brownie points for being so versatile.

From a culinary perspective, flax is a great addition to baked goods both sweet and savory. They can also be sprinkled in a variety of dishes to add a hint of nutty flavor without actually adding nuts.

From a health perspective, while flax may sound wonderful and it is... all things in moderation. Unsoaked flax seeds have the same issue that many seeds and nuts have, which is their nutrients are protected by phytic acid. The only way to get to the nutrients and break down the phytic acid is either by soaking or by cooking. (I'm sure there are other ways but those are the quickest and easiest). I either soak mine or give them a quick low heat sauté and then grind them once they have cooled.

Flax seeds have been touted as a superfood because they are high in fiber and high in essential fatty acids. There have been a variety of studies conducted on the benefits of flax seeds; some demonstrating that the chemical compounds can help lower cholesterol, decrease oxidative stress, balance blood sugar and decrease intestinal inflammatory response. If you do include consumption of flax seeds in your diet, make sure you are consuming enough liquids and maybe spreading out the consumption through a variety of meals rather than one large amount. This will inhibit the potential for intestinal blockage.

CHEESY ALMOND AND FLAX SEED CRACKERS
1 cup finely ground almond flour (meal)
1/4 cup finely grated Parmesan cheese
2 tablespoons ground flax meal
1/2 teaspoon of a savory herb (this is optional, I have used rosemary, oregano and/or thyme)

1/4 teaspoon salt

1/8 teaspoon paprika

1 large egg (if you choose to just use egg white, make sure you add 1 tsp of olive oil)

Preheat oven to 350 degrees. You will need to roll the dough out between two pieces of baking or parchment paper. Combine all ingredients in food processor. Scoop onto parchment, place another sheet over the top and roll out to about 1/4 inch or pie crust thickness. Remove the top parchment and use a knife or pizza cutter to cut crackers into squares. Move the crackers while still on parchment to a baking sheet. Bake for about 15 minutes. When they are nicely browned, remove them from oven and let them cool before enjoying. Keep in an airtight container.

DAY 131 – ANNATTO (ACHIOTE)

Interesting... earthy, pungent, piquant with a suggestion of heat, but no heat; annatto has a subtle yet distinctive flavor combination. Tasting annatto in its unadulterated form is reminded me of those times when you forget a word and it's right there on the edge of your tongue waiting to be remembered. I knew I had tasted it before, it evoked memory of flavor experience but try as I might I could not clearly identify any particular dish. This makes annatto very intriguing, in my book.

Annatto is made from the seeds of the Achiote tree, which originates in Central and South America. According to historical records, it was originally used externally for things like body paint and even ink by various indigenous groups from Brazil to Mexico. At some point, it started making its way into cuisine and is now pretty commonly used for a variety of culinary purposes. Since then it's made its way around the world as is cultivated globally in most warmer climates. It is a very common additive in conventional foods and can be found as a coloring agent in things that are yellow, orange or red. It is what gives most conventional cheddar cheese the bright orange color.

Annatto is versatile and subtle and can be used in a variety of foods, both sweet and savory. The powder can be added to sauces, soups, stews, or it can be combined with other spices to make a flavorful paste. Wondering what dishes you may have tasted achiote in? Carnitas, Chili, Biryani, Ropa Vieja, just to give an example of the global influence for this seed. The coloring potential makes it an inexpensive replacement for dishes requiring saffron. You can also make it into a paste and add it to chocolate to make a traditional treat worthy of Aztec gods.

From a medicinal perspective, annatto has a rich traditional history from various cultures that is finding its way into the scientifically supported realms. Historically, it has been used as a skin protectant for things like insect repellent, sun protection, and even leprosy. It has also been used to lower blood pressure, cleanse the liver and as an antiviral/antibacterial agent. Research suggests that it can indeed be beneficial in reversing liver damage. It has been studied as a blood sugar stabilizer with positive results and it demonstrates promise as an intervention for oxidative stress and a systemic anti-inflammatory.

All in all, annatto is an interesting and exotic flavor adventure for the mainstream westernized diet, could be worth giving it a try! (:

DAY 132 – AGIORGITIKO

That's easy for you to say! Easily influenced, the flavor of this grape changes like a chameleon depending on what it is accompanying. Agiorgitiko is a variety of grape that is indigenous to Greece. I tried it for the first time in the form of a traditional Greek table wine called Katoi.

The very first taste was 'interesting' to say the least and being the complete food and flavor geek that I am, I was motivated to begin pairing it with foods to see how they influenced the flavor. Feta cheese, yum, kalamata olives, double yum... potatoes, not so yum. What I found utterly fascinating and also completely obvious was that when paired with foods that would be within the same terroir or environment of this grape, it opened up and became extraordinary. When paired with foods that were not native to the area it was merely so-so. Yet, another reason it is worth paying attention to the origin and terroir of your food and drink.

This grape has quite the interesting history with several nicknames affiliating it with various Greek myths and historical events. In Nemea, wine made from Agiorgitiko is called "The Blood of Hercules" because it is referenced as the wine that Hercules drank before dispatching the Nemean Lion (one of his many epic accomplishments in Greek mythology).

The literal translation of Agiorgitiko is "St. George's Grape". While it appears there is a vast array of variations to the story of St. George, there does seem to be some agreement by historians that his name means, "worker of the land". Historical records suggest that before he became a Roman soldier, he did indeed work the land of his home, Cappadocio, which may be well have included tending vineyards. Of course, there is also the potential that they are named such because they were cultivated in a town named after St. George. Either way, I personally prefer the name Agiorgitiko because you can use it as a litmus test of wine consumption. When you can no longer say the name, you can no longer drink the wine. (:

This grape is quite versatile, if not paradoxical, on the one hand hardy and on the other hand very prone to disease. It also has a flavor that is most definitely influenced by viniculture (how it is grown) and terroir (where it was grown). Given that, it can have a very wide flavor palate making it a challenge to pin down to one simple description.

From a health perspective, of course first and foremost, all things in moderation, but then, as a red wine, Agiorgitiko offers all the same valuable benefits of red wine with its notable quantity of resveratrol and other antioxidants.

DAY 133 – TATSOI

Crisp, refreshing, slightly bitter, with a cool suggestion of zesty sweetness as the aftertaste; Tatsoi reminds me slightly of a cross between young mustard greens and watercress. Tatsoi is an Asian green that is also sometimes called Spinach Mustard. It is a member of the Brassica family, so imparts all the healthy goodness of its veggie compadres; cabbage, broccoli and brussels sprouts. It is a very attractive plant with its deep green leaves, complemented by light colored veins and stalks. Tatsoi is indigenous to China but initially gained popularity through Japanese cuisine. It is now making its way around the globe as an interesting addition to palatable greens and can be found more and more readily in U.S. markets.

From a culinary perspective, Tatsoi can be used much the same way as spinach. Add it to fresh salads for an interesting complexity of flavor. It can also be stirred into soups or sautéed up with other veggies. I used it as a fresh pizza topping last night, mixed up with some fresh basil and it was quite tasty.

From a health perspective, Tatsoi has so many of the same fantastic benefits of its brassica mates. It is rich in vitamins and minerals. Calcium, potassium, phosphorus, iron, all contribute to healthy bones, tissue, and blood, as well as nervous system balance. Vitamins A, C, and K and beta carotene contribute to overall health and wellness. Adding tatsoi to your diet can help manage systemic inflammation, oxidative stress, and boost immune function.

One word of caution...tatsoi, as with all brassicas, contains progoitrin, which with significant consumption can impact thyroid function. Just one more reason to be sure you are eating a wide variety of foods rather than consuming the same old thing every day. (:

DAY 134 – BANANA (RECIPE)

Smooshy, sweet, almost cloyingly sweet in my opinion; bananas are a very popular fruit and can be found in cultures around the world. Technically, the banana is a berry according to the ranking of its botanical genus. It originates in warmer climates but has managed to make its way into the mainstream market of almost every culture around the globe.

Bananas are a nicely contained option for a quick snack. They are packed with potassium and B vitamins, making them a great option for cardiovascular and nervous system health. Research demonstrates that consuming a banana one hour prior to athletic activities keeps potassium levels higher in the blood and increases the body's ability to repair and recover. Bananas are also a great option for insuring digestive balance. The combination of fiber, pectin, and fructooligosaccharides make it a great option for gastrointestinal health. The banana supports the cultivation of pre and probiotics.

Bananas have the interesting property of being a little bit of everything. Yes, they have a higher sugar content but the pectin and fiber help balance it out and the starch actually feeds the healthy bacteria in your colon. If you're suffering from, dare I say it, diarrhea or constipation, bananas actually can help in both cases. From a commerce and cultivation perspective, they are hardy and at the same time quite fragile.

From a culinary perspective, bananas are again versatile...they add well to both sweet and savory dishes. They are delicious raw and they are also delicious cooked. They can serve as a moistening agent in baked goods and they are a great foundation for grain free pancakes.

Here's a recipe for some crazy delicious grain free…

BANANA CHOCOLATE CHIP PANCAKES
1 ½ large ripe bananas
2 eggs
½ tsp. vanilla extract
¼ tsp. ground cinnamon
1/8 tsp. baking powder
Chocolate chips

Blend all ingredients together. Cook like regular pancakes... I put them in small circles in the pan and then sprinkle the chocolate chips on top of the raw batter while it is cooking. You can also do blueberries or any other type of fruit.

DAY 135 – BURDOCK ROOT

The taproot of Burdock is more flavorful than one might think; it is slightly earthy with a hint of bitter and subtly pungent. The combination of flavors is surprisingly refreshing. Burdock root is very popular in Asian cuisine and is making its way back to popularity in western cuisine. There was a time, however, when Burdock was quite popular in European cuisine. As a drink it was paired with dandelion to create a popular alcoholic beverage of that very name, "Dandelion and Burdock". Dandelion and Burdock was also referred to as Hedgerow Mead in Medieval times. It has since become a non-alcoholic version, which enjoys an equally rich history and can also be relished as a tea as well as a soda.

Burdock and dandelion root can be roasted and made into a drink that serves as a 'coffee' substitute, sometimes with chicory and fennel added in to give it a richer flavor. Once roasted the roots can be either soaked, like tea, or ground finely and used in place of coffee grounds. I use this blend as an after meal digestive tea and it is really quite nice. Burdock root is also a really great addition to soups and stews. It is delicious pickled and also adds a really lovely complexity when added to other culinary endeavors.

From a health perspective, Burdock is considered a diuretic, diaphoretic, and blood purifier. Diaphoretic means it induces sweating; which in turn detoxifies the body, via lymph and circulation. As a diuretic, it detoxifies the liver by cleansing while also supporting liver function.

I enjoy burdock throughout the year in the form of tea as mentioned, and it also takes a front and center role in the spring as an addition to broths, soups and stews that help detox my system. Burdock is high in essential minerals and other nutrients, as well as fiber. Research suggests that it increases digestive properties and can help manage blood sugar. Studies have been conducted on the use of burdock root to help manage diabetes with evidence of success.

Burdock is also beneficial in reducing blood clots, which also adds the cautionary note of being careful if one is taking blood thinners already or perhaps undergoing a surgical procedure.

DAY 136 – CHUTNEY (RECIPE)

Straight from my cheese and pickle sandwich; today's flavor comes from the pickle part...it's a rhubarb lemon chutney. It is sweetly sour, with a slightly chewy, jammy quality. Chutney is a combination of preserved fruits, vegetables, and spices, similar to relish. True chutney originated in South Asia and made its way through various cuisines around the world. Today's chutney was a combination of citrus, rhubarb, and small, sweet onion, making it a delicious addition to my cheese and pickle sandwich. Chutneys are meant to be a sweet and savory condiment to complement meals and snacks. They are one way to help get all of the qualities of taste included in your meal as well as adding various nutrients without adding extra entrees or larger quantities of food.

Chutneys are made by reducing vinegar, sugar, fruit, veggie and spices down to jam-like consistency. Preserved foods have been part of human food culture for thousands of years. The first recorded use of preserved food was 700 BC although it is assumed preservation of foods was going on well before then.

From a health perspective, chutney one property that chutneys are meant to serve is to aid in digestion. They sweet and sour blend acts as a digestive aid. Other health properties vary with the combination of fruit or vegetables.

Here's a simple summer chutney recipe:

FRESH FRUIT CHUTNEY
1 tablespoon sesame oil
4 cups chopped onion

1 tablespoon minced garlic
8 cups prepared fresh fruit
1 cup dried fruit, chopped if larger than raisins
1 cup muscavado sugar (if you can't find any, you can use white granulated or brown)
1 cup vinegar
1 cup water
2 small fresh chile peppers, seeded and slivered lengthwise, or 1 teaspoon crushed red pepper
1 teaspoon salt
Preparation

Heat oil in a Dutch oven over medium heat. Add onion and cook, stirring occasionally, until light brown, 6 to 10 minutes Add garlic and cook, stirring, until fragrant, about 30 seconds. Add fresh fruit, dried fruit, sugar, vinegar, water, chiles and salt. Bring to a boil over high heat, stirring often. Reduce heat to maintain a lively simmer and cook until thickened, 30 to 40 minutes. To test doneness, put a spoonful of chutney on a plate and draw a spoon through the center. If no liquid seeps into the middle, it's done. Return to a simmer to thicken more if necessary.

If freezing or refrigerating, ladle the chutney into clean canning jars to within 1/2 inch of the rim. Wipe rims clean. Cover with lids. Let the jars stand at room temperature until cool before refrigerating or freezing. Or process in a water bath to store at room temperature.

DAY 137 – TRAMINER

Today's flavor is isolated from a duo of flavors that blend together and create the amazingly synergistic white wine from La Petraia, Segreto. Traminer grapes have an interesting history. It is believed that the original varietal was a green skinned, white grape cultivated in Tramin, South Tyrol, which is in Northern Italy. Over the centuries it has made its way down the slopes and into various other vineyards across Europe and beyond.

The Traminer grape is a very close relative of the sauvignon grape and is quite versatile as far as white wine grapes go. It apparently adapts well to its environment, taking on the influences of its growing environment and viniculture. In this particular blend of Segreto, the Traminer grape is blended with Voigner to become a gentle white wine that is sweet, but not overly so, and mellow with hints of honey, lavender and oak. All of which can be found in the close proximity of these grapes as they grow to maturity.

Personally, I typically do not drink white wines, however, this Primaia Segreto is amazing. Understanding the influence of terroir, coupled with a deep appreciation for all things authentically created, provides a great foundation for the pure enjoyment of Primaia Segreto.

One reason I have not necessarily enjoyed white wine is because I assumed, erroneously, that it was less healthy than white. However, being the research geek that I am, I decided to find out if that was indeed true. Surprise! I found quite a bit of current research touting the benefits of white wine grapes. In fact, current research suggests that it is packed with almost every bit of benefit that red one contains. For example, red wine has been applauded as a heart healthy friend, but lo and behold, so is white. Even more interestingly, the heart healthy benefits of the white grape are not derived from the same source.

In red wine it is the resveratrol that contributes so much its reputation for health; however in white wine it is a different antioxidant entirely. Tyrosol and hydroxytyrosol, both of which are also found in olive oil, and are what contribute to the beneficial reputation of the Mediterranean diet. Research on white wine also shows promise for helping regulate blood sugar and decreasing instance of diabetes, as well as activating specific anti-aging genes thought initially to only respond to resveratrol.

If you are really thinking to add wine to your health arsenal, you will want to be sure that you are purchasing "cleanly" processed wines, organic and/or biodynamic when possible as with the wines from La Petraia. Trust me on this one, before you begin assuming that organic wines are too expensive or unobtainable, you will be surprised to know that there are some very inexpensive and well made wines from organic and sustainably farmed vineyards. If you are drinking cheap, conventional wines you are often killing off the amazing benefits with the chemical processing that occurs so it ends up being an unhealthy option. This is slightly less true for 'old world' wines which have some pretty strict processing rules in both Italy and France; even if they aren't organic.

As with all things delicious, and especially alcoholic, moderation is key... and if you've been limiting your palate to reds because you think it's healthier, I hope this inspires you to broaden your horizons. It definitely has inspired me.

If you want to know more about La Petraia, check them out here. They have an amazing and heartwarming history that is worthy of accolades and deep appreciation.

DAY 138 – BROAD BEANS (RECIPE)

Crunchy-ish, fresh and earthy, with an ever so slight hint of bitter; fresh Broad Beans are a beautiful addition to an evening meal. Broad beans as they are called in the U.K. also go by the moniker Fava Beans and are one of the oldest cultivated foods in human record. Archeologists believe the initial domestication and cultivation of the Fava Bean began sometime around 9,000 BC in the area, which is now considered Syria and Turkey.

In due course, they made their way across the continent and eventually around the world. Broad Beans have an interesting and dichotomous history. Some cultures have completely shunned them such as the Egyptians, who believed they housed the souls of the dead. While other cultures have embraced them as completely sacred and included them in sacred rites and feasts.

Today for the most part, they are just considered food. From a culinary perspective, there are multitudes of ways to prepare them. Fresh Broad Beans have a subtle flavor that can lean toward the bitter side the more mature they are. This is because they are high in oxalic acid, which will cook out but can still leave a bitter aftertaste.

Dried Broad Beans, or Fava Beans, are better soaked and then prepared. They have a slightly stronger bean taste, although much less bitterness. Beans can be added to soups, stews, and other foods. They can also be served on their own, sautéed with butter and herbs, which makes them perfectly delicious. Historically, they have also been prepared as a puree, similar to hummus.

From a nutritional perspective, Broad Beans are an amazing source of fiber, protein, and various minerals and vitamins. Research suggests that these beans have a significant amount of isoflavones and plant sterols that help protect against breast and prostate cancers. They also lower cholesterol and balance blood sugar levels. Research also demonstrates that Fava/Broad Beans are a significant source of L-Dopa which is a precursor to Dopamine in the brain and can help protect against Parkinson's Disease and also various dopamine dependent mood disorders.

Word of caution: There is a small percent of the population who have a rare condition called Favism, which means they are unable to process the chemical compounds found in Broad Beans so if you're one of these few, then you don't want to try these beans. (: Also if you are at all sensitive to oxalates, you want to be sure to cook them well, or opt for the dry bean.

BROAD BEAN HUMMUS

1 1/2 cups fava beans (if you use dry you will need to soak them overnight and then cook them)
2 cloves garlic
1/3 cup olive oil
1/4 cup lemon juice
2 tablespoons (or more) reserved cooking liquid
1 1/2 teaspoons salt
1 teaspoon ground cumin
1/2 teaspoon sweet paprika
1/2 teaspoon hot paprika or cayenne pepper

Prepare the Broad Beans, dried beans should be soaked and then cooked until tender. Fresh beans should be boiled until tender. Then combine all ingredients in a food processor and blend until smooth. Enjoy...

DAY 139 – GRAVADLAX

Today's flavor comes straight from Mark Gainfort's fishing boat via the Griffin Inn in Dale, Pembrokeshire, Wales. Gravadlax pronounced like battle ax... is a type of cured or preserved fish. It originates from Nordic cuisine and typically is made from Salmon, cured with either sugar or salt.

Today's Gravadlax is actually Sewin, or sea trout, which has been marinated in beetroot and vodka. Oh my gosh! The flavor is inspired. It's subtle and at the same time distinctive. Typically, I am not a fan of cured fish, not being partial in the least to things like lox, however this fresh take on the recipe is completely delicious. It was also amazingly aesthetically pleasing with the bright red of the beetroot creating colored nuances that were tremendously compelling.

This particular sea trout, otherwise known as Sewin, came straight from the bay in Milford Haven, fresher than fresh and sustainably harvested. Sea trout bears a close resemblance to salmon but has a subtler flavor and lighter colored flesh. Even so it contains all the delicious nutrients of salmon with much less political upheaval or particular environmental pressure. It is rich in Omega 3 fatty acids and higher purine proteins, making it an excellent option for health and well-being.

Remember also that Salmon is a good mood food, with research demonstrating that it contributes to brain health and nervous system balance. It's also a delicious option for cardiovascular health and immune function. Omega 3's decrease oxidative stress and systemic inflammation. Couple that with the beetroot which has its own amazing nutrient base and you've got a dish that is worth savoring and also knowing you have tipped the scales of health your way (no pun intended). (:

My thoughts are, it's worth figuring out how to get your hands on some Sea trout, beetroot and vodka and attempting to add gravadlax to your dietary repertoire...or better yet, if you're in the area, make your way to the Griffin Inn in Dale and have some that has been prepared by the Master.

DAY 140 – LOGANBERRY

Berries, berries, berries... sweet, juicy, tart, sour; all at the same time, delicious. Today's flavor is the lesser-known Loganberry. Although, it is quite possible that you've had a Loganberry and mistaken it for a raspberry, they are indeed distinctly different berries. The Loganberry is said to have originated in the U.S.; specifically in the Santa Cruz Mountains of California. So, it's a wonder that my first known taste of a Loganberry was in the welcoming and cozy kitchen of Monk Haven Manor, in St. Ishmael's, Pembrokeshire, Wales.

These particular berries were part of the cornucopia of lovely edibles harvested straight from the garden below the house and lovingly turned into a delicious jam made by the expert hands of Jan Mathias, proprietor of Monk Haven Manor. What better way to enjoy the fantastic home baked bread than with a slathering of homemade Loganberry and Raspberry Jam?!? Of course, the morning's gentle banter and delightful camaraderie with Jan and her assistant Jo Evans, made every breakfast morsel infinitely more delicious.

The Loganberry is a hybrid cross between a blackberry and a raspberry. It has the delightful red color of a raspberry but the flavor, size and texture of a sweeter blackberry. From a culinary perspective Loganberries, though not quite as popular in the mainstream market, actually make a better fruit for kitchen endeavors. They are a little bit hardier than the raspberry having a full rather hollow center and imparts their own unique flavor; not too raspberry-ish and not too blackberry-ish. They are, as demonstrated, delicious in jams, pies, cakes, salads, on their own, and even tossed into game based savory dishes.

From a health perspective, the loganberry delivers all the nutritional goodness of its counterparts. They are a powerhouse of vitamins, minerals, antioxidants, and other phytonutrients to keep you on a wellness track. They are high in fiber, and vitamins A, B, C, D, E, and K; all of which contribute to bone and tissue health, immune balance, and a healthy nervous system. Their naturally high pectin content contributes to collagen production. They contain potassium, copper, manganese, magnesium, zinc, etc, etc., which makes them a fantastic option for decreasing systemic inflammation and oxidative stress. Research indicates that just one half cup of berries a day contributes to prevention of cardiovascular disease, cancer, and various neurodegenerative diseases.

We all know that laughter, good food, and good friends support optimal health, so I highly recommend finding delightful people to share your Loganberries with, as we were lucky to do at Monk Haven Manor.

DAY 141 – GORSE FLOWERS

Subtly sweet and fragile, with hints of earth; gorse flowers have such a subtle flavor that you can almost miss it if you're not slowing down and savoring each bite. For all of their subtlety in the flavor department they are visually stunning. They have tiny bright yellow petals on showcased on dark green, spiky branches. Gorse bushes are native to Western Europe, though they've made their way around the world, and can be found on coastal landscapes adding a sense of idyllic visual delight to panorama's that might otherwise be flat and sparse. In the spring and summer when they are most fully in bloom, they give off the slight scent of coconut when the sun warms their petals.

Today's flavor comes from the kitchen of the Lavender Café in Solva, Pembrokeshire, Wales. I was allowed to sneak a little taste of their local foraging efforts when they found out what a flavor junkie I am. These particular gorse flowers had just been foraged earlier in the morning from the nearby coast and surrounding area and were being prepared to add to salads and other sweet or savory dishes. Apparently, gorse can also be made into quite a delicious wine.

From a health perspective, there is little empirical research touting the health benefits of gorse, there are plenty of folk herbal remedies. Gorse is high in tannins giving it all the benefits of tannic acid; which include, immune support, cardiovascular support, lowering cholesterol, and balancing blood sugar. Tannins are also antimicrobial, antifungal, antiviral, making gorse a great preventative for foodborne illnesses and bacterial infections. Gorse is also a Bach Flower Remedy used for feelings of hopelessness.

DAY 142 – HAKE

Flaky and dense, with the subtle flavor of the sea, Hake turns out to be quite a delicious fish. I have to admit it is one that I have avoided trying because of the name, which may not make sense to some of you but to others it will resonate completely (apparently it's a 'girl thing'...you can read more here).

Anyway, back to Hake, which I am now a very huge fan of. Hake is a white fish, in the same family as Cod and Haddock, found in the ocean depths around Europe and America. In the U.S. Hake is sometimes referred to as Ling or Ling Cod, a point which I had no idea of until this particular tasting adventure.

Today's meeting with Hake comes straight from the table of a Bohemian Mojo adventure. (you can read more about that here). This particular piece of Hake, which I must admit wasn't on my plate, so many thanks to Alun for sharing, was taken from the sea that very morning and delivered up steamed with minimal distraction, so the fresh flavor of the sea was subtly obvious and a welcome surprise. Fish when fresh from the sea does not have that cloying 'fishy' flavor, which is a sign that it's been on land too long. The texture was firm and flaky, which is definitely the texture I prefer in fish.

From a culinary perspective, Hake is a versatile fish. It's subtle flavor but hardier texture make it a good choice for more challenging culinary adventures but it also is delicious simply served with minimal taste distraction.

Nutritionally, there has been little research about the health benefits of white fish as opposed to salmon and smaller, cold-water fish. It is acknowledged that white fish do contain Omega 3 fatty acids and other nutrients similar to their Salmon cousins but specific research is sparse. However, recently two studies on Hake specifically revealed that frequent consumption of hake improves blood pressure, lowers cholesterol and reduces weight. A secondary study reveals that frequent consumption of Hake also reduces weight and decreases LDL-Cholesterol levels.

DAY 143 – FIG

Sweet and earthy with a mouth feel that is a texture revelation, soft and smooth with intervals of grainy little seeds; I am a huge fan of the fig. Figs are delicious raw, baked, sautéed, dried. Just about any way possible to prepare them makes them delicious. They are also versatile being an amazing addition to both sweet and savory dishes. Just to illustrate my point, today's flavor comes straight from a scrumptious cheddar, tomato and fig quiche served up at Woodruff's Organic Café in Stroud, UK. Upon initial perusal of the menu, I thought how odd to find those flavors all mixed together in a savory quiche. So odd, in fact, that I had to give it a try. It was delicious, simple flavors, both savory and sweet, with the fig adding a depth of both flavor and mouth feel complexity that was delicious. Figs are probably one of my favorite foods, not least because as a child I loved fig newtons.

They are native to the Middle East and parts of Asia but have been cultivated all over the world. When I lived in the Sonoma, California area there were fig trees galore growing everywhere and I could pick my fill when they were in season. Not surprisingly, it appears that the fig tree was one of the first plants cultivated by humans, cultivated well before grains and other domesticated fruits and vegetables.

From a culinary perspective, figs are a wonder. Obviously, eating them raw is a nice option, as is eating them dried, however, they can also stand alone to make some pretty amazing small plates. They can be added to a variety of sweet and savory dishes ensuring a level of fully encompassing culinary experience that will wow the palate. You can get dried figs year round but fresh figs are seasonal and available late spring, summer and early fall depending on location.

Nutritionally, figs are a great source of nutrients. They contain polyphenols, which add to their ability to decrease oxidative stress, systemic inflammation, and cardiac disease. They also are a great source of potassium, manganese, copper, and vitamin's B6 and K. While we typically think only of eating the fruit (or actually false fruit as it's often referred to) science also demonstrates that eating the leaves can also be valuable for things like blood sugar balance, lowering triglycerides, and contributing to protection against cancer.

I say, if you can get your hands on some fresh figs, do it! One of my favorite ways to eat them now that I'm all grown up (and know what's really in a fig newton, ugh) is to cut them in fourths and bake them with goat cheese, drizzling them with honey before I serve them.

DAY 144 – SAMPHIRE

With such a romantic name, it is no wonder the flavor is subtle, yet complex. This particular Samphire is accompanying my Cod dinner, so it has been prepared as a tasty side, plain, simple, and delicious. There is only a slight taste of the sea, enough to delight the palate without overpowering. It leaves me wondering what it tastes of when it is straight from the coastline. The texture is crisp and chewy, reminding me of a cross between fresh young asparagus and pine nuts. There is even the slightest hint of nuttiness.

Samphire is considered a sea vegetable, even though most of the Samphire found in stores or restaurants grows in tidal marshland rather than directly out in the sea. It is sometimes called sea asparagus or sea pickle. Samphire has a rich history as not only a food source but also in the making of glass and soap.

From a culinary perspective, Samphire is making its way into haute cuisine and is becoming more and more available in the marketplace. It can be eaten raw, however, tends to be bitter due to its high saponin content. The best way to prepare it is to boil it for a few moments and then rinse and eat. It has such a subtle salty flavor it is a nice addition to any number of culinary endeavors without being distracting.

From a health perspective, sea vegetation is incredibly nutrient dense. It delivers an amazing amount of vitamins and minerals, like manganese, calcium, phosphorous, iron, and of course is rich in iodine. Samphire is also high in Vitamins A, C, D and B. Historically it has been used as a digestive aid and diuretic. Research suggests that it is beneficial in protecting the liver from oxidative stress, repairing cellular DNA, and increasing cardiovascular health.

DAY 145 – CALENDULA

Slightly sweet and earthy, calendula flowers have a flavor that is subtle, yet distinctive. Calendula has a long and interesting history of use from both a culinary and a medicinal perspective.

In the kitchen, calendula adds a subtle earthy sweetness, that some have described as zesty, to various dishes, along with a splash of color. It can be added to dishes, both, sweet and savory, raw or cooked. When cooked with foods the calendula imparts a lovely yellow color similar to saffron, in fact, in some instances, calendula, also known as poor man's saffron, is used as a substitute for saffron. It can be used in egg dishes to brighten up the yolk color and also in baking to again, give an added dimension of flavor with a lovely yellow tone. The flowers can be added to salads or used as an edible garnish to liven up a variety of dishes.

From a medicinal perspective, Calendula is a powerhouse. It is packed with antioxidants and bioflavonoids that contribute to overall health in a delightfully aesthetically pleasing way. It is well known for its skin reparative qualities, making it a fantastic wound healer and intervention for rashes, eczema, psoriasis and any number of skin irritations and injuries. It is antiviral, antimicrobial, and anti-inflammatory; making it a great option for decreasing systemic and local inflammation, as well as preventing free radical damage to tissue. It can be consumed as a tea for stomach upsets and menstrual discomforts or applied topically as an ointment, salve, or lotion to help with skin issues.

Edible flowers don't often make their way into the typical, daily food repertoire but the nutrient density they provide coupled with the aesthetic pleasure can't be beat. I say get your hands on some edible deliciousness from the garden or fresh herb section of your local market and delight your palate.

DAY 146 – CHERRIES

Juicy and refreshing, tart or sweet, cherries are a delicious harbinger of summer. Depending on the climate and varietal, cherries can come into season anywhere between late April to late August. Cherries are a drupe or stone fruit, which mean they are in the same family as the olive, peach and plum and any other fruit with a pit in the center.

From a culinary perspective, cherries are amazingly versatile and delicious in both savory and sweet dishes. You can even make a liqueur out of the cherry pits, but you have to be careful because cherry pits have cyanide in them. You definitely don't want to interrupt your dining enjoyment.

You can eat cherries raw, by the handful, or you can add them to any number of foods. My personal favorite happens to be the good old-fashioned cherry pie; simple and not too sweet (if you use tart cherries), all in a deliciously flaky crust. What more could you ask for? When you're not adding them to desserts, you can also add them to savory dishes. They make a great addition to stews, soups, and salads; especially meat dishes.

From a health perspective, the benefits vary depending on the type of cherry. All cherries offer a pretty great dose of Vitamin C and a variety of antioxidants, but it's the tart cherries that pack the most punch. Tart cherries are loaded with vitamins, minerals, and even interesting things like carotenoids, and anthocyanins. Anthocyanins are the chemical compounds that act as a preventative measure against oxidative stress and the development of different types of cancer. It is also the compound responsible for relieving the potential for muscle strain after a workout.

Cherries also contain a substantial anti-inflammatory quality, making them a great option if someone is suffering from systemic inflammation and things like gout. Cherries also help balance sleep disturbance, they contain a good amount of natural melatonin. Research also suggests that consuming tart cherries can help decrease your risk of stroke. All in all, cherries are a great seasonal fruit. I say, get them while they are ripe but then not when they aren't in season.

DAY 147 – BUCKWHEAT (RECIPE)

Nutty and chewy, with hints of sweet, grass, and even some bitter; the flavor of buckwheat is an enjoyable addition to my afternoon meal. It's one that I love but don't really have too very often for some reason. Buckwheat, despite its name, is not actually a type of wheat or even in the grass family; rather it is considered a pseudo-cereal and is part of the broadleaf plant family, along with amaranth and even rhubarb. The seeds from the buckwheat plant are similar to sunflower seeds, with a hard outer shell and a softer inside, although not quite soft enough to eat raw without soaking or otherwise breaking down the cell structure.

Buckwheat has been part of the human dietary repertoire since about 8,000 BCE, with actual recorded reference to cultivation occurring in 4,000 BCE. It is thought to have originated in areas of Asia and then made its way around the globe. It's a mainstay ingredient for many cultures, from

Japanese Soba noodles to French Galettes, which are basically Buckwheat crepes (quite delicious, I might add). From a culinary perspective, Buckwheat is quite versatile; it can be prepared as the whole grain or used as flour. As the whole grain it is can be eaten hot or cold, added to salads, stews, soups, stir fries.... even eaten as a delicious breakfast cereal. As a flour it can be used in much the same way as most millings. The only thing to be aware of is that it has no gluten so it makes for more dense baked goods.

From a nutritional perspective, Buckwheat is a great source of plant-based protein as well as a variety of vitamins, minerals, and other phytonutrients. It is a great source of magnesium, manganese, copper, zinc, and B-vitamins. Buckwheat contains tannins, catechins, and rutin; all of which contribute to its antioxidant qualities and aid in the reduction of systemic inflammation and oxidative stress.

Various studies have demonstrated that Buckwheat can be beneficial in preventing high blood pressure, regulating blood sugar, preventing colon cancer, and it's also a good mood food.

RAW BUCKWHEAT PORRIDGE

2 cups soaked raw Buckwheat Groats (note: Whole buckwheat groats are not the same as Kasha. Soak 1 cup of groats in 2 cups of water for a couple of hours).
3/4 c. milk (nut or regular)
1 tbsp soaked chia seeds
Honey to taste (or other sweetener if desired)
Pinch of kosher salt
1 tsp pure vanilla extract
1 tsp cinnamon
Place soaked buckwheat groats in food processor or blender, along with the almond milk, chia seeds, and vanilla. Process until combined and slightly smooth. Now add in the sweetener and cinnamon to taste

DAY 148 – ALMONDS (RECIPE)

The particular Almonds in question have been soaked and then oven roasted. They have a crispy, nutty, flavor, with a subtle hint of sweetness. When they were raw they were slightly bitter due to the high tannin content of the skin. Soaking them allows the skin to be removed and inhibits the phytic acid that is also found in raw nuts, grains, and seeds.

Almonds are also a drupe, like the cherry and the olive and other 'stone fruits'. They come in a wide variety from bitter to sweet. While it appears the common Almond that we are typically used to eating originated in the Mediterranean, it has become an incredibly popular ingredient in cuisines around the world. Everything from beverages, to baking ingredients (flours and pastes) can be found around the globe.

Almonds have gained a crazy amount of popularity in the health world and given a place of superior status for health benefits, although in truth, there are other nuts that are as worthy, just perhaps not as globally recognized. They are best when somehow processed, such as soaking and then made into whatever the end result will be. Eating too many of them raw can cause gastrointestinal irritation. Historically, sweet and bitter Almonds have been part of culinary and medicinal endeavors. The sweet Almond has properties that are more healthful and is easier on the human digestive system. The bitter almond actually contains high amounts of cyanide and other toxins and can be quite a problem if too many are consumed... in the case of the bitter Almond, too many is not actually that many, so be sure of your Almond sources.

From a culinary perspective the Almond has so many uses, there is no way possible to mention them all here. It is an incredibly versatile little nut. My favorite Almond foods are Almond butter, marzipan and almond paste. I also use Almond flour quite a bit as a grain free baking option.

From a health perspective Almonds have been getting a lot of glory. My thoughts are that's because they are so versatile although the Almond is a rich source of nutritional benefits. It is high in vitamins, minerals, fiber, protein; making it a great snack or food option. Research suggests that including Almonds in your dietary repertoire can help you manage your cholesterol, decrease your risk of heart disease, protect against diabetes, prevent gallstones, and increase your mood. The fiber also supports gastrointestinal health while the combination of minerals, fats, and protein are a great source of energy.

Does this mean you should go nuts about eating these nuts? Not really, all of the studies I reviewed showed people consuming small amounts on a daily basis; roughly ¼ of a cup. Also, you will definitely want to read ingredients if you purchased whole cooked Almonds. They are often baked with added ingredients like undesirable oils. If you are going to eat them, I highly recommend getting them raw, soaking them and then you can easily oven bake them and seal them once they are cool. They will last quite a while so long as they are not left sitting in the sun or heat.

ALMOND FLOUR CHOCOLATE CHIP COOKIES

1 ½ c. almond flour
1/4 c. butter, room temperature
1/4 c. sugar
1 egg
1/4 tsp salt
1/2 tsp vanilla extract
1/4 tsp baking soda
1/4 c. chocolate chips

Cream the butter and sugar together until smooth. Mix in the egg. Next, add the almond flour, vanilla, salt, and baking soda and mix until it's all incorporated. Fold in the chocolate chips. Line a baking tray with parchment paper. Scoop the batter into even portions onto the parchment paper and bake for 12-15 minutes until golden brown. Let cool slightly before removing the cookies from the tray.

DAY 148 – BROCCOLI LEAVES

Crisp and chewy with an earthy bite; broccoli leaves are becoming one of my new favorite foods. I've been using them to make wraps. Today's flavor comes from my bacon, lettuce, and tomato (plus cheese and pickle) Broccoli leaf wrap. Delicious!!
Broccoli leaves are the foliage around the broccoli "flower" and look a lot like collard greens but have a bit of different taste. As the heat of summer begins to make its way into our daily lives I love to find foods that help refresh and cool my palate. Broccoli leaves are just one of these foods.

From a culinary perspective, you can definitely use Broccoli leaves anywhere you would use collard greens, kale, or any other broad-leafed green veggie. They are great raw, steamed, sautéed, or stir-fried. I personally prefer them raw.

Nutritionally, you guessed it; Broccoli leaves have many of the same fabulous benefits of their florets and then some. The leaves are higher in fiber and higher in beta-carotene than the broccoli head we are used to eating. They also contain a significant amount of vitamin A and C, more than the floret. Remember that research demonstrates that the flavonoids in broccoli increase colon health and decrease the potential for colon cancer (and other cancers). Broccoli is also high in vitamin C, K, an A. It is beneficial for cardiovascular health and helps lower blood pressure. Studies suggest that sulforaphane, a chemical compound found in broccoli, can also help repair and prevent damage to small blood vessels caused by diabetes. Broccoli also has the amazing ability, due to a unique trio of phytonutrients, to detoxify the body on a cellular level.

DAY 149 – TAHINI (RECIPE)

Nutty, earthy, with a hint of sweet and a slightly bitter aftertaste; those are the immediate flavor sensations that I experience when I taste Tahini. Tahini is a paste made from ground up sesame seeds. Traditionally, the seeds are hulled first, which removes some of the bitter aftertaste that can be part of the tahini experience, however, not all versions use hulled sesames because the nutritional value changes. Hulled sesame seeds equals decreased nutrient density, albeit a sweeter tahini. If you are going to make your own tahini one way to decrease the bitterness and still leave the hull intact is to soak them overnight.

Tahini is a common ingredient in a variety of Middle Eastern and Mediterranean cuisines and has been for thousands of years. The first recorded reference to Tahini was found in written manuscripts from 4,000 BCE in the Fertile Crescent regions. It has since made its way around the world into a wide variety of cultural cuisines. If you've ever eaten hummus, baba ganoush, or halva then you have had tahini. It's also great just as a nut butter spread on toast or veggies.

From a nutritional perspective Tahini's health benefits vary depending on whether or not the sesame seeds are hulled. Tahini with the hull has much higher nutrient content. For the most nutritional impact you would want to have Tahini that is from raw, un-hulled sesame seeds and go for the organic if it's an option. Tahini is a rich source of a variety of vitamins and minerals. It's very high in copper, which research demonstrates can have a beneficial impact on rheumatoid arthritis. It's also high in magnesium, potassium, and calcium. Studies suggest that these minerals can help with things like protecting against colon cancer, decreasing bone loss, lowering blood pressure, and also PMS.

One caution about sesame seeds; they are high in oxalates, which is what makes them bitter, so cooking or soaking is in order to break them down.

Curious how to use Tahini? Try this amazing recipe:

BEETROOT HUMMUS
1/2 lb beets, scrubbed clean, cooked, peeled, and cubed
2 TBS tahini sesame seed paste

5 TBS lemon juice
1 small clove garlic, chopped
1 TBS ground cumin
1 TBS lemon zest (zest from approx. 2 lemons)
Generous pinch of sea salt or Kosher salt

To cook the beets, cut off any tops, scrub the roots clean, put them in a covered dish with about 1/4-inch of water in a 375°F oven, and cook until easily penetrated with a knife or fork. Peel once they have cooled.

Place all ingredients in a food processor (or blender) and pulse until smooth. Taste and adjust seasonings and ingredients as desired. Chill and enjoy.

DAY 150 – SUGAR SNAP PEAS

Crisp and refreshing, sweet and earthy; Sugar Snap Peas are a deliciously snappy addition to a meal or break. I love to have them handy for dipping or just enjoying a handful raw as a quick and refreshing snack.

It appears that Snap Peas originated in Europe, different than their shelling pea counterpart. Also, unlike their counterpart, Snap Peas are meant to be eaten with their outer shell intact. The peas inside remain relatively small and unobtrusive, which is what keeps them from splitting open when they are mature like regular garden peas do.

Sugar Snap Peas are versatile and can be enjoyed raw or cooked in a variety of savory dishes. They make great crispy, crunchy, and refreshing additions to a salad or even as a side dish to a meal. They can be stir-fried, boiled, or baked, although truthfully, if they are cooked it should be only briefly as the whole point of them is their refreshing, crisp 'snap', which can be cooked away and you will end up with a lifeless, not so exciting, addition to your dining experience.

From a nutritional perspective, Sugar Snap Peas are not quite as overall nutrient dense as garden peas but they've still got some good stuff going on. They are higher in vitamin C, A, K and folic acid than garden peas. They are lower in calorie and have a different starch content making them a great source of fiber while still keeping them on the lower end of the glycemic index. They are a great source of B vitamins and supply a nice dose of minerals like zinc, copper, calcium and iron.

Like the garden pea, Sugar Snap Peas are a great source of antioxidants like lutein, zeaxanthine, and carotenes. Recent research on the little Snap Pea demonstrates that it also contains antifungal properties. Studies demonstrated that a particular protein found in the Snap Pea inhibited the translation and growth of a variety of toxic fungi.

All of that being said, I think they are simple and delicious treats. They are not too sweet and provide a refreshing experience to the palate.

DAY 151 – TOMATO

"Tomayto, Tamahto...let's call the whole thing off."

Juicy, slightly sweet and acidic, with a firm texture, those are the qualities of the heirloom Tomato I am enjoying at the moment. Typically, I am not a fan of the Tomato, however, this is about the time of year when my palate is happy to enjoy them. Especially, beautiful heirlooms with their abundance of variation in color, shape and flavor. I love to enjoy them raw with some herbs, olive oil, and balsamic vinegar and/or cheese.

There's actually quite a bit to say about Tomatoes both from a nutritional perspective and also a commerce perspective. Sadly, Tomatoes are some of the more scientifically tampered with fruits, not necessarily genetically modified, though those exist on the market, but mostly just hybridized to create a product that travels well and uniformly colors rather than tastes good. This is why conventional Tomatoes tend to taste bland and grainy. Organic or farm fresh Tomatoes are the most delicious. A Tomato is perfect when it tastes of the sun and the elements that helped it to grow, even if it isn't perfectly uniformly colored and doesn't last for weeks on the shelf (in fact, a tomato, or any food for that matter, that lasts for weeks on the shelf is a little bit scary).

First recorded domestication of the Tomato was in South America around 500 BC, although it's found in warm cultures around the globe. Since that time it has been hybridized to create so many variations that it boggles the mind. It's a staple ingredient in many cultures and often serves as a foundation for sauces, soups and stews, and a great number of other savory dishes. I mentioned that I enjoy Tomatoes raw and rarely eat them cooked. However, roasted Tomatoes are a perfect example of the umami flavoring that we all tend to crave. For me, it's a texture thing, umami is delicious but if the texture is not right, there's no way I'm going to enjoy it.

From a nutritional perspective, Tomatoes are an amazing source of nutrients. They are, of course, rich in vitamins and minerals, especially

Vitamin C. Even better, though, they are an amazing source of phytonutrients and antioxidants; rutin, lycopene, zeaxanthine, quercetin, kaempferol, beta-carotene, the list goes on. All that nutrient density makes them have a significant beneficial impact for your health. Research shows that consuming Tomatoes can help decrease cardiovascular issues, including heart disease, increase bone density, boost immune function, decrease oxidative stress, and decrease the risk of various cancers...namely prostate and lung (as far as studies are concerned).

The only downside to the Tomato? It is in the nightshade family, and while it's not necessarily the Tomato itself that is poisonous (the leaves are), if you are experiencing systemic inflammation or auto-immune issues, it could be good to decrease your intake. That being said, the benefits of consuming them are pretty significant so it's worth not cutting them out of your diet entirely if you can help it.

Another thing, many people store their Tomatoes in the refrigerator. This actually decreases their nutrient viability and causes the sugars to break down in a way that impacts their flavor. Keep them at room temperature and eat them before they spoil.

CHAPTER 6 - JUNE

DAY 152 – HONEYSUCKLE

Honeysuckle has a subtle sweetness, akin to the flavor of cantaloupe but so much lighter and more mysterious. When I was a child, I used to collect the Honeysuckle flowers from the bushes surrounding our backyard and tuck myself away in a corner, enjoying the lightly sweet syrup that could be harvested from the stem of each flower. Then I would gather all the flowers and arrange them in patterns in the grass. Edible art...who knew I was so far ahead of my time? (:

Although, I still harvest the occasional Honeysuckle flower if I'm rambling through the countryside, I hadn't really thought of them as a culinary entity. Then recently I had the opportunity to enjoy some as a tea. It was delicious and it inspired me to investigate further. Apparently, Honeysuckle is quite the culinary treat for both sweet and savory dishes. There are recipes for Honeysuckle simple syrup, Honeysuckle cupcakes, Honeysuckle cordial, Honeysuckle ice cream, Honeysuckle biscuits, and jellies, even Honeysuckle chicken. In fact, the list goes on and on. I'm inspired to get a little creative with some honeysuckle in my kitchen. The first recipe I will try once I get my hands on some flowers is the cordial.

From a medicinal perspective, Honeysuckle has long held a place in Traditional Asian Medicine, as well as, Homeopathy and Bach Flower Remedies. As an herbal intervention it appears to be beneficial for inflammation, immune function, digestion, dysentery, colds and flu, and more than I can name. There is also empirical data to support the beneficial use of Honeysuckle. Research shows that it has broad-spectrum antimicrobial activity; inhibiting a variety of bacteria, including strep and influenza. Studies also show that it has significant systemic anti-inflammatory properties. There have been studies demonstrating that Honeysuckle has a beneficial impact on cholesterol; as well as demonstrated anti-cancer properties.

As a Bach Flower Remedy Honeysuckle is useful for keeping people in the present moment rather than getting lost in the past. As a homeopathic remedy, compounds containing Honeysuckle have been used to eliminate asthma and respiratory issues, as well as digestive problems.

Mostly, it's just tasty. It's delicious straight from the flower and lovely as a tea. The other preparations are on my kitchen list!

DAY 153 – BLACK PEPPER (RECIPE)

Sharp, piquant, spicy heat; black pepper is so commonly used in food it is easy to take it for granted and miss its amazing potential. Piper Nigrum as it is officially known, is the flowering vine, the part that becomes Pepper is the 'fruit' that is produced by the vine. Even though Pepper is spicy and has heat, it is not the same as a capsicum pepper, which are fleshy fruits and in a different family.

Pepper is one of the most popular spices in the world for both culinary and medicinal endeavors. It is also among some of the oldest spice and medicinal interventions recorded and currently the top on the commerce list.

From a culinary perspective, I would venture to guess Pepper can be found anywhere that the preparation of food occurs; households, restaurants, cafeterias, etc. It seems to accompany food with almost unconscious wild abandon; in jars on tables, little packets in boxes, and even wrapped up tightly with little plastic knives and forks. Of course, it rarely travels without its counterpart "salt". It's unfortunate that it is so ubiquitous that it is easy to take it for granted because truly there is a nuance to Pepper that it akin to the variations and nuances in wine.

The flavor of Pepper is impacted by terroir, when it was picked, how it was processed, and even what it is served with. There is Black Pepper, white pepper, red pepper (not the same as cayenne), green pepper...all of which are variations of the growth and terroir of the plant and each carries its own subtle yet distinct difference in flavor. The more I'm learning about Pepper, the more I'm in love with it and all of its variations.

From a medicinal perspective Pepper has quite a history as well. Pepper stimulates the taste buds and encourages the production of digestive fluids. It also has diuretic and diaphoretic properties, making a good resource for detoxifying the body. Research demonstrates that it is antimicrobial, antifungal, and antiviral, perhaps those organisms don't like the chemical compounds that also make it seem hot to the palate. Studies have been conducted that demonstrate it is also an anticonvulsant, aiding in the elimination of convulsions and seizures. The chemical compounds also make highly beneficial for eliminating systemic inflammation and oxidative stress.

The next time you sit down at the table and reach for the Pepper, maybe take a moment to give it closer attention and appreciation. Here's a grain free sweet recipe with a Black Pepper kick:

CHAI SPICE SUGAR COOKIES
2 c. almond flour
¼ c. coconut flour
¼ c. coconut or date sugar
½ tsp. baking soda
¼ tsp. cream of tartar
¾ tsp. ginger
¾ tsp. ground cinnamon
¾ tsp. Black Pepper
¼ tsp. ground cardamom
¼ tsp. ground cloves
¼ tsp. salt
¼ c. coconut oil, melted
¼ c. maple syrup
1 tsp vanilla
1 large egg
sugar or coconut for rolling...

In a mixing bowl, stir together the dry ingredients (almond flour through salt).
In a separate mixing bowl, mix together the melted coconut oil, maple syrup, vanilla and egg (make sure the melted oil is not actually hot).
Add the dry mixture to the wet and stir just until combined.
Wrap the dough in plastic wrap and refrigerate for 2 hours or until firm enough to roll into balls.
Preheat the oven to 350°F (175°C) and line a baking sheet with a piece of parchment paper. Roll the dough into 1" balls, roll in the sugar, and place 2" apart on the prepared baking sheet.
Bake for 8-10 minutes or until the tops are firm and no longer wet. They will not brown but may crack a little. I've also tried pressing them down flat, they are lovely this way as well and still have a nice texture.
Remove to a baking sheet or wire rack to cool completely

DAY 154 – PISTACHIO

Crunchy, chewy, nutty and slightly earthy Pistachios are a delicious addition to my morning breakfast. The Pistachio is a desert plant and seems to have originated in the more arid regions of the Fertile Crescent before making its way to arid climates around the globe. Pistachios have been a part of human diet for thousands of years with evidence of early nut-cracking tools and Pistachio remains dating back to 78,000 years ago. Although the Pistachio is often lumped into the 'nut' category, it is actually a seed, similar to the cashew.

From a culinary perspective Pistachios are an amazing addition to both savory and sweet dishes, not to mention a stand-alone food that is delicious and nutritious. Seeds and nuts alike are a great source of energy and protein; Pistachios being part of that equation. There are many examples of traditional foods that include the delicious Pistachio, from chicken and fish to baklava. I personally love to give them a quick toast in a pan and then add them to salads, stir-fries or baked goods.

From a nutritional perspective Pistachios are a great addition to your healthy diet. They contain higher amount of protein than many nuts and are lower in calorie. They are significant source of vitamins, minerals, and phytonutrients. They are high in potassium and phosphorous and have trace elements of other minerals like zinc, copper, manganese, and calcium. Research suggests that Pistachios contribute to heart health and contributes to balance cholesterol, as well as managing blood sugar.

Several other studies demonstrated that people who ate Pistachios for 24 weeks lost an average of 0.7 inches from their waists, reduced cholesterol by 15 points, improved their blood sugar, and lowered inflammation. The consumption of Pistachios seemed especially beneficial for individuals with metabolic syndrome. The only caveat: avoid bleached or processed pistachios.

DAY 155 – NECTARINES (RECIPE)

Sweet and juicy, with a texture that is just the perfect combination of smooth and pulpy chewable goodness. It's that time of year when the fruit selection is broadening and one of my favorites on the scene is the Nectarine. Interestingly, peaches and Nectarines are supposedly from the same family, even potentially can come from the same tree depending on a recessive gene situation, but I find them to be totally different to my palate. Not least, because of the obvious non-fuzzy quality of the Nectarine, but also because, to me, their flavor and mouth feel are entirely different.

From a culinary perspective, Nectarines can compliment both sweet and savory dishes and add a dimension that will delight the palate. Nectarines sautéed and reduced can add just the right bit of complexity to game or other savory dishes that have a substantial texture and mouth feel. As sweet option, they fit in, quite deliciously, anywhere that any stone fruit would fit. To me Nectarines are not quite as sweet as peaches so I find them more inviting to my palate.

From a health perspective, fruit sometimes gets a bad rap because of their higher sugar content. However, when eaten as the whole fruit, you also get the pectin, the fiber, and any other nutrients, enzymes, etc that come in the whole fruit package. Eating the whole Nectarine (except for the pit, of course) provides you with some amazing benefits to your health. They are loaded with vitamins, minerals, and phytonutrients.

They are a great source of potassium, iron, zinc, copper and phosphorous. Remember that potassium helps lower blood pressure, prevents heart disease and is a main participant in nerve to muscle communication. Nectarines are also a great source of vitamins B, A, and E, which can help with things like bone and tissue strength and repair, as well as, boosting immune function. They're a rich source of flavonols like zea-thanthine, which helps prevent eye issues like macular degeneration.

One of my all time favorite ways to eat nectarines (besides baked in a tart or straight off the seed) is this:

FULL FLAVOR NECTARINE SALAD
6 nectarines, sliced
1 TBS dry white wine
dash or two of tabasco or other hot sauce
dash or two of balsamic vinegar
salt and pepper to taste
1 TBS fresh cilantro, minced

Mix all the liquid ingredients and then toss with the nectarine slices. It's spicy and sweet and savory; just right for a summer pick me up.

DAY 156 – RAMPS (U.S.)

Piquant yet slightly sweet with a chewy yet crisp mouthfeel; ramps are a delicate and delicious treat. Ramps are native to North America and are in members of the Allium family; like onions, leeks, and garlic. Wild ramps have a delicately piquant flavor that is slightly oniony minus the bite or heat that onions and garlic can sometimes have. When ramps start showing up on the menu, (and in nature) it's a sign that spring is here and summer is on its way. The ramps that I just ate to inspire the flavor for the day were slightly caramelized so the outside was chew and slightly sweet but the inside was still crisp and fresh tasting.

From a culinary perspective, ramps are quite popular in the foodie/foraging world in the U.S. especially in the south where there are festivals held in their honor and a multitude of inventive and tried and true delicacies prepared. You can use them in the same way that you could use any onion or garlic but it seems best to just work with them in their whole food state because their flavor is so unique.

From a nutritional perspective, ramps have many of the same qualities of other foods in the Allium family. They are antibacterial, antiviral, antifungal and high in vitamins and mineral. Ramps are especially high in Vitamin A, B, and C, as well as minerals like selenium and chromium. Research suggests that including allium members in your is highly beneficial in lowering blood pressure and reducing the risk of cardiovascular disease. They are also immune boosters and an excellent resource for fighting flus and viruses. Alliums are beneficial for healthy digestion and help stimulate production of health flora and fauna in the gut while eliminating the baddies, including parasites.
Research suggests that allium is also useful in preventing a variety of cancers, most notably prostate cancer. It also aids in decreasing oxidative stress as well as systemic inflammation.

DAY 157 – CHICKPEAS (RECIPE)

Tasted fresh green Chickpeas for the first time; they were chewy and slightly sweet with a hint of earthy goodness. Chickpeas are a legume; also known as a pulse. The Chickpeas I have encountered in my life have always been dried first, the soaked to revive and they have always been the white variation. As such, they have not been one of my favorite foods. So, I must admit my culinary ignorance and share with you I had no idea they also grew in green. I realized upon reflection as I was eating my fresh green Chickpeas that I knew precious little about them; other than the basic nutrient content. Finding them on my plate was an unexpectedly delicious treat.

There are three main varieties of Chickpea, (also called a garbanzo bean) white, black, and green; although the black Chickpea is not really black just darker than its counterparts. Interestingly, it is the small dark variation that seems to be the closest descendent to the ancient Chickpea seeds found in various archeological digs across the European continent. The other two varieties, white and green, are cultivated varieties and have become mainstays in many cultures around the world. They can be eaten as the whole bean, ground into a puree and used in things like hummus, or dried and ground into a flour and used to make a variety of flatbreads and other culinary endeavors.

I tend to relate foods made from Chickpeas to cuisine from the Middle-East and India, however, there are also quite a few dishes in Italian, French and other European cuisines that use Chickpeas as a main ingredient. My dinner last night was a delicious meal of fresh green Chickpeas served with Panisse; a fried bread made from Chickpea flour. Very delicious. Now I'm on a mission to find more fresh Chickpeas and make them into fun and delicious meals.

From a health perspective Chickpeas are a great source of fiber and nutrition. They are a unique source of a variety of phytonutrients and provide some pretty cool health benefits. Recently the focus of research on the Chickpea has been on its unique fiber content. Most of the fiber in the Chickpea is insoluble with the added benefit of increasing the amount of nutrient that makes it to your colon and the transit time. Recent studies demonstrated that people who ate garbanzo beans compared to people who ate the same amount of fiber but from other foods, also found a decrease in LDL, and an increase in insulin regulation. The antioxidants in Chickpeas also contribute to decreasing systemic inflammation and oxidative stress.

After researching the topic, I have found that green Chickpeas are being sustainably cultivated in various states across the U.S. They are not only a body friendly food but also a planet friendly food, in that they act as a natural soil fertilizer and increases depleted nitrogen content in soil. Chickpeas are being recognized as one of the top crops for sustainable agriculture.

I asked the chef for his panisse recipe and he graciously shared. If you are up for some delicious fried goodness, give these a try! (gluten free, protein dense, and delicious) This recipe occurs in two steps and the batter for the panisse can be made a day ahead.

PANISSE
4 c. water (or broth)
3/4 tsp salt
2 tsp olive oil

2 1/4 c. garbanzo flour
1-2 tsp garam masala (or spice of your choice)
salt and pepper, to taste
oil, for frying
Begin to heat the water, oil, salt and pepper, as it is heating and before
it boils, begin whisking in the flour so that it doesn't form lumps, add
the spices, and continue stirring until the mixture is thick and smooth
and begins to pull from the sides of the pan holding its shape. Scoop
into a greased 9-inch cake pan, cover and refrigerate for at least 3
hours. This will allow the mixture to set. When you're ready to fry
them take the mixture out of the fridge, slice into small rectangles
(batons) and then quickly fry, drain, and serve. If you are avoiding
fried foods, that's okay... I found some recipes for baking, 375
degrees for 10 minutes. I always encourage experimentation and
finding your own most delicious option.

DAY 158 – CHERIMOYA

Sweet, with a hint of vanilla and honey and a texture that is smooth and
creamy; it's not for nothing that the Cherimoya is also called a custard
apple. I think the Cherimoya is a most interesting fruit with their daunting
outer covering that gives the illusion of scales and reminds me of the skin
of a dragon.

The Cherimoya is an example of a fruit that really needs human
intervention to survive. For the most part, they must be hand pollinated in
order to insure that fruit will be produced. It has trained us well. For a fruit
that originated in the Andes, it can now be found appropriate climates
around the globe.

From a culinary perspective Cherimoya is really best when unadulterated.
Because it is so creamy and delicious, it can be frozen to serve as an ice
cream substitute. It can also be pureed and made into delicious custard
filling for things like tarts or puddings. I like to eat them just as the whole
fruit. They have large black seeds that can be easily removed as the rest of
the fruit is enjoyed.

From a health perspective Cherimoya is a good mood food as well as heart
healthy and packed with select group of antioxidants that do some
interesting things. Several studies suggest that a particular alkaloid extract
found in the Cherimoya can act as an anti-depressant, contributing to
increase in the neurotransmitters that act as the foundation for dopamine
modulation.

These same alkaloid compounds have demonstrated anticonvulsant and anti-anxiety activity. Because of the fruits ability to help the brain manufacture GABA they have also demonstrated the potential to help decrease inflammation in the brain that contributes to things like migraine headaches. The Cherimoya also contains some pretty powerful cytotoxins, which research has found effective against certain cancers and even malaria.

DAY 159– PEAR

M.R. "You don't know what a pear tastes like?" N.C. "I don't know what a pear tastes like to you" M.R. " Sweet... ...juicy. Soft on your tongue. Grainy like sugary sand that dissolves in your mouth." ~City of Angels

Juicy and fresh tasting, crisp to the bit and then sweet and grainy; Pears come in such a wide variety. They are as prolific as the apple, with several thousand varieties. I always wonder, with so many varieties, why we only see three or four different types on our market shelves. Where are all the other varieties? How does one get to taste those? Pears and I have an interesting relationship; it always takes a brief moment to get past the childhood memory of canned Pears, which were back then a tasty treat for the most part, but nonetheless quite smooshy. For a person who is almost more sensitive to texture that taste, that can be a bad combination. Nonetheless, fresh Pears are nothing like canned even when they are very ripe and soft.

Pears and the cultivation of Pears have been a part of human culinary endeavor for thousands of years. Archeological digs in various areas throughout Europe have produced evidence of Pears as part of prehistoric diet. Roman writings from first century A.D. discuss the grafting of Pear trees, the storage of the fruit and some culinary preparations...all of which include the use of honey. Because of all the different varieties Pears also have an extended 'season' for eating; with some harvesting options even extending into the winter months. They come in all shapes, sizes and even colors. One of my favorites is the Crimson Pear, which has a deep red skin with honey colored inner fruit.

From a culinary perspective Pears are incredibly versatile and interesting in both sweet and savory dishes. They are delicious raw, stewed, baked, and even fried as well as made into jams, ciders, and juices. One favorite way to eat them is to bake them with goat cheese in the middle and drizzle them with honey... yum! However you decide to eat them just be sure to leave the skin on!

Pears are also highly nutritious and along with the apple make up the top two most nutrient dense fruits. This is due not necessarily to their high phytonutrient content, but more to the combination and variety of nutrients. Where the Pear is concerned the skin is an integral part of its nutritional value; it contains about half the fiber and about three times phytonutrients contained in the rest of the fruit.

Studies suggest that red skinned Pears contain even a higher amount of phytonutrients and have demonstrated that they are beneficial in regulating insulin production. Research indicates that including Pears in your diet helps regulate blood sugar, improve insulin sensitivity, decrease heart disease, and act as a systemic anti-inflammatory. Studies also suggest that the flavonols found in Pears are beneficial in decreasing the risk of certain cancers, particularly esophageal.

DAY 160 – CUCUMBER

Juicy and refreshing Cucumbers also have the palate quenching quality of tasting a little salty and sweet all at the same time. The Cucumber is a member of the gourd family originating in Southern ? and making its way around the globe. As an ingredient in the human diet, they have been found in written records dating back to prehistory. Cultivated and hybridized to meet a variety of desired culinary needs, the Cucumber can be found in many shapes and sizes, not to mention colors varying from shades of green to yellow. The type of Cucumber will dictate the nuances of flavor, the thickness of skin, the length, color and even the palatability.

From a culinary perspective Cucumbers are an interesting addition to a variety of culinary endeavors. They are refreshing and easily added raw or pickled to dishes both sweet and savory. They can brighten a summertime meal or even add a refreshing note to a drink. My favorite ways to eat them? Pickled, of course, but then also chopped fresh into yogurt with garlic and mint, and lastly quick in summertime they are an amazingly refreshing treat when they are marinated in vinegar and honey to make a deliciously refreshing salad.

From a health perspective the Cucumber doesn't disappoint with its wide variety of nutrients and phytonutrients. It contains a specific type of polyphenol which research suggests contributes to the decrease in certain cancer risks, most notably ovarian, breast, uterine and prostate. It contains a combination of chemical compounds that contribute to the reduction of systemic inflammation and oxidative stress. Cucumber also is an excellent source of silica, which is one reason it is beneficial in decreasing joint and tissue inflammation. Research has demonstrated it can be a beneficial addition to your diet if you are suffering from inflammatory issues such as gout or arthritis. The silica and combination of other minerals and vitamins decreases uric acid in the system contributing to decreased inflammation. Cucumbers are also good topically. They can help decrease the pain and inflammation of burns, especially sunburn and also help with other minor skin irritations.

DAY 161 – ZUCCHINI (RECIPE)

Fresh tasting with the slightest hint of salt and earth, mild in all of its flavor elements, the Zucchini is one of many vegetables making its way to the market in more abundance now that summer is here. Sadly, I'm unable to do justice to it simply because it is one of my least favorite vegetables, however, it is popular and does have its good points so it is only fair to include it as a flavor and food. That being said, as summer arrives, with it comes more varieties of summer squash and I really do love 8 Ball Zucchini, mostly for their versatility as a fun way to serve up some nutrient dense finger foods. They make great little pizza crusts and foundations for finger sandwiches.

Cucurbita pepo, also known as summer squash, is one of the more cultivated vegetables around the globe making it available year round rather than just during summer and fall months as their name might suggest.

From a culinary perspective, Zucchini is an amazingly versatile food in both the sweet and savory world. I use them more for structure and foundation to a meal or dish than for the flavor they impart (for me it's a mouth feel thing). I have dehydrated them in long. flat strips to use in place of pasta for lasagna with great results. I've spiral cut them into noodles for fun all veggie pad thai; I've even used them as a main ingredient in brownies because they hold moisture so well. Overall, if I'm not looking for function rather than flavor then Zucchini is fantastic (feel free to differ with me).

From a health perspective Zucchini is in the Curcubita family, which gives them almost all of the amazing benefits of their relatives in the squash world; including pumpkins and cucumbers. To ensure the highest nutrient density you want to leave the skin on your Zucchini (so make sure it's organic and wax-free) and then you will reap the benefits of antioxidants like zeaxanthin and lutein; which help with things like oxidative stress and systemic inflammation. Members of the Curcubita family, including Zucchini, have a unique chemical combination that includes pectin and certain polysaccharides that work together to reduce insulin resistance and help regulate blood sugar.

Added bonus? The seeds of summer squash have antimicrobial properties. If you dry them and then grind them into powder they also act as a flea deterrent and natural pest repellent.

ZUCCHINI BROWNIES
1 c. almond butter
1 1/2 c. grated zucchini
1/3 c. raw honey
1 egg
1 tsp vanilla
1 tsp baking soda
1 tsp cinnamon
1/2 tsp nutmeg
1/2 tsp allspice
1 c. dark chocolate chunks
Directions

Preheat oven to 350. Grate your zucchini and combine all ingredients in a large bowl. (This goes a lot faster if you have a food processor with a grating attachment) Pour into a greased 9×9 baking pan. Bake 25-30 minutes or until a toothpick comes out clean.

These brownies are amazing. I usually have to leave them in the oven a little longer than 30 minutes (40 minutes is my oven's magic number) so just check in on them before you turn the oven off to let them cool.

DAY 162 – PEACHES
Sweet, juicy, chewy, with hints of grass and vanilla nestled in the delicious peachy flavor, Peaches are a summer time treat. I have a love/hate

relationship with Peaches, I love their delicious flavor and texture but I'm not a fan of their fuzzy skin, which actually irritates me.

The Peach is a stone fruit which seems to have originated in Asia but has since been cultivated all over the world. While there are many varieties of the Peach, there are two main 'type'; the clingstone, which means the flesh clings to the seed and the freestone, which means the flesh is free of the seed. From a culinary perspective, Peaches are a special treat to both savory and sweet dishes. In the kitchen, the freestone is the better Peach to work with because of the obvious ease; pie, jam, Peaches and Goat Cheese Crostini, Peach mole'...so many Peach options.

From a health perspective Peaches provide many of the same nutrients that their drupe family counterparts provide. This means the phytonutrients in Peaches contribute to a decrease in systemic inflammation and oxidative stress. They also have a group of beneficial flavonols that contribute to blood sugar regulation and insulin balance. Peaches are also a good source of quercetin, which works with vitamin C to boost heart health, immune function and decrease the risk of various cancers.

QUICK AND EASY RAW PEACH COBBLER:
1/4 c. walnuts
1/4 c. cashews
3 dates (soaked overnight)
cinnamon
pinch of salt
2 fresh peaches, sliced

Blend the nuts, dates and spices to make a crumble and mix in with your sliced peaches. Enjoy.

DAY 163 – KALE

Fresh, crispy, slightly bitter, with a healthy dose of grass and earth, kale has a dense texture and mouth feel. Today's flavor is inspired by a kale salad I just made for this afternoon. Kale, pumpkin seeds, nectarine slices and a light olive oil and lime dressing. Kale is in the brassica family, which also includes broccoli and cauliflower. It has been a darling of the vegetable world in recent years and can be found in marketplaces around the globe. Interestingly, according to historians, kale was one of the more popular vegetables across Europe with first recorded use and cultivation in the 5th century A.D., until the middle ages when cabbages became more widely cultivated.

From a culinary perspective Kale is pretty versatile. It's easily sautéed, stir fried, baked, boiled, steamed and even grilled (yum). Personally, my favorite way to enjoy Kale is raw or baked crispy. If consumed raw then it should be massaged with your hands until it is a dense green, this helps break down the cell wall, making the nutrients more easily digested and assimilated. To bake Kale, I heat the oven to about 350, space the kale leaves on a cookie sheet, removing the larger part of the stem but still keeping some intact. And then bake for about 10 or 15 minutes until they are crispy. You have to watch carefully because they can go from barely brown to burnt really fast if you are not paying attention. I remove them from the oven, sprinkle them with salt or nutritional yeast and then crunch on them when cool. Seriously yum!

From a nutritional perspective, Kale is packed with all the healthy goodness that its brassica family members contain. Vitamins, minerals, phytonutrients abound. Kale has received much critical acclaim as a powerhouse of antioxidants and other phytonutrients. Studies suggest that the amount of quercetin and kaempferol in Kale contribute significantly to decreased risk of a multitude of cancers. The chemical compounds in kale also contribute to decreased cholesterol, increased immune function and a decrease in oxidative stress. They also decrease systemic inflammation and contribute to detoxification of cells.

Kale, in moderation, is a good thing, however, overconsumption of Kale can contribute to hypothyroidism. So if you are one of those Kale in everything, smoothie drinkers, (like I used to be) you will want to vary your vegetables and not rely on kale as much. Other caveats about Kale…it has a significant amount of vitamin K so it is one you will want to avoid if you are taking blood thinners. The oxalates in Kale can also inhibit calcium uptake in the body.

DAY 164 – GRUYERE CHEESE

A perfect storm of sweet, savory, nutty, pungent, salty, all combined in an unassuming little piece of cheese. Today's flavor comes straight from my breakfast omelet; heirloom tomato, baby spinach, fresh chives, and Gruyere cheese. The flavors come together so well, I feel like I'm on vacation.

Gruyere cheese (pronounced Grew-yair) is named for the village of its origination, Gruyeres, Switzerland. The making of traditional Gruyere is an art. The milk must be obtained from cows that have been fed only grass or hay. Milk from just two milkings are allowed in a batch and it must only be prepared in copper pots. The milk must be full fat and unpasteurized. The aging process occurs in stages that can take anywhere from 5 –16 months. Traditionally prepared Gruyere tastes infinitely different than conventional manufactured Gruyere cheeses out on the market so if you have a chance to get your hands on the real deal, I encourage you to do so.

From a culinary perspective, Gruyere is a flavorful, easy melting cheese that can be added to a variety of savory dishes without overpowering or disappearing. It's amazing raw, in quiches, on sandwiches, and don't forget fondue!

From a nutritional perspective, cheese provides a good source of complete protein and minerals and vitamins, like calcium and vitamin B12. Cheese is umami and satisfies the palate as well as stimulates digestion and nutrient uptake. You have umami taste receptors in your gut that appear to help regulate the digestive process as well as signal satiation. Research suggests that consuming a good quality cheese in moderation can also help regulate blood sugar in insulin balance.

The key to eating cheese, besides enjoying every delightful morsel, is to make sure that you are going the extra step and purchasing full fat, quality cheese. It may cost a little bit more but you will also eat less because it will be more satisfying to your palate and body.

DAY 165 – BLACKBERRY (RECIPE)

A perfect combination of sweet, tart, and almost tannic; blackberries are a juicy and refreshing summertime treat. Blackberries are not, technically, a berry. Rather they are an aggregate fruit, which means it grows around the 'stem' and each little rounded pocket is a drupe that contains its own tiny seed. In this way, they are actually similar to a pineapple. I think this is one reason I love blackberries, it takes me forever to eat them because I tend to want to chew each little seed. (:

From a culinary perspective Blackberries are versatile, adding an interesting twist to dishes both sweet and savory. They make a great jam, pie, tart, and even wine. Or how about Blackberry barbecue sauce, Blackberries in salad, or even on a pizza? Delicious. Personally, I love to eat them raw just as a delicious and nutritious snack.

From a health perspective Blackberries are a great source of vitamins, minerals, and a wide variety of other beneficial phytonutrients. They are packed with vitamin C and have a decent amount of vitamins A, K, E, and B. They are a great resource for Omega 3 fatty acids as one cupful contains over 400 mgs of Omega 3's. They are also a great source of fiber and contain the natural sweetener xylitol, which research suggests help regulate blood sugar and insulin production.

Blackberries contain significant amounts of copper, manganese and other minerals that help maintain endocrine balance among other things. As for antioxidants? The Blackberry is packed with them, quercetin, anthocyanins, kaempferol, and gallic acid. All of which serve as protective mechanisms against systemic inflammation, oxidative stress and a wide variety of cancers. A variety of studies have been conducted on the Blackberry revealing that its chemical compounds contribute to weight management, blood sugar balance, beneficial for peristalsis and healing to the intestinal lining. Blackberries are also antimicrobial and antimutagenic, with studies showing that they contribute to the suppression of tumors.

Summer is here, grab a handful of blackberries and enjoy! Or you can try this (:

RAW FOOD BLACKBERRY CHEESECAKE.
Crust:
1 1/2 c. pecans
1 cup pitted dates
1/4 tsp. sea salt, divided in half

Filling:
1 c. blackberries
1 c. cashews, (soak overnight or at least 3 hours)
1/2 c. coconut oil
¼ c. maple syrup or honey or date sugar (I actually tend to leave out the sugar if the berries are sweet enough).

Blend the crust ingredients in a food processor until crumbly. Press into a pie plate and refrigerate.
Puree the filling ingredients and scoop into the pie-crust. Refrigerate until firm...serve and enjoy!

DAY 166 – STEAK (BEEF)

Umami, with hints of sweet and salt; cooked meat evokes a primal response in the palate. It's the Maillard Reaction that gives cooked meat the flavor of umami. The application of heat denatures the proteins and when they are recombined with the sugars that are present, it creates the smell and flavor that stimulates salivation. It's just kind of how we are wired.

While eating red meat is a HUGE topic for a variety of reasons too numerous to address in this small post on taste and flavor, it is safe to say that the average consumer is so inundated with misinformation that it's no wonder it is such a hot topic. Here's a little bit of useful information to help sift through all the confusion.

First and foremost, all red meat is not created equally. Where and how it was raised and what it was fed directly impacts the nutrient density and chemical compounds available in the end result. There is a drastic difference between the quality of grass-fed/pasture centered and grain fed, lot-centered meat. For the most part conventionally raised meats are grain fed (and heaven knows what else) and raised in conditions that can require the regular use of antibiotics in order to attempt to maintain the health of animals living in such close quarters. We've all heard that consuming saturated fats from things like red meat contributes to heart disease, increased cholesterol, and any number of other inflammation based ailments.

However, research over the past years is demonstrating that it isn't necessarily saturated fats in general that are the culprit contributing to ill health, rather it is a specific type of fatty acid. One that is found in significantly higher amounts in conventional grain fed beef. Grass fed beef on the other hand, according to data collected over the past two decades, contains a different concentration of fatty acids, making it significantly better for overall health. The caveat being that you have to make sure it is pasture raised and not simply grass-fed. Because like all things consumerist, someone has figured out that if you simply chuck some alfalfa pellets into your feedlot, you can label it grass fed. Ugh.

"Research spanning three decades suggests that grass-based diets can significantly improve the fatty acid (FA) composition and antioxidant content of beef, albeit with variable impacts on overall palatability. Grass-based diets have been shown to enhance total conjugated linoleic acid (CLA) (C18:2) isomers, trans-vaccenic acid (TVA) (C18:1 t11), a precursor to CLA, and omega-3 (n-3) FAs on a g/g fat basis. While the overall concentration of total SFAs

is not different between feeding regimens, grass-finished beef tends toward a higher proportion of cholesterol neutral stearic FA (C18:0), and less cholesterol-elevating SFAs such as myristic (C14:0) and palmitic (C16:0) FAs. Several studies suggest that grass-based diets elevate precursors for Vitamin A and E, as well as cancer fighting antioxidants such as glutathione (GT) and superoxide dismutase (SOD) activity as compared to grain-fed contemporaries. "(Daley, et al., 2010)

Furthermore, how you cook your meat also has a direct impact on the antioxidant levels and concentration of beneficial nutrients. Research demonstrates that rare to medium and slowly cooked at lower temperatures provides the best combination for the most obtainable nutrients.

It's also helpful to know that not everybody is designed to eat meat and not every body is designed to *not* eat meat. Some body types work very well on a plant based diets and some don't. It's important to listen to your own body to begin to identify what your real needs are despite what anyone around you says. For indigenous peoples around the world eating meat has been a significant part of a healthful and conscious diet for thousands of years. Whether or not it is the right and healthy thing for your body depends on your body type, the type and quality of meat you are choosing, and how you prepare it.

All of that being said, I believe it is very important to be picky about what kind of meat you do choose to eat. Sustainably reared and humanely dispatched is really the only way to go for reasons too numerous to mention, not the least of which are your health and the health of the planet. It may cost a little more but it is well worth it.

Other ways to contribute to sustainable and humane animal husbandry, besides searching the store for it, is to get a couple of friends together and participate in a share program. Some small Farmers and Ranchers are creating share agreements that allow you to "purchase" an animal and what it produces and they raise it for you. You can do this with products like milk, eggs and wool too.

DAY 167 – BAKING SODA (RECIPE)

Zingy and slightly salty Baking Soda, or sodium bicarbonate as it's conventionally known, is more of a mouth feel than an actual flavor. It has a slightly salty taste and a mouth feel that is metallic. Baking Soda is a mineral, or rather a component of the mineral natron. While it has historically been derived from natural sources in its most natural state, it is possible to formulate Baking Soda from chemically processing ore in a lab. The process is kind of interesting if you like science. However it's one that leaves me slightly skeptical so I opt for baking soda that has been minimally processed and is 'harvested' straight from its source as nahcolite. Baking Soda has a multitude of uses, ranging from extinguishing grease fires, decreasing acid in the body, cardiopulmonary resuscitation, decreasing lactic acid, cleaning teeth, as a cleaner, and even to eliminate the itch from bug bites.

From a culinary perspective Baking Soda is used as a leavening agent and also as a way to soften the grain in certain vegetables and even tenderize meat. As a leavening agent using a little bit of baking soda interacts with heat to create carbon dioxide, which introduces a fluffy quality to baked goods, pancakes, etc.

I use a touch of Baking Soda when making veggie/fruit based grain free pancakes, breads and cakes because it gives them a lighter quality without needing to add any flour. Word of caution, too much baking soda is detectable and changes the flavor, so just a pinch does the trick. In fact, that's the inspiration for today's flavor...too much baking soda in my cake!!

What's the difference between Baking Soda and Baking Powder? Baking Soda is just Baking Soda; it's a pure mineral (even the lab version). Baking powder is actually a combination of Baking Soda, some form of acid, and cornstarch. It will create a different chemical reaction when heat is applied.

From a health perspective, while there has much emphasis on being sure to purchase aluminum free Baking Soda, there is very little danger of purchasing Baking Soda with aluminum in it, even if it doesn't say "aluminum-free", it's actually baking powder that you want to worry about where aluminum is concerned. That being said, I do prefer to have a more naturally derived source for Baking Soda rather than something chemically created, which is a personal preference.

The action of Baking Soda is to decrease or regulate acid and increase an alkaline state. For that reason from a health perspective, it has been used as a way to eliminate overactive stomach acid and heartburn as well as acidosis. It also can be used to treat skin conditions, either topically by spot treating or soaking in the bath. It is a great deodorant because it creates an uninhabitable environment for most bacteria and it can also be used for mouth and teeth care.

There is also some interesting research that demonstrates including Baking Soda as part of a therapeutic intervention for kidney disease and various cancers can be very beneficial. Apparently ingesting baking soda in appropriate amounts can help create a more alkaline state in the body. This aids in balancing metabolic acid/alkaline levels without impacting blood balance too drastically and thus increases the potential for eliminating tumors. This is interesting research and worth looking into further.

GRAIN-FREE PANCAKES

Okay so I'm going to use carrots and nettle in this particular recipe but seriously you can replace those veggies with any other veggie or fruit. I have yet to find one that doesn't work. For example the last cakes I made had blackberries, peas, carrots...all mushed up to equal about 2 c. of base. I've even been known to mix in nut butters and different seed combinations. Go crazy... (:

1 ½ c. grated carrots
½ c. nettle
2 eggs
dash of vanilla
dash of garam masala (or whatever spice/herb combination strikes your fancy)
¼ tsp baking soda
1 tsp olive oil

Process the veggies to your desired texture. I like them a little bit chunky but it works well pureed or any variation in between. Move veggies to mixing bowl, add rest of ingredients and mix well. Add baking soda last and let sit for a few minutes. It will start to get a little bubbly. Coconut oil on your griddle, drop by the spoonful onto the heated griddle and voila you're on your way to some delicious pancakes.

DAY 168 – VIDALIA ONION (PICKLED)(RECIPE)

Tangy, sweet, sour, crunchy, and smooth; the first bite of a home pickled Vidalia Onion is a flavor adventure. So there's a couple things going on in today's flavor, inspired by the pickled Vidalia Onions that found their way onto my dinner plate last night. First of all the Vidalia Onion are a specific variety of onion grown in particular counties in the state of Georgia (U.S.). They are relatively new to the onion world, being an accidental hybrid that occurred in the depression era and then, according to historical data, began to make a name for itself.

The vidalia has now become the Georgia state vegetable and its name is legally protected and references only a twenty county region in the South. What's the big deal about Vidalia Onions? Well, most of all, they are sweet. This gives them a particularly interesting influence in a variety of dishes. They don't have the 'heat' or pungent quality that other onions have because they are lower in pyruvic acid. While Vidalia isn't the only sweet onion on the market, it is one of the only ones to have its own counsel.

Other interesting facts about the Vidalia? They are harvested by hand due to their sensitive nature. They have their own mascot (yep...his name is Yumion). They have a counsel that decides each year when they can be shipped and available for sale; any shipments that would like to go out earlier than the designated date must undergo an intensive quality inspection to insure they are up to snuff.

From a culinary perspective, because they are sweet they make an interesting addition to many culinary endeavors but they are really best (in my opinion) when eaten as close to whole as possible. For example, they make great onion rings whether fried, pickled, or just plain raw. The added little flavor punch to the onions I was eating came from quickly "pickling" them. Slice them into rings and let them sit for several hours (or even a day or two) in a mixture of vinegar and water with a touch of sugar (or honey). They are fresh tasting, crisp and deliciously sweet and sour and you can still taste the influence of the onion.

From a health perspective, Vidalia Onions are an onion so they possess many of the same qualities that their allium counterparts possess. There is an interesting correlating statistic that in the counties where Vidalia Onions are grown there is about half the incidence of stomach cancer. It could be all that sweet onion eating. Other research demonstrates that consuming onions can also boost immune function especially for things like cold and flu. Sweet onions have a few less antioxidants and powerhouse nutrients that their sulfuric counterparts have but they still have plenty of health benefits that make them worth including in your dietary repertoire.

HONEY PICKLED ONIONS

One Vidalia Onion sliced (although any sweet onion will work)
1/4 c. of honey
1/2 c. of warm water
1/2 c. of white balsamic or apple cider vinegar

Mix honey in warm water to dissolve, add balsamic vinegar. Add onions making sure they are fully immersed in the liquid. Let sit for several hours and enjoy.

DAY 169 – CRUNCHY (RECIPE)

Have you ever had those moments when you find yourself in the kitchen roving the pantry and refrigerator looking for the perfect crunch? No matter what else you might find to eat you are just not satisfied until you feel and hear that perfect crunching crunch...you know the one. When that happens to me it seems like nothing will satisfy but a corn tortilla chip... and not because I love corn or corn chips, but just because they typically have the perfect combination of crunch and chew.

One sense that is rarely included in the discussion of taste and flavor is the Trigeminal Sense, yet it has a huge impact on food choice and the perception of palatability. It is also referred to as the 'chemical sense'. Not because it senses for chemicals but because it responds to any potential "irritants" that you ingest. It's responsible for stimulating salivation when you eat something sour and for causing you to sweat when you eat something hot.

Trigeminal stimulation by spicy, crunchy, or sour foods is a pain response, and triggers a multitude of actions, including opioid and endorphin responses, to quell the potential pain. Interestingly, it is typically the end response that we find stimulating and enjoyable, rather than the actual food we are eating, because of the natural "pain" response. Who knew every time you dropped a Wasabi bomb on your tongue you were actually taking a happy pill?!?!? (Wasabi bombs are not for the faint of heart...more about that in the wasabi flavor day).

Back to the phenomenon of the *CRUNCH*... the reason you crave the perfect crunch especially when you are stressed, is because your body knows that by stimulating the Trigeminal nerve, you can in turn stimulate a parasympathetic response. In other words, the relaxation response. Of course, it has to be the "perfect" crunch and not just any old chomping (which is why a carrot stick will never be able to replace a corn chip) because it also needs the added sensation of inner ear stimulation. When your jaw crunches, the sound is delivered to your ear, which in turn enhances the perception of texture and palatability.

The Trigeminal nerve is a very large nerve responsible for sensation and motor function in your face. It is called Trigeminal because it branches off into three main sections; the ophthalmic (your eyes), the maxillary (your nasal sensation, sinus, palate) and mandibular (mouth, jaw and aids in the action of chewing). The Trigeminal nerve through a series of intricate pathways plugs into the Vagus Nerve, which when activated can lead to a reduction in stress signals (and a bazillion other things far too extensive for this brief entry). Grind your teeth at night? You can thank your trigeminal nerve…or better yet, you can give it the opportunity to *CRUNCH* its way to stress relief.

Quick lesson on stress management, it is the parasympathetic side of your nervous system that is responsible for things like resting and digesting. Research suggests that the Vagus/Trigeminal interface gives some people hypersensitivity to mouthfeel, which in turn can contribute to the use of food as a source of stress management.

Ultimately, in these situations, it's not really the food that is desired, it's the stimulated physical response to crunching and chewing. Crunching food is a good thing; it's what we are designed to do. Crunching good, quality food is even better. I've learned to keep some crunchy good options around for those times when nothing else will do but the crunch! Try this recipe for Spicy Roasted Chickpeas if you want to pack a healthy trigeminal double whammy. Spice, crunch, and insulin management all rolled up into one.

SPICY ROASTED CHICKPEAS
4 c. of chickpeas (I either soak dried ones overnight or now that I've discovered fresh green, I use those, you can also use canned, just go for BPA free lining)
2 tbs Olive Oil
Spice of your choice – to taste

Drain the chickpeas, coat them in olive oil, toss them in the spices and bake them at 400 for about 30-40 minutes. When their crisp, remove, cool, and enjoy! They will keep in a sealed jar (after they are cooled) for actually quite some time.

DAY 170 – WASABI

Pungent and hot, with a sensation similar to that of horseradish or hot mustard powder, Wasabi is a plant in the Brassicaceae family. It is often called a 'horseradish' although it really is not a true horseradish. For culinary use, it is the stem that is prepared and eaten and not the root. True Wasabi is a little challenging to come by, especially in restaurants, in fact, chances are the last time you had Wasabi with your sushi it was probably not really Wasabi, rather a blend of horseradish, mustard, corn starch and green coloring, which is what most of the Wasabi in the culinary mainstream consists of.

Wasabi originates in Japan and has been a significant part of the traditional Japanese diet since about 754 AD, however, archeological records note the presence of wasabi in Japanese culture as early as 14,000 BC. Initially, it seems, Wasabi was a medical intervention. It is possible it made its way into the diet as it was recognized for its powerful bactericide/insecticide qualities, which helped minimize the potential for food poisoning or other repercussions of eating foods like raw fish. Eventually, Wasabi made its way into the western world and isn't just for sushi anymore.

From a culinary perspective, the Wasabi stem can be grated or powdered and used directly in foods or as a condiment on the side. It is highly volatile due to the chemical compounds similar to horseradish so a small amount goes a long way. The heat from Wasabi is different from the heat from a pepper or capsaicin which is oil based. Wasabi compounds are not oil based which is one reason it manifests in your sinuses so quickly but also disappears pretty quickly.

From a health perspective, true Wasabi has a variety of interesting qualities. It contains a particular blend of chemical compounds that are specific to the wasabi plant which research demonstrates to be highly anti-oxidant. It contains several different types of isothiocyanates, which research suggests, could be very beneficial in decreasing the risk of various cancers. Wasabi is antiviral, antibacterial, antimicrobial and contributes to increased immune function. It can also aid in digestion and help balance gut bacteria. Because of the volatile quality, it has also been utilized as an inhalant for fainting in place of smelling salts. Research also suggests it is beneficial in reducing blood pressure and decreasing triglycerides.

The volatile quality also can be a mood booster, the body responds to the 'heat' of the wasabi by producing endorphins meant to calm the system; making Wasabi a potential 'good mood' food. (:

Oh yeah, that wasabi bomb mentioned in the Crunch entry? It involves taking a small piece of pickled ginger, wrapping it around a small (pea-sized or less) bit of wasabi and eating. Not for the faint hearted and I cannot in all good conscience recommend it. But I must admit I do love the rush!

DAY 171 – DRAGONFRUIT

Juicy, succulent, slightly sweet with a mouthfeel similar to berries, especially the strawberry; which is what this Dragonfruit reminds me of. Dragonfruit or Pitaya, originates in Mexico and Central America, although it has made its way to various Asian countries and is widely cultivated in places like Thailand and Vietnam. It is actually the fruit of a cactus, similar to a prickly pear. I'm always curious when I see daunting looking vegetation, about the first person to give it a try. The Dragonfruit's visage definitely gives one pause, even in all of its beauty.

As is true of any good fairy tale containing a dragon, the story of the dragon fruit from start to finish is a tale of romantic intrigue and anticipation. The cactus produces a bud, which becomes a flower that lives for one night only and must be pollinated on that night if it is to become a fruit. The bud grows and when ready it blooms in all of its magnificent glory and waits for some night visitor to help it actualize its full potential. They rely on bats and other night insects to help with the process. Then the next morning the flower begins to wilt and die, if it was successfully pollinated it will become a beautiful fruit. If not...):

I have seen Dragonfruit from time to time in the market but never actually tried one until this morning. Purchased just for today's flavor, I sliced it open with anticipation, not sure at all what I would find. It is an absolutely beautiful fruit. The little black seeds beautifully contrast the deep red flesh; for all of its visual intensity the flavor is actually quite subtle. Simple and refreshing, I could see including this fruit in summer foods to create a fresh and visually stimulating dish.

From a culinary perspective Dragonfruit can add to both savory and sweet dishes, although it appears that it most definitely lends itself to the sweeter side. A quick search on the culinary side of things reveals recipes for ice cream, mousse, smoothies, and even salsa. I think I will be turning what's left of my Dragonfruit into a salsa.

From a health perspective, the Dragonfruit supplies some great nutrients.

Vitamins A, C, and B. Minerals like phosphorous and calcium, as well as, quite a few antioxidants specific to 'tropical' fruit. Research suggests that Dragonfruit can aid in regulating blood sugar levels, help lower cholesterol, and increase immune function. It is high in fiber and the seeds are high in Omega 3 fatty acids.

DAY 172 – PASSIONFRUIT

The scent of Passionfruit is by far its most compelling attribute. A heady combination of sweet and earthy, the retronasal impact contributes a great deal to the flavor of the Passionfruit. It has an interesting mouthfeel, sort of crossing between a berry and a papaya; with a flavor that is both sweet and tart. Because the smell was so intensely sweet, I was a little surprised to experience a hint of tart and an astringent quality upon first taste.

There are several different varieties of Passionfruit, which originates in South America but has made its way to other landscapes with subtropical climates.
The fruit is a product of a very interesting and quite beautiful flowering vine. In the U.S. the chances are you will find the purple Passionfruit more readily than the gold. If you've never eaten Passionfruit it is an adventure for several reasons, not the least of which is how it looks when you cut it open. Then there is the interesting combination of the intensity of smell and flavor, which are slightly but pleasantly at odds with each other. The best way to eat a Passionfruit? Just cut it open and scoop it right out of its skin, seeds and all.

From a culinary perspective Passionfruit can add an exotic note to any dish, both sweet and savory. It can be an added or featured flavor to the obvious dessert items like smoothies, ice cream, pies, and puddings; and it also is an interesting addition to savory dishes like rice, or ginger Passionfruit chicken. This morning's Passionfruit flavor was half of one scooped into oatmeal with pumpkin seeds. Super delicious.

From a health perspective Passionfruit is like its tropical fruit cousins, packed with vitamins A and C. They are also a rich source of potassium and magnesium. They're high in fiber and with the addition of the seeds they pack in plenty of antioxidants. Research suggests that eating the pulp and including the seeds can help lower blood pressure and provide other beneficial support to the entire cardiovascular system. Interestingly, studies show that the seeds have a beneficial impact on the lungs, decreasing shortness of breath and symptoms of asthma. Some studies have been conducted using an extract derived from the peel and shown success in decreasing joint pain and stiffness for people suffering from osteoarthritis.

DAY 173 – RAMBUTAN

Sweet and a little tangy; a Rambutan has a texture similar to a grape or a lychee with a large seed in the middle. The Rambutan is a tropical fruit that originates in Southeast Asia. It is an interesting looking fruit with its long spiny, 'hairy' outer coating. For someone who is kinesthetically dominant, the Rambutan is super entertaining! They are visually interesting and fun to touch. They feel tickly to my fingertips, which makes cutting and peeling them an interesting experience. The inside fruit is smooth and shiny, with a firm but squishy mouthfeel. Its name is also loads of fun to say. Rambutan.

From a culinary perspective Rambutans are pretty straight forward. They can be eating raw, in salads, made into jams, jellies, candies, even ice cream. They are fun to freeze (if you like frozen food) as the fruit and then pop into drinks as flavorful "ice". They have such a mild and pleasant flavor that it seems better to serve them whole so there is an entire eating experience.

From a health perspective, the Rambutan contains a moderate amount of vitamin C. Interestingly; research demonstrates that the ones cultivated in Hawaii have a higher mineral and vitamin C content. I'm guessing this is due to environmental conditions. That being said the Rambutan is pretty basically a mild mannered fruit and best eaten just for the enjoyment, which is as important as nutrient density. There is research being conducted on the inedible parts of the fruit, for example, studies suggest that an extract made from the skin of the fruit could be beneficial for weight management and the roots can be effective against yeast and candidiasis.
For now, I just say...enjoy the fruit!

DAY 174 – TAMARIND

Sweet and sticky, Tamarind reminds me a little bit of sticky taffy or caramel. It definitely satisfies the sweet tooth without the sugary overload of an actual piece of candy. You just have to be sure to carefully chew around the very interesting seeds. Tamarind pods come from the Tamarind tree, which originates in tropical regions of Africa but has made its way around the world. Tamarind trees are impressive in stature and can reach a height of up to 100 ft. producing hundreds of seed-pods at a time. The pods can be left on the tree for up to 6 months without suffering any significant impact to the freshness or flavor, making them incredibly versatile.

Young pods are a bit sourer and can be used in culinary endeavors that require a more diverse flavor spectrum running from sweet to sour. More mature pods are sweet and tasty without being sugary or cloyingly sweet. Tamarind is a popular ingredient in cuisine from many cultures and shows up in the form of drinks, chutneys, jams, candies, curries, ice creams, pastes...it seems to fit into any dish imaginable.

From a health perspective, the Tamarind has some very interesting properties, not the least of which is its fiber content. As a folk remedy Tamarind has been used to treat digestive issues, including nausea and even intestinal parasites. Research is revealing that tamarind has antimicrobial, antibacterial, and antifungal qualities. Studies also demonstrate that the chemical compounds in Tamarind make it useful for gall bladder and liver issues, as well as, decreasing cholesterol and blood pressure.

DAY 175 – APRICOT

Juicy, sweet, and earthy, apricots are an easy summer treat. They are small enough to be a quick refreshing snack without any hassle. The Apricot I sampled for today's flavor is a beautiful burnished burgundy color, with a firm texture and even subtle hints of spice as the flavor settles. Apricots are a stone fruit, like the plum, peach and cherry. There is disagreement concerning origination of the Apricot tree, which has made its way around the globe regardless of where it originally began.

From a culinary perspective, fresh Apricots are a seasonal delight and can end up in all sorts of dishes from sweet to savory. It's an ingredient featured in a wide variety of cultural cuisines. One of my favorite dishes is Apricot Chicken, featuring fresh or dried apricots, saffron, cardamom and a number of other succulent spices. Dried Apricots are delicious, however, you want to make sure you are choosing unsulfured, which are not as aesthetically pleasing but are much better for you.

Apricots have the added bonus of containing a pit that can be eaten and is sometimes used in conjunction with, or as a substitute for, almonds. Apricot kernels are an ingredient in Amaretto, which is an Italian liquor and also in some jams and traditional almond cookie recipes. That being said the kernels are best eaten in moderation as they contain a chemical toxin that converts to cyanide in your stomach and can have some pretty uncomfortable side effects if too many are eaten at once.

From a health perspective Apricots are a great source of many of the same nutrients that their stone fruit cousins contain. They contain vitamins A and C, copper, potassium, and a wide variety of antioxidants and polyphenols. Research suggests that they are helpful in decreasing systemic inflammation and oxidative stress. Studies have shown that the chemical compounds found in the Apricot are especially beneficial to the liver. They also contain a significant amount of lycopene, which is beneficial for decreasing the risk of cancer. Other antioxidants found in the happy little Apricot; quercetin, catechins, proanthocyanidins and more; all of which contribute to your overall health and wellbeing.

A quick and easy way to bump up your dinner menu is to halve a few Apricot remove the seed and bake them. Once they are a little browned and juicy remove from the oven and top with goat cheese and honey. Delicious!

DAY 176 – MESQUITE

Nutty, slightly sweet, earthy, with a hint of something almost smoky or akin to molasses Mesquite powder is a traditional food currently making its way back to the marketplace. The Mesquite tree grows plentiful in the arid southwest. They can grow very large, reminding me of the Tamarind tree; the leaves and the pods look similar. The entire tree provides a wealth of resource in the form of wood, medicine, food, shade, building material, and on and on, so they have been an integral part of native cultures in the southwest.

To make Mesquite flour the pods are collected and dried thoroughly and then the entire pod including seeds and outer shell are ground into a powder. The powder can be used to make little cakes, breads, thicken stews or soups. It's really quite tasty. I have used Mesquite powder more from a supplement perspective as an added ingredient to bump up the nutritional density of various meals but sadly, did not really appreciate it as a food source until now.

From a culinary perspective the Mesquite tree provides several different culinary options. The pods can be made into flour and the flowers can be made into tea or added to foods as a decorative and edible flower. The flour is sweet and dense and can easily be made into little breads or cakes by simply adding enough water and then they can be fried. I also found a recipe for making a Mesquite flour drink, which when fermented becomes fizzy, alcoholic, and apparently quite tasty. The pods can also be roasted, soaked and then reduced to a syrup that is similar to molasses, which can then be used as a type of sweetener. I'm really interested in exploring more with the mesquite tree!

From a health perspective, mesquite pods are high in protein and high in fiber. And although also high in fructose, between the fiber and protein content, they actually regulate blood sugar rather than contribute to an insulin spike. It also contains a significant amount of calcium, potassium, magnesium, and zinc, which are more readily absorbed because of slower digestive time and the glutinous quality to the fiber.

Research demonstrates that consumption of Mesquite flour can help regulate blood sugar and insulin production. It has antifungal, antibacterial properties and also contributes to improved immune function. Once the pods are made into flour the protein is easily assimilated through the digestive properties, making it an excellent source of bio-available protein and great for repair on the cellular level.

I think it's great there's a resurgence of recognition for mesquite as a nutrient dense food source. It's just a shame it's been isolated in the form of trendy "superfood" fame. Appreciating the entire Mesquite tree and understanding where it comes from, paying attention to its role in the health of not only people but also the earth is a good way to reconnect to food and well-being.

DAY 177 – YOGURT

Creamy, tangy, slightly sweet, and a hint salty; full-fat yogurt from pasture raised, grass-fed Jersey cows tastes like all the elements of flavor wrapped up with earthiness, as though you can taste the fields and sunshine. As a fermented food, Yogurt can be a great way to maintain the pre and pro biotic balance in your digestive tract. Fermented milk in the form of Yogurt, can be found in cultures around the world, whether cow, sheep, goat or even buffalo. In many of those cultures there is a strong recognition that Yogurt is highly beneficial to health and wellness. In India, Yogurt with honey is referred to as food for the gods and even the Roman philosopher, Pliny the Elder wrote about the benefit of thickened milk with its agreeable acidity.

From a culinary perspective Yogurt is super versatile. It can be added to a variety of dishes from savory to sweet. It can also be used as its own stand-alone meal as well as a nutritious and satisfying snack. Yogurt can be added to a marinade for meats; the lactic acid helping to break down the protein and acting as a tenderizer. It can be folded into sauces, like curries and lentils. It can be added to baked goods, although, you lose the much of the bacterial good stuff when heated to the point of die-off. It can also be enjoyed mixed in with a variety of ingredients or as a type of dip or condiment. One of my favorite savory ways to enjoy yogurt is mixed with cucumber, garlic and dill. For a sweeter snack, mixing it with fresh fruit and seeds makes a great meal.

From a health perspective, the bacteria found in real Yogurt are beneficial for your body (emphasis on 'real'). Dairy Yogurt is a great source of complete protein, and a wide variety of vitamins and minerals. Studies suggest that eating ½ c. of fermented food a day, like Yogurt, can boost immune function, help regulate blood sugar, decrease digestive issues, and increase bone density.

Yogurt, if it comes from a quality source like a grass-fed Jersey Cow, contains elements of all the key nutrient groups making it an amazing wealth of well-rounded nutrient density. Research also demonstrates that eating Yogurt can help to balance mental and emotional well-being. This happens partly because of the good bacteria contributing to gut health balance, but also the full range of vitamins and minerals (namely the B's) lay the foundation for the development of things like glutathione, which contributes to increased antioxidant activity and decreases the potential for mood and neurodegenerative disorders.

So what's the down side? You have to be a savvy consumer as precious few of the conventional brands we find on today's market shelves possess the health qualities traditionally found in *real* Yogurt. Most conventional brands have a very small bacteria count and contain additives, including sugar, that end up doing more harm than good. It's best to eat plain Yogurt and add your own goodies, and also choose Yogurt that is from a quality source and contains nothing but the milk and the bacteria that helped ferment it.

You can also try making your own, which is not really as complicated as it seems and can produce some very delicious and creamy Yogurt. Also, if you're wondering about the current fad of Greek yogurt and whether or not it is 'better' for you...it's actually not. The whey in regular yogurt contains thousands of bacteria; when it is strained off to make thicker 'Greek' Yogurt, those bacteria are lost.

DAY 178 – SHALLOT (RECIPE)

As a member of the Allium family I think of the shallot as onion's daintier cousin. It is milder, and more refined, with a subtle flavor that is similar to onion yet distinct in its own right. In the US, it's pronounced a SHAH-let and in the UK a shuh-LOT but however you say it makes no difference to its flavor impact to your meal.

While it tastes more like an onion, the Shallot looks more like garlic and grows in a segmented bulb similar to the garlic. The outer covering is often a lovely shade of red maroon sometimes varying to copper and the inner flesh is pearly with hints of rose coloring.

From a culinary perspective Shallots can be used in much the same way as onions. They impart a more delicate flavor and texture making them a great addition to culinary endeavors even when raw. I tend to use shallots much more often than onions, tossing them in salads, sautéing them in eggs or veggies, or caramelizing them for more complexity. Interestingly, while I tend to swap onions for Shallots, I wouldn't really do it the other way around, if a recipe calls for a Shallot it may need the mild flavoring and to substitute an onion could overpower. This is why I tend to keep plenty of Shallots on hand.

From a health perspective Shallots are in the allium family so all of the goodness that you find in garlic and onions, you will find in the shallot and then some. Shallots have a higher nutrient density than the onion and pack quite an antioxidant punch. They are high in chemical compounds that convert into allicin, which is in turn beneficial for lowering cholesterol, improving liver function, lowering blood sugar, and even inhibiting the potential for cell mutations that contribute to cancer. Shallots are also anti-viral, anti-fungal, anti-microbial making them a great addition to your diet during the flu season (although, including them year round will definitely build your immune function). They are high in vitamins and minerals, especially vitamin A, potassium, iron, copper, and believe it or not, calcium.

Here's a yummy way to make CARAMELIZED SHALLOTS, which are a delicious addition to a meal:

Ingredients:
- 1-2 tbsp coconut or olive oil
- ½ lb shallots, peeled but left whole
- 2 tbsp butter
- 1 bay leaves
- thyme sprig

1 cup of stock

Heat oil in a large frying pan and cook shallots over a high heat for 5 mins. When they are golden, remove from pan and drain off the oil.

Add the butter, bay and thyme and toss with seasoning. Cook for 5-8 mins, stirring so that the butter doesn't burn.

Pour over the stock and lightly simmer until the shallots are tender and the sauce is reduced and sticky.

DAY 179 – MARSALA

Cloyingly sweet and slightly acidic and tangy, Marsala is an aperitif or dessert wine, very similar to port or sherry that is often used in cooking. Like port and sherry it is typically also a fortified wine, meaning it has been enhanced with a distilled spirit, typically Brandy. This increases the alcohol content, and the shelf life, and imparts a distinctive flavor.

Marsala originates, and is named for, a specific region in Italy. It comes in variations of sweetness and is typically produced from white grapes. When used as an aperitif it is sipped before a meal as a preparation for digestion. As a dessert wine, it accompanies the end of the meal and similarly can help stimulate digestion.

From a culinary perspective, Marsala wine is used in a wide variety of dishes both sweet and savory. Most notable dishes include, the Italian dish Chicken Marsala and the desserts, Zabaglione and Tiramisu. One of my favorite, and perhaps unlikely, ways to use Marsala, besides in Zabaglione, is in a winter dish of Brussels Sprouts. I sauté shallots and Brussels Sprouts, then remove them and add Marsala to the pan, reducing it down to a thick syrup. I then pop the shallot and Brussels Sprouts back in and sprinkle on some roasted Hazelnuts. It seems extra delicious on a cold winter evening.

From a health perspective, being the research geek I am, I've searched databases far and wide to find a nugget of "health" benefits specifically concerning Marsala Wine. Sadly, I have found none. However, I have found an Italian saying; "Wine makes good blood" and think there is always something to be learned from folk sayings. I'm also aware, and have already shared, that there are health benefits to the moderate or occasional consumption of both red and white wines.

Lastly, I did find a research study listed in the Journal of Internal Medicine concerning fortified wine and blood sugar levels; a group of researchers found that drinking a moderate amount of fortified wine, either while fasting or eating a meal, had no significant impact on blood sugar levels. So, perhaps, Marsala and other aperitifs and digestifs are meant to just be consumed for their own sake and enjoyed in moderation or on special occasions where they can be incorporated into a meal and appreciated for their own unique qualities.

DAY 180 – SATSUMA

Tangy and refreshing with the perfect blend of sweet and sour the Satsuma is a variety of mandarin orange. It originates in Japan and appears to be a result of artistic cultivation during the Edo period, according to Japanese botanist, Chozaburo Tanaka. The Satsuma became popular for its flavor intensity and ease of peeling and eating. It is seedless with a skin that is thin and easily detached from the inner fruit. In the 1700's, the Satsuma began to make its way around the world, being cultivated in climates that are humid and temperate. It is also known as the "Christmas Orange" because it is placed in stockings as a special holiday treat. There are varying and interesting historical explanations as to how this became a tradition.

From a culinary perspective, the Satsuma is as versatile as its relative: the tangerine. It is delightful to eat on its own; a perfectly packaged, refreshing snack. It also can add some zip to a drink or dish either by squeezing the juice over or dropping in some whole sections. I love to use the juice of Satsuma's as a dressing for salads and veggies. The citrus gives it a preservative quality and the flavor imparts an exotic, sweet, and zesty quality.

From a nutritional perspective, like its cousins, the Satsuma is an excellent resource for Vitamin C and fiber. Its volatile oils, like thymol and limonene, add an extra element of health with their ability to aid in digestive issues and promote cell regeneration. They even act as a natural pesticide. It also contains significant amounts of minerals like potassium, magnesium and manganese. Research demonstrates that including citrus, like Satsuma, in your diet can help with oxidative stress, systemic inflammation, cardiovascular issues, high blood pressure, and gastrointestinal ailments. It also acts as a fortifying agent for blood and cellular structure, increasing the growth and repair of healthy red cells.

DAY 181 – MOZZARELLA DI BUFALA

Creamy, tangy, sweet and salty, Mozzarella di Bufala is a delicious soft, young cheese made from the milk of water buffalo. Chances are if you've had the real deal in the summertime months, it's been part of the ever-popular Caprese Salad; tomato slices, with mozzarella slices, and fresh basil. Not all Mozzarella is made from buffalo milk so if you're looking for this particular type of cheese, you will want to make sure it contains the words "bufala". If you're thinking, 'how the heck did water buffalo get to Italy?" You are not alone. It is a question that has several different answers and no consensus. The one consensus is that the first reference to cheese made from the milk of water buffalo is in the 12th century.

From a culinary perspective, Mozzarella di Bufala is considered a "fresh" mozzarella meaning it is typically packaged in whey and has a stretchy, chewy quality. It is delicious unadulterated with other ingredients but also makes a fabulous creamy cheese addition to any culinary endeavor that features cheese. You can add it to pizzas, eggs, pastas, veggies, and salads, raw or melted. Just know that it doesn't melt the way a harder, drier cheese melts, so if you're looking for that stringy quality of melted cheese, it would be best to couple this with a drier version of mozzarella.

From a health perspective, Buffalo milk is higher in protein, fat, and various vitamins and minerals than cow's milk. It is rich source of bio-available calcium, magnesium, zinc and phosphorous as well as a Vitamins B and A. It is lower in cholesterol than cow's milk and contains an enzyme that provides it with a longer "shelf life" than cow's milk. The molecular structure of the milk solid is similar to cow's milk so there is no guarantee that if someone is allergic to cow's milk they won't be allergic to buffalo: although there is, indeed, research that suggests this is the case. I imagine it just depends on the type of allergy and exactly what molecular part of the milk someone is allergic to. The cheese and yogurt made from buffalo milk contain all the creamy goodness with the added benefit of fermentation; so pre and probiotics galore.

CHAPTER 7 - JULY

DAY 182 – GREEN CURRY

In the heat of summer, the spicy, tangy, sweetness of green curry cools and satisfies my palate. Green Curry or Kaeng Khiao Wan, as it's traditionally called, is a Thai curry made from green curry paste which consists of delicious things like; green chilies, kaffir lime zest, cilantro, coriander, lemongrass, cumin, garlic and more. The exact combination of spices and herbs can vary from region to region. Once the paste is prepared, it is then mixed with coconut milk, fish sauce, basil, and a variety of protein and veggie; again depending on location.

I grew to love green curry as a summertime dish while traveling through Thailand. Initially, when someone suggested I try a hot curry to combat the heat of the day I thought they were crazy, but decided to give it a try. Amazingly, they were right, the spiciness of the curry elicited a cooling response in my body and I felt cooler and more adjusted to the heat. Then I started thinking about it and realized that many cultures that exist in hot climates have the spiciest food...hmm... enter the detective hat. Eating spicy food elicits a gustatory facial sweating response, which also prompts the back of the neck and hairline to sweat. The sweat initiates a cooling response similar to placing a cool, wet cloth on the back of the neck. Fascinating! Now back to the green curry....

From a culinary perspective, making authentic Green Curry from scratch can feel super daunting in the westernized kitchen as some of the ingredients are quite unfamiliar to the typical market. I highly recommend finding an Asian market close by and going on a sensory adventure. Not only will you more than likely find all of the needed ingredients you will also have the pleasure of seeing, smelling, touching exotic fruits and veggies that are not typically available in your grocery store.

If, however, you're not up for grinding some Green Curry paste in your mortar and pestle, you can always purchase a jar of it and start with that. Just be mindful of the ingredients and look to avoid any flavor enhancing chemicals or additives. Once you prepare the basic curry sauce, you can add any number of veggies and protein. My current favorite is salmon with some broccoli, zucchini, peas and a couple of slices of avocado.

From a health perspective, traditional Green Curry is jam packed with healthful herbs and spices. Galangal is a root that is in the ginger family and has many of the same properties as ginger. Turmeric is anti-inflammatory. Cilantro is anti-microbial, anti-viral, anti-fungal and aids in decreasing cholesterol while also helping the body detox. The list goes on and on...

There is research on curry in general, which suggests that consuming curry based dishes can help lower cholesterol and blood pressure, reduce the risk of cardiovascular disease, increase digestive balance, and decrease systemic inflammation and oxidative stress. What's not to love!??

DAY 183 – LYCHEE

Sweet and juicy with a satin smooth mouthfeel; the Lychee is similar to the rambutan in both flavor and texture. They are both members of the soapberry family, which are native to subtropical climates. They are considered soapberries because some part of the plant, whether root, leaf, or seed contains saponins and can be used as soap. Recorded use of the Lychee fruit can be found in Chinese written records as early as 2000 BC. It is a delicate fruit that begins to deteriorate quickly once ripe and removed from the branches, consequently, most Lychee fruit are dipped in a chemical compound to extend their shelf life and keep them from turning brown. The compound used is classified as GRAS, which means, "generally recognized as safe".

From a culinary perspective, Lychees are absolutely delicious as a fresh, raw snack or side to a meal. They can be made into puddings, ice creams, sorbets, or added to salads. The creative culinary options are endless for this sweet little fruit.

From a health perspective Lychee, just as the fresh fruit, contains a moderate amount of nutrients like Vitamin C and B. They have a decent amount of fiber and can help balance digestive function. Studies suggest that 9 Lychee contain the recommended daily allowance of Vitamin C. There are several suggesting that Lychee as an extract helps to reduce inflammation and oxidative stress. Three studies in particular demonstrated that efficacy of Lychee fruit extract for tissue repair and decreased inflammation in long distance runners and other endurance athletes.

DAY 184 – FAUX "PEANUT" SAUCE (RECIPE)

Salty, sweet, tangy...umami; this raw food version of "peanut" sauce is uber delicious and nutritious. Traditionally Peanut Sauce is made from roasted ground peanuts and includes coconut milk, sugar and other very interesting herbs and spices. It can be found in a variety of cultural cuisines, including Indonesia, Thailand, and Africa. It seems that in the U.S. the most popular rendition of Peanut Sauce is in the form of Satay, which is roasted meat or veggies on a skewer and then dipped into the sauce. Finding authentic peanut sauce made from traditional ingredients with traditional effort can be a challenge but one worth the hunt if possible.

From a health perspective, traditional peanut sauce is actually quite good, containing a wide variety of nutrient dense ingredients. Unfortunately, most of the conventional versions of peanut sauce that you will find today contain high amounts of sugar and other additives attempting to recreate the umami flavor with cheaper ingredients. The ingredients provided in the recipe above are all nutrient dense and provide a number of health benefits ranging from decreasing oxidative stress to enhancing digestive balance.

My favorite way to enjoy it? Spiral cut some raw zucchini and carrots then mix it all together. It's a savory, nutty dish that hits and satisfies all the flavor notes in your palate. You can use either almonds or almond butter or peanuts, or peanut butter or a combination of all of the above. I personally like a combination because I do not have an allergy to peanuts.

In the meantime, if you want a delicious, nutritious and easy to make home version, you can try the recipe below.

SAVORY NUT SAUCE
½ c nuts pureed into butter or nut butter
1 Tbs Nama Shoyu or Braggs amino acid
1 Tbs of minced garlic
1 Tbs ginger
2 Tbs lemon or lime juice (I combine both)
dash of chili pepper or jalapeno
1 Tbs lemongrass (you can leave out if unavailable)
1 - 2 dates (optional)
Water (the amount depends on how thick you want your sauce)

Mix all ingredients in food processor or blender until desired consistency. Can be stored in the fridge for several days and just added to veggies or used as a dip.

DAY 185 – RASPBERRIES

Tangy, sweet, and sour, fragile little raspberries are a delicious addition to my morning yogurt. Of course, I had to wear them as little hats on my fingers before I could put them in the bowl. It's just a thing.

Raspberries are a member of the rose family and when left to their natural devices, ripen during the mid summer months. Each berry is actually a conglomeration of little drupe fruits, with seeds contained in each little bulb that makes up the whole little berry. The berries form around the core of the bulb and when they are picked it's left behind which is why they are hollow and make such good accessories!

From a culinary perspective if you haven't enjoyed a Raspberry, straight from the garden or forest, then you are most definitely missing out. Freshly foraged Raspberries have a flavor spectrum unique to themselves. Second best are organic berries from the market, which can be added to any number of sweet and savory dishes if not enjoyed just as is. They can be pureed quite easily and used in sauces, dressings, puddings, baked goods, and smoothies. Truly, the sky's the limit if you are creative in the kitchen. I actually enjoy them raw because I like their texture as well and don't want to miss out on that if they are smooshed into other ingredients.

From a health perspective Raspberries are little packets of nutritional goodness. They are high in a wide variety of vitamins, minerals, and phytonutrients; some of which are specific to the raspberry. A good source of vitamin C, just a cup a day provides the recommended daily amount. They are high in manganese and fiber too, both of which aid in blood sugar management, bone, tissue and skin health, and anti-oxidant activity. They help decrease oxidative stress, systemic inflammation and cell mutation that can lead to various cancers.

The most interesting thing about Raspberries in the health world is research around a little ketone specific to the raspberry called rheasmin, which has the potential to boost intracellular metabolic function. In plain language it can decrease the risk of obesity and fatty liver disease. Combine the rheasmin with several other flavonoids that are specific to the Raspberry and the rose family and you have a combination that works very well for the metabolism of fat and sugar.

Just an added note about Raspberries... research also demonstrates that their nutrient qualities are significantly increased if they are organic or pesticide free, and if they are ripe.

DAY 186 – LENTILS

Chewy, nutty little discs of goodness; Lentils are a versatile and nutritious addition to your dietary repertoire. I like Lentils and find them interesting additions to my plate, mostly because their texture compels me to slow down and chew each one individually. Sometimes it makes for a very long meal.

Lentils are considered a pulse, which is a plant in the legume family that is harvested for the dry seed. While green beans and peas are in the legume family as well, they are not considered pulses because they are consumed fresh. Lentils have been part of the human diet for thousands of years and have made their way into most cuisines around the world in some shape or form. Lentils grow in a pod with about two or three seeds per pod. The seeds are harvested and dried before they make their way out into the market and to your table. Lentils are beneficial not only to your body but also to the planet. They contribute to healthy soil and are a low impact crop, so much so, the United Nations declared 2016 the Year of Pulses in an attempt to bring more awareness of the value of pulses to the human diet and to the planet.

From a culinary perspective Lentils are versatile and easily added to a variety of dishes. There are a few different varieties of Lentils, giving them each a different shape, size, color, texture and even flavor. French green Lentils, split yellow, petite red, they all have their own personality to add to a given dish. My favorite ways to enjoy Lentils are either made into a loaf and then baked and eaten much like meatloaf or added to soups and stews. If you keep a small jar of them prepared and in the fridge, you will have them handy to just add to any number of dishes with ease.

From a nutritional perspective Lentils are seriously nutritious little treasures. They are a fantastic source of protein and fiber as well as a multitude of minerals and vitamins. Research demonstrates the high mineral content and combination of minerals helps decrease things like heart disease, systemic inflammation and oxidative stress. They can also help manage insulin fluctuation, decreasing the potential for diabetes and other glucose related issues. Lentils are also a great source of iron.

DAY 187 – BLOOD ORANGE

Citrus Sinensis

Sweet, sour, bitter, tangy, all rolled up into a juicy and refreshing bite of citrusy deliciousness. Blood Oranges are also visually beautiful once they are cut open to reveal the crimson inner pulp. From the outside, they resemble a small regular orange. There are three different varieties of Blood Orange; the Moro, which is a more recent variety, is a deep red with a pinkish hue to the skin. The Tarocco is an Italian variety, it is the one used to make Italian blood orange soda. The Sanguinella is a Spanish variety. The blood orange thrives in Mediterranean climates and it is the low temperatures during the winter nights that give them the lovely red inner fruit.

From a culinary perspective Blood Oranges are so beautiful and tasty that they can be used in a variety of culinary endeavors. They can be used anywhere that citrus is used, depending also on the variety of orange since some are sweeter than others. How about some Duck a la Blood Orange, or Blood Orange Osso Buco, or maybe some Blood Orange ice cream or Blood Orange olive oil cake?

From a health perspective Blood Oranges have all the vitamin and mineral goodness that regular oranges have with the addition of anthocyanins. Of course, they are packed with vitamin C even more than regular oranges and between the fiber and other antioxidants they are an awesome resource for health. Research suggests that the anthocyanins in the Blood Orange are amazing antioxidants, they are anti-inflammatory, anti-oxidative stress, anti-cancer, anti-carcinogenic...they're pretty anti anything that isn't serving your best health and wellness.

DAY 188 – LIME (RECIPE)

Refreshing, juicy, tart, slightly sweet and sour. I find Limes add something extra refreshing in the heat of summer. Limes are a member of the citrus family and while many people think a Lime is a Lime is a Lime, there are actually quite a few varieties of Lime, each with their own little twist of limeness. (:

It appears the Lime originated in Indonesia but has made its way to tropic and subtropical areas around the globe. First recorded use of Limes is in literature dating back about 4,000 years. It has been used in a variety of medicinal, preservative and culinary endeavors across time and culture. One obvious way that Limes were utilized as medicine was in ship crossing, the Vitamin C kept the sailors from getting scurvy, hence the name Limey for English sailors. Initially, the use of Lime Juice was supposedly simply to make the water and other drinkable items more palatable, but when doctors noticed that sailors drinking the Lime Juice were among the healthiest they realized it had an added benefit.

From a culinary perspective Limes are preservative, sweet, sour, tangy, and can add a nice acidic level without actually impacting the flavor of a dish too drastically. I love the flavor of Lime as an added back note to spicy dishes or anytime I need a refreshing kick. It also makes a cooling tonic, add lemongrass and ginger and you've got a really refreshing treat.

From a health perspective Lime is like its citrus relatives. It is full of vitamin C and other vitamins and minerals. They are also a great source of Limonin, which help reduce the risk of various forms of cancer; most notably mouth, throat, skin, and stomach. Research also suggests the flavonoids in Limes can help decrease the risk of auto-immune diseases such as rheumatoid arthritis, type 2 Diabetes, and Graves. Limes help decrease oxidative stress and systemic inflammation.

RAW KEY LIME "CHEESE" PIE
Crust:
1/3 cup almonds
1/3 cup cashews
1/3 cup pecans
6 -8 medjool dates
1 tsp vanilla extract

Filling:
2 ripe avocados
4 dates (soaked and pureed)
3 tbs Lime juice
1 tsp vanilla

¼ cup cashews
dash sea salt

Topping:
1 cup soaked & drained cashews (soak for an hour or more so they blend smooth and creamy)
2 tbs dates (soaked and pureed)
1 ½ tsp vanilla

Pulse crust ingredients in a food processor until crumbly. Press into a pie plate or small muffin cups. Set in refrigerator to firm. Puree all filling ingredients, pour into crust, place back in refrigerator to firm. Mix all topping ingredients in blender, pour over firm filling ingredients and place back into fridge to set. Once firm, slice and enjoy!

DAY 189 – COCONUT MILK

While Coconut Milk is slightly sweet, for me the flavor is more about the mouthfeel. Good Coconut Milk has a rich and creamy mouthfeel; because it is made from the fatty meat of a ripe coconut so contains a good amount of coconut oil. Traditionally, Coconut Milk is prepared by grating, or grinding, coconut meat and mixing it with whatever fluid is left from the coconut or with water. The mixture is then strained and the resulting liquid is Coconut Milk; used in any number of sweet or savory dishes in tropic and sub-tropic cuisines. Coconuts originate in tropic and subtropical climates but these days can be found in markets around the world, with the advent of canned products Coconut Milk can be found even more easily on market shelves.

Personally, I am not a fan of the BPA's found in can linings or the additives that get put into conventional Coconut Milk (guar gum, carrageenan, and sometimes enriched vitamins) so I tend to make my own upon occasion as a treat. When I make it I puree the coconut meat with the liquid and water for the desired consistency and I leave the pulp in for added fiber. It can, however, be easily strained for a more milk like consistency.

From a culinary perspective Coconut Milk can be found in any number of traditional cuisines originating in sub-tropic or tropical climates. It is used to make sauces, soups, desserts, and even in marinades. It can really be used in any recipe that calls for regular milk without disrupting flavor or texture.

From a health perspective fresh Coconut Milk has all the goodness of coconut. The fat in Coconut Milk is a medium chain triglyceride which, research suggests, can help lower cholesterol, balance blood sugar, and stabilize thyroid. Coconuts also contain lauric acid, which can be a very effective anti-bacterial, anti-fungal, and anti-microbial. It protects against oxidative stress and eliminates free radicals.

Coconut is also low in sodium, high in potassium and other vitamins and minerals, high in fiber and can be a great way to stabilize your appetite. Coconut Milk is a nice replacement for people who can't have animal milks although, if you are allergic to tree nuts, it could present a problem for you.

DAY 190 – PAPAYA

Sweet and juicy, with the tiniest hint of citrus or earthiness, and a mouthfeel that is smooth and almost creamy Papayas are nice summertime treat. For some reason, when I eat a Papaya it reminds me a little bit of the creamsicles that I used to love when I was a kid. Papayas grow well in tropic and sub-tropic climates. They are native to Central America but have made their way to various places around the world.
\
From a culinary perspective Papayas are versatile and interesting to use in a variety of dishes both sweet and savory. The seeds are also edible and have a spicy, peppery flavor. Papayas contain papain making them a great option for naturally tenderizing meats or tougher vegetables. They can be pureed into a cream and used as a marinade or added to dishes to give a creamy texture. They are delicious as is; raw and yummy. I love to just scoop them right out of their skin and enjoy, eating a few seeds along with.

From a health perspective Papayas are a great source of nutrients and very high in vitamin C, B, and A. Also a good source of potassium and magnesium, they help balance electrolytes and intracellular fluid retention. Research demonstrates they are beneficial for cardiovascular health and promote immune health. They are high in the digestive enzyme papain, which helps digestive processes and repair of the gastro-intestinal lining. It also has great anti-inflammatory and antioxidant properties making it a great resource for eliminating systemic inflammation.

Studies show it is useful in decreasing the incidence of auto-immune disorders such as rheumatoid arthritis. It also contributes to tissue repair and research has been conducted on athletes, finding that they have a quicker recovery time when papain is included in their diet.

Papaya seeds have their own health qualities, being antifungal, antibacterial, and antiviral. They are also anti-parasitic and can help expel parasites and repair any damage to the intestinal tract.

DAY 191 – MAHI MAHI

Mahi Mahi has a texture that is flaky and smooth, it is light pink to white in color and very mild in flavor as far as fish goes. Mahi Mahi is a warm water fish ranging from areas in the pacific like Hawaii and into the south Atlantic. It is also known as the dolphinfish but don't worry, they are not related to the dolphin in any way (other than they both live in the ocean). According to FishWatch, Mahi Mahi is one of the more abundant fish harvested for commercial use, however, they are still closely monitored to insure preservation of numbers.

From a culinary perspective, Mahi Mahi is quite a versatile fish because it is so mild in flavor. It is wonderful grilled, baked, steamed or any number of other ways. My favorite ways to prepare Mahi Mahi is en papillote (steamed in paper) or just grilled stovetop with shallots and herbs.

From a nutritional perspective, Mahi Mahi is a good choice for quality protein and other nutrients. It is higher in complete protein than salmon and other fish and, alternately, it is lower in fat than salmon while still supplying plenty of Omega 3 fatty acids. It is a great source of other vitamins and minerals, such as Vitamin B and potassium and selenium. Studies suggest that consuming at least 6 oz. of fish a week can greatly increase your physical and mental health.

DAY 192 – ELDERFLOWER (RECIPE)

Sweet, earthy, refreshing with a taste that sparkles; elderflower cordial is such a delight that it inspired me to want to know more about the elderflower. The elderflower is a bright little flower looking quite similar to Queen Anne's lace (aka Cow Parsley) except the elderflower comes from a deciduous bush that can actually grow quite large. Interestingly as delicious as the elderflower tastes, all other parts of the plant are toxic (except for the ripe berries).

From a culinary perspective the Elderflower is small and sweet smelling; almost like honey or honeysuckle. In fact, it used to be classified in the honeysuckle family until a more thorough investigation of its DNA revealed that it was not part of that family at all. The flowers are in season across Europe, parts of Asia, and even Africa from May to July. They are most popularly used in drinks such as cordials or spritzers although there are quite a few recipes for using Elderflower in both sweet and savory meals. How about some Duck breast with Elderflower, goat cheese, and peas? The Elderflowers just need to be cooked first, either by steeping them in water or by soaking and then drying to be added to dishes.

From a health perspective the elderflower actually has some really great properties for health. They are packed with bioflavonoids and are antifungal, antiviral, and antibacterial. Research demonstrates Elderflower extract can be effective in killing pathogens in a hospital setting, including MRSA. Elderflowers are also antiflammatory, helping to eliminate system inflammation. They help reduce blood sugar and manage glucose levels. Research suggests they are a potent digestive and diuretic, helping to cleanse the kidneys and bladder and eliminate constipation. Elderflowers are also analgesic, helping to alleviate pain, both systemic and localized.

CORDIAL
10 large elderflower heads
900g granulated sugar
600ml litres water
2 lemons

Pick off any insects and beasties you see on the flowers. Eeek!
Heat the sugar and water in a large saucepan until the sugar has dissolved. Strip large ribbons of zest off the lemons with a vegetable peeler, lose the knobbly ends, then slice the lemon and place in a large bowl with the Elderflower heads.
Pour the hot syrup over the lemons and Elderflower heads and give it a good stir. Cover the bowl with a cloth or a big plate and leave it for 24 hours.
Strain the mixture with muslin or kitchen paper in a sieve and pour into sterilized bottles. I used a couple of small glass ones for the fridge, which should be used within a month, and a small plastic bottles for the freezer for future use.

DAY 193 – POPPY SEED

 Tiny, crunchy seeds that taste earthy, and nutty with slightly bitter undertones; Poppy Seeds are a chewing adventure. I absolutely love Poppy Seeds, mostly because they are fun to chew. Poppy Seeds are harvested from the dried pod of the poppy flower. Even though the poppy flower is more commonly associated with opium these days, that wasn't always so. The seed had a much-venerated place in cuisine from a wide variety of cultures. German bakers have long used them to make desserts and cakes, mostly notably Mohnkuchen (one of my absolute favorites), and they are also a feature in Jewish, Indian, and Asian cuisines. Poppy seeds have a long history in the culinary world with first recorded use coming from Ancient Egypt.

From a culinary perspective, Poppy Seeds are versatile and can find their way in savory and sweet endeavors. When baking with them I reconstitute them first in honey and milk and then use them as a paste in several different types of baked goods and puddings. They can be tossed dry in soups and stews or salads or even with pasta.

From a health perspective, Poppy Seeds have a dubious reputation, however, that reputation is really unwarranted. They are highly nutritious little seeds. They are high in minerals like copper, zinc, and calcium and high in vitamins like B. Poppy Seeds are an excellent source of antioxidants and other nutrients like oleic acid. Folk medicine and other indigenous traditional medicines utilize Poppy Seeds for a variety or reason. First, they make a great nervous system tonic, restoring the ability to sleep well and rest and relax. They are a great expectorant and work to balance the endocrine system. Research suggests that Poppy Seeds not only taste delicious but also be used to lower cholesterol, balance blood sugar, and can have a mild sedative effect.

Just FYI... poppies lose any of the narcotic properties found in opium once the pods and seeds ripen and dry out, so although rumor has it you may test positive on a drug test, you will not actually experience any effects nor will you test positive if a more extensive test is given. You would also have to eat an incredibly huge amount of these tiny but delightful wonders.

DAY 194 – MANCHEGO

Firm and buttery tasting, with the sharp earthiness of sheep milk; Manchego cheese is mild and delicious. True Manchego cheese is a protected origin label and comes specifically from the La Mancha area of Spain. It must be made from milk produced by Manchega sheep and it is aged anywhere from 60 days to 2 years. Unfortunately, in the U.S. we do not recognize designated labels and produce cheese that is called Manchego even though it is often a blend of cow, goat, and sheep milk and produced differently; giving it a very different flavor. Personally, I think having true Manchego cheese is a distinct treat and one that should be preserved and appreciated when encountered.

From a culinary perspective, Manchego cheese is lighter in flavor and can be used in a variety of dishes calling for light cheese. Of course, the time that the Manchego is aged will also help designate its best culinary use; with the more aged being firmer and denser with an almost nutty flavor.

From a health perspective, several things stand out for Manchego. First, it is a sheep milk cheese, so supplies different nutrients than dairy. Second, it is a light cheese, so again it supplies different nutrients than cheeses that might be denser or deeply colored. Sheep milk tends to have more nutrients than cow's milk. It is higher in iron, zinc, phosphorous and calcium as well as, vitamins A, D, E. It also is a significant source of Omega 3 fatty acid based mostly on the sheep's diet of grass. Sheep milk also tends to be easier to digest and assimilate than other dairy.

Most tasty treat: Manchego cheese aged at least a year, drizzled with fresh honey. Second favorite tasty treat: Young Manchego with fig jam and Marcona almonds.

DAY 195 – CABERNET SAUVIGNON

Blackberry jam and butter, with earthy, oaky undertones; Cabernet Sauvignon is one of the more popular red wine grapes in the world. Cabernet grapes grow in vineyards around the world but as popular as these grapes are in the wine industry, they are relatively new to the scene. DNA testing from UC Davis suggests that they are a hybrid that appeared in the grape world around the 17th century. One thing that makes the Cabernet grape so popular is that it is a very hearty grape. It is also a versatile grape with nuances that are dependent on the age it is harvested and the time fermented.

From a culinary perspective Cabernet is considered a bolder wine; one that pairs better with fatty, heavier meats or rich pastas. To know what food a Cabernet will best pair with depends on the region where it is grown and at what age the grapes were harvested. What a fun and complex little grape. (:

From a health perspective Cabernet grapes are a rich source of antioxidants and other phytonutrients. Resveratrol is among the most popular being in the limelight of pop culture health and fitness. Research suggests that resveratrol decreases incidence and potential of cardiovascular disease as well as balancing cholesterol and reducing the formation of blood clots. Resveratrol also protects against cell damage and mental decline.

The ellargic acid found in red grapes also contributes to metabolic increase and increases the body's fat burning potential, mostly by decreasing the body's ability to produce new fat cells and delaying the growth of fat cells already present. Of course, all this good stuff about red wine is dependent on moderation and type of wine. So, if you're going to have a glass, make it just a glass or two tops, and make sure it is a consciously produced wine. Old world wines from France, Italy, and Spain tend to have more stringent fermentation guidelines, otherwise, I say go for the organic, or better yet the sustainable and/or biodynamic wines.

DAY 196 – COD

A flaky, heavy textured white fish, almost sweet: Atlantic Cod is a mild and delicious fish. Today's cod was straight from the Atlantic Ocean this very morning, steamed and served up with a very simple white wine, butter sauce. Served on a bed of asparagus and samphire, it doesn't get better than this. This particular cod was harvested out of the Dale peninsula in Wales, just at the mouth of the Milford Haven Estuary. Part of the daily catch for the Griffin Pub, it was then expertly prepared by Chef Simon, to make its ultimate end as a welcome feature on my dinner plate. Once almost a staple on both sides of the Atlantic Ocean Cod has become a relatively popular fish simply because of scarcity through overfishing.

From a culinary perspective it's mild flavor and dense, flaky meat makes it an exceptional choice for the ever-popular 'fish and chips' and also for a variety of other simple fish dishes. Deep-fried, steamed, baked, served in stew, soup, or even fish pie, Cod is an exceptionally simple ingredient.

From a health perspective, Cod is an amazing source of complete protein. It is also an excellent source of Vitamins B12, B6, and B3 as well as a super resource for minerals like selenium and iodine. It's a great option for Omega 3 intake which helps decrease a wide variety of ailments. Research indicates that eating just 10oz of Omega 3 rich fish can help decrease heart disease and triglycerides. Studies show an increase in heart rate variability and muscular tone and demonstrate that eating the appropriate amount of Omega rich fish can add to mental, physical and even emotional balance.

DAY 197 – COCKLES

Chewy with a flavor that hints of the seashore, cockles are small clams. Today's cockles were purchased by the cupful from Swansea Market in Wales. I have to admit I was skeptical at first, however, they proved to be quite tasty. Cockles are a bi-valve in the Mollusk family and can be found in cultural cuisines all around the world. The small common Cockle is more edible than other varieties in the same family.

From a culinary perspective Cockles can be steamed, stewed, baked, boiled or eaten raw. They have a delicate and distinctive flavor that is of the sea, but also has the tiniest hint of butter. I have not tried them warm yet but look forward to a nice bowl of warm cockles to warm the cockles of my heart. (:

From a nutritional perspective, you want to be sure the cockles you are eating are from an unpolluted source as bi-valves that act as a filter and can retain some of the toxins or pollutants found in the environment. If you can get some good ones then enjoy them! They are a very good source of quality protein. They are high in zinc and selenium as well as Vitamins A in the form of retinol. Zinc is a crucial part of cellular metabolism and immune function; it's also critical for protein synthesis. Vitamin A is important for tissue health and repair. It's also critical for eye health and can reduce the risk of macular degeneration.

Alive, alive-oh ....try some cockles if you can. Just avoid eating them during their breeding season, which is March to July.

DAY 198 – BARA LAWR (LAVER BREAD)

Breakfast starts with the sea on toast. Bara Lawr tastes of the surf and the very ebb and flow or the tide. It took me a moment to get used to the flavor, but then I was able to appreciate the depth of sea flavor in small amounts with my eggs and tomato and toast.

Laver Bread…isn't…bread that is….at least not in the sense that I know bread. I had heard quite a bit about Laver Bread, so was very excited to give it a try. When we finally were able to make it to Swansea Market in Wales, to purchase some local Laver Bread (Bara Lawr in the ancient Welsh language) I was skeptical to say the least. It was, first of all, most definitely not bread and second of all, it looked quite like overcooked spinach or worse. Hmm...what had I gotten myself into? This morning's breakfast was the great unveiling...

Laver Bread is basically seaweed, in fact, it is the same seaweed used to make sushi. In Japan it is called Nori and is preserved as sheets of seaweed used to wrap sushi. However, for Welsh Laver Bread the sheets of seaweed are cooked down to a dark green pulp, which is what we purchased in the market. It is then cooked again with bacon and/or oatmeal to make a sort of paste or almost porridge like dish of seaweed.
Initially, for a number of reasons I was a little nervous to try it. However, I persevered and after the obligatory 9 bites (it takes your brain 9 bites to decide whether you really like something or not and are not just giving in to whim) I decided that it was quite okay and in smaller amounts was really a good accompaniment to my meal. In fact, truth be told, I would and will have it again.

Bara Lawr has been a tradition Welsh food for centuries; in fact, it was recorded in writings in 1607 as a food that was a "survival" food for people forced from their homes by the Vikings in the early 5th/6th centuries. It was recognized as a high energy and nutrient dense food.

From a culinary perspective Bara Lawr is made by gathering seaweed then cooking it down to a paste which can then be used in soups and stews or fried up with bacon to make small seaweed pancakes.

From a health perspective Bara Lawr is an amazing source of nutrients. It's seaweed, after all. It is rich in minerals and vitamins; especially Vitamins b12, iron, calcium and iodine. Seaweed is considered a "superfood". It is a powerful anti-oxidant and anti-inflammatory, which can help reduce the risk of inflammation related ailments like rheumatoid arthritis and autoimmune disorders.

Research also suggests that consuming seaweed can help eliminate mood and mental imbalances like depression and anxiety. Seaweed also helps regulate estrogen and estradiol which manage PMS and other hormonal imbalances. It is also beneficial for gastrointestinal repair, helping with ailments like IBS or Crohn's Disease.

So, if you're able to give it a try, some Bara Lawr could be a great accompaniment to breakfast; boosting your appetite and your health.

DAY 199 – GLAMORGAN SAUSAGES

Savory, with the delicious influence of leeks and cheese, Glamorgan sausages are a traditional Welsh offering. They are made from cheese, bread, leeks and other herbs and they are absolutely delicious. Of course, what's not to love about bread and cheese??? There seems to be some disagreement and speculation about when Glamorgan Sausages, actually known as Selsig Morgannwg in Welsh, came onto the scene in Welsh tradition.

One school of thought suggests they arrived in response to rationing during the two World Wars. However they are mentioned quite gloriously in writings by travel writer George Borrow, from the Victorian era and there's mention of something similar in writings by the monk Gerald of Wales in the 12th century. So, it's quite possible they have been around as a mealtime mainstay for quite some time.

My first experience with Glamorgan sausages was an absolutely delicious one. They are crispy on the outside and deliciously creamy and oniony on the inside; a perfect match for my breakfast egg.

Glamorgan sausages can be made from any stale bread and while, historically Glamorgan cheese was used, since that is no longer available any hard, melty-type cheese can be used, though Caerphilly or cheddar seem to be the best choices. Fresh leeks, eggs and various herbs and spices all mixed up and then fried and you're in business with a delicious vegetarian option that is sure to please even the pickiest eater.

From a nutritional perspective...well, okay, there's really no way to candy coat it, they probably aren't completely the best option for nutrient density, however, with fresh, sustainable ingredients, eaten in moderation they are a great source of protein, fiber, and the nutritional benefits of leeks. Remember, leeks have many of the same beneficial qualities that onions and garlic have. They are high in phytonutrients that help protect cell structure and reduce low-level systemic inflammation.

DAY 200 – OSSAU IRATY

Buttery, creamy, with a hint of earthy nuttiness, Ossau Iraty is a traditional Basque cheese. I stumbled across a wedge of Ossau Iraty quite by accident and I am completely smitten. It is delicious! I must confess, sheep cheese is beginning to hedge to the top of my favorites list. This particular cheese originates in the Pyrenees and is the only cheese from the Pyrenees with a controlled designation of origin, the AOC.

The AOC is a French designation legally recognizing any cheese using the name Ossau Iraty must comply with the designated criteria and come from the designated area. The specific area being the Ossau Valley and Iraty forest in the Northern Basque country of France.

Ossau Iraty is a cheese produced from sheep milk. It is typically made in small batch by hand during winter and spring months and then allowed to ripen for three months. It is a cheese with quite a rich history, with first mention found in records from the 1st century.

From a culinary perspective, Ossau Iraty is a firm and mild cheese that can be used in a number of culinary endeavors. It is lovely as an opening or a finish to a meal with some lovely fruit jam or berries and it can also be easily used in main courses as an addition to soups, stews, or salads or other cheese based dishes.

From a health perspective, Sheep's cheese is again a fantastic choice for a variety of reasons. First, it supplies different nutrients than dairy; not only more protein but also an easier to assimilate protein. It also provides more nutrient density than cow's milk being higher in iron, zinc, phosphorous and calcium as well as, vitamins A, D, E. It also is a significant source of Omega 3 fatty acid based mostly on the sheep's diet of grass.

DAY 201 – ROSEHIPS

Sour, tangy, crisp and refreshing; Rosehips are the fruit of the rose plant. The garden is full of them right now although they are not ready for harvesting. It's definitely worth saying, "well done bees and butterflies!" since the appearance of Rosehips is a sign that pollination has been successful.

Rosehips range in size and color depending on the type of rose and are best harvested around first frost. They can be dried for future use or eaten raw or made into jams, jellies, syrups or even wine. I've found several recipes that recommend they can be used anywhere a cranberry can be used...cakes, breads, and pies.

From a health perspective, first and foremost, Rosehips are an amazing source of Vitamin C and Vitamin A. They also contain a variety of antioxidants; carotenoids, flavonoids, polyphenols, leucoanthocyanins and catechins, which help with things like cardiovascular disease, systemic inflammation, and insulin management. Rosehips are considered to be a good cancer preventative. Sipping a cup of rosehip tea is not only great for the skin but also boosts immune function and acts as an antiviral, antifungal and antibacterial intervention.

Research demonstrates a daily dose of Rosehip can help lower blood sugar, cholesterol, and blood pressure. Studies also demonstrate that Rosehips can minimize the pain and inflammation experienced during rheumatoid arthritis and also in chronic back pain. It has also shown promise in helping to decrease joint pain from osteoarthritis, in fact, several studies demonstrated better results at alleviating pain and inflammation than non-steroidal anti-inflammatory drugs typically used as mainstream intervention.

Rosehips can also be made into a topical skin gel that can help skin cells repair and replenish. It is great for helping to eliminate scarring, acne, and burns. It also helps replenish collagen and skin elasticity.

At the moment, I have only tried rosehips as tea and as jam but as soon as harvest time comes round I will be experimenting with a wide variety of culinary adventures.

DAY 202 – DUCK EGG

With a texture that is smooth and almost creamy, duck eggs can be a delicious switch up on your breakfast plate. So what's the difference between a duck egg and a hen's egg; besides, of course, the obvious? Well, yes, duck eggs are bigger and they have tougher shells and larger yolks. To me they do have a slightly different taste from a hen's egg but it is hard to say what the difference might actually be...perhaps just 'egg-ier'.

From a culinary perspective duck eggs are higher in fat and protein so they are a luscious addition to any baked goods, custards or creams. They can be used and eaten in any way that you eat hens' eggs. Just be aware that the higher protein can make them rubbery if they are overcooked so watch them closely.

From a health perspective duck eggs are, as mentioned, higher in protein and fat, which accounts for their "creamier" consistency. They are more nutrient dense than their chicken counterpart being higher in vitamins B, D, E, and A. They are higher in Omega 3 fatty acids and things like selenium, zinc, manganese, copper and more. It also seems that people who are allergic to hens' eggs can typically tolerate Duck Eggs: there are fewer allergen factors in the protein.

One caveat about duck eggs; make sure they are from a local or sustainable source, otherwise you're contributing to some pretty horrific conditions for them...(which is, unfortunately, true of almost all conventional animal husbandry)

DAY 203 – RADISH

Crispy, refreshing, with a little bit of heat, radishes are cooling and heating all in the same bite. Radishes are part of the Brassicaceae family along with other crucifers, like mustards, and cabbages. The common Radish, Raphanus sativus, was first domesticated in pre-Roman Europe. Even though the 'common' Radish is the name of these little gems, they are anything but common and come in a wide variety of colors, sizes and even flavors.

From a culinary perspective, the common Radish is typically eaten raw, chopped, shredded and added to a variety of culinary endeavors. You can eat the root, leaves, seeds and flowers. Sprouted Radish seeds are a delicious and zingy addition to a breakfast plate or salad. There are a few recipes out there that include cooking Radishes but I've not tried them. Another cooking adventure to think about (:

From a health perspective radishes are completely amazing; again, anything but common! The chemical compounds in Radishes help regulate bilirubin and remove any excess. This means Radishes are a happy liver food. They have been studied as beneficial additions to diet for people suffering from jaundice and chronic liver disease. Radishes are high in fiber and can also help the lining of the intestine replenish and repair. The combination of macro and micronutrients helps eliminate mucus, fight bacteria/virus/fungus, and decrease systemic inflammation. They are high in Vitamins C, B, and K as well as folate.

They are a good source of potassium, manganese, copper, and iron. Studies demonstrate they help regulate metabolism and have been a beneficial addition to diet of individuals trying to manage blood sugar levels and avoid diabetes. Externally, Radish juice can help decrease pain and inflammation as well as eliminate pain and itching from bug bites.

DAY 204 – BOYSENBERRY

Sweet, juicy, with the taste of summer sun and the sweetness of rain; Boysenberries are a delicious addition to my day. Wandering the Farmer's Market in Stroud, UK, we happened upon a stand with fresh wild berries. I decided to try the Boysenberries. I popped the first one in my mouth and it occurred to me that while I've had many Boysenberry products in the US, I don't think I've ever had a fresh boysenberry. I assumed they were just like a blackberry and while in the realm of shape and stature they are quite similar, from a flavor perspective they are indeed their own unique experience.

The Boysenberry is a hybrid cross between European raspberry and common blackberry. Records indicate that it originated in the U.S. on the Northern California coast. From the 1920's on it began to make its way around the world. They are similar to blackberries in that they are an aggregate fruit, meaning that each globe contains a seed and technically are an individual berry merging into one large berry.

From a culinary perspective Boysenberries can be added to any number of culinary endeavors both sweet and savory. Boysenberry is absolutely one of my favorite kinds of pie and also jam...but it's also a great addition to game dishes. My new favorite way to eat Boysenberries is direct from the vine.

From a health perspective Boysenberries are a great source of vitamins, minerals, and fiber. They are packed with vitamins C, E, and A. They are high in potassium, magnesium, manganese, iron and calcium. Research suggests that the antioxidants in Boysenberries promote brain health, they play a significant role in boosting memory and decreasing the oxidative stress that contributes to Alzheimer's Disease.
Studies also show that the chemical compounds found in the Boysenberry are especially beneficial in decreasing the risk of colon and esophageal cancers. They also have excellent anti-inflammatory qualities, helping to decrease inflammation related ailments. From a nutrient perspective the best way to eat berries and maintain the most nutrient density is either fresh or frozen.

DAY 205 – WILD STRAWBERRY

Sweeter and more satisfying than any candy I've ever had, the Wild Strawberry is truly one of nature's tasty gifts. I know I've already covered the domestic strawberry as a flavor, touting the difference in taste between conventional and organic, but the wild strawberry is a taste sensation all of its own.

The first thing that came to mind as I savored its sweet and juicy deliciousness, was how very horribly we've lost the plot when it comes to domesticating and hybridizing our food. We hybridize and genetically modify for things like longer shelf life, easier transportation, higher yield but it seems we've forgotten that food should also taste good. These wild strawberries evoke a nostalgia that I didn't know I had.

The other thing that Wild Strawberries remind me of is the seasonality of our food and the gift of cycles. I find a deeper appreciation and mindful connection to them, knowing they are only here for a brief amount of time and the only thing to do is to enjoy them to their fullest. We have grown accustomed to having whatever we want whenever we want it and perhaps in doing so have lost the art of anticipation.

Wild Strawberries tend to be smaller than domestic strawberries, although this can vary with the terroir and variety. They have that intensely sweet and rich and unique strawberry flavor that could never be recreated in a lab. From a culinary perspective, a little bit goes a long way. These strawberries are so flavorful they make a nice addition to both sweet and savory dishes. I've added a few of them to my breakfast plate and enjoyed them again later with some cheese and Sourdough rye flatbreads.

From a health perspective, the intensity of flavor also signifies the density of nutrients. Wild Strawberries pack a significant nutrient punch thus serving as a reminder that one of the other great losses we have inflicted on ourselves as we hybridize our food, is nutrient value. As I was searching peer-reviewed journals for scientific data on strawberries I was quite pleasantly surprised to find there was a significant amount dedicated specifically to wild cultivars.

A small handful of Wild Strawberries provides the recommended daily allowance of Vitamin C and they are also a significant source of Vitamins A and E. They are packed with phytochemicals that provide a plethora of health benefits. For example, research suggests they contain chemical compounds that contribute to cardiovascular health and Wild Strawberries especially demonstrated a particular anti-thrombotic effect allowing blood to flow more freely through the heart and body.

Studies also show that particular cultivars of the woodland strawberry contain phytonutrients that decrease the risk of esophageal cancer and reduce cell proliferation in certain types of breast cancers. Wild strawberries are a significant source of quercetin, which has the demonstrated impact of reducing the risk of colon and other gastrointestinal cancers. There's also been some interesting research showing that the phytonutrients in strawberries, in particular, wild cultivars inhibit the production of enzymes associated with systemic inflammation. They also contain nutrients that inhibit the production of tumors.

Wild Strawberries have been part of the human diet since the Stone Age according to archeological finds. They can be found in fields and wooded environments across the European and North American continents. Get out in it. Go find them!

DAY 206 – EMMER

Chewy and nutty with the slightest hint of bitter; Emmer is fun to chew when prepared as the whole grain. Emmer, or triticum dicoccum is a type of wheat. Specifically, it is one of the original wheat strains and is considered an ancient or heritage grain. Einkorn, Spelt, and Emmer make up the three strains of our most ancient domesticated wheat. Sometimes Emmer is referred to as farro, especially in Italy where all three heritage grains fall under the heading of "farro".

Emmer is one of the first domesticated crops in the history of man. Wild strains similar to the original grains can still be found in the areas of the Fertile Crescent from Iran to Israel. Fascinatingly, its inclusion in our diet seems to go back as far as 17,000 years. Grains were found in sites excavated in various locations across the area now known as Turkey. Sort of boggles the mind that a grain currently so vilified has been part of the human diet for such a long time.

So what gives? Why all the sudden the issue with wheat in the human diet? Is it just a trend? Is there really an issue with wheat? Many scholars suggest it is because very little, if any, of what we consume as wheat today is actually from these ancient grains. We have, unfortunately, hybridized the wheat to the extent that the current domestic grains no longer resemble the molecular structure of the historical grains.

From a culinary perspective, the best way to eat Emmer wheat is as the whole grain, which requires soaking overnight before cooking. The soaking helps break up the hull and neutralize the phytic acid that would normally make the nutrients in the grain less available or in some cases altogether unavailable. Studies suggest that even if you are making flour from the grain soaking it first then drying and grinding is the most effective way to maintain the viability of nutrients. Once soaked, the grains can be rinsed and then cooked much like rice, or they can be dried and ground into a flour to be used in that way. I like to eat Emmer wheat upon occasion as a breakfast cereal, especially in winter, or as a warm side to a savory dinner. They can also be added to soups and stews, just remember if you have purchased the kind that still contains hulls (which I recommend) you need to soak them first even if adding them to a soup or stew.

From a health perspective, it is, first of all, important to eat the whole grain whenever possible. Research suggests that Emmer wheat has a nutritional value very close to that of oats. It is high in protein, high in fiber (if the whole grain is used) and high in vitamins and minerals. It contains a specific carbohydrate known to boost immune function and contribute to balanced blood flow, contributing to appropriate clotting and tissue repair for wounds.

Emmer is also a significant source of calcium, copper, lithium, magnesium, phosphorus, potassium, selenium, sulfur and zinc, whew! ... much more so than new breed wheat. Believe it or not Emmer grains are high in phenols and other phytonutrients that help decrease systemic inflammation and oxidative stress. Emmer grains contain other phenols and catechins, including also gallic acid, which is the same compound found in foods like blueberries and green tea, notable in the way it helps protect the liver and provides protection against carcinogenic influence of free radicals.

So, in the midst of all this good stuff, why the outcry about the evils of wheat? First of all, I want to be very clear to acknowledge that Celiac Disease is no joke and if someone is genuinely suffering from CD then they will want to avoid any kind of gluten containing foods at all costs. That being said, many people are jumping on the gluten free bandwagon and shunning wheat because of digestive distress that may not really be due to gluten at all. Researchers are suggesting there may, in fact, be several factors that are putting people off the wheat and distress could be related to one or all depending on your body type and the type of wheat.

First, there are the new strains with slightly increased molecular structure. It has been suggested these new strains are significantly altered with a decrease in nutrients and an increase in the stuff that creates disturbance. To a small degree this is true, however don't be fooled into thinking this is the entire issue. Wheat over the past 100 years has indeed been hybridized for higher yield and weather resistance and it does also contain a slightly higher prolamine count per grain head.

What are prolamines? Those are the things that people with Celiac Disease are really allergic to. Prolamines contain a combination of gluten proteins, gliadin, cysteine and other interesting stuff. It may be that some bellies are more sensitive to the higher prolamine content and therefore have less tolerance for newer strains of wheat. It has also been suggested by research that the higher gliadin actually acts as an irritant among other things (including an  appetite stimulant!) and that it contributes potentially more than the gluten to gastrointestinal distress.

One other often ignored factor but supported by several studies is that it is not necessarily the wheat that is the issue, whether new or ancient strain, rather it is the processing. Grains contain phytic acid; they always have. It is their way of protecting themselves from the predators of the world (us included). Modern day processors are not going through the trouble to soak grains before grinding, they simply get the grain, process it and then turn it into a manufactured product of some type. Some studies indicate that even though the final product has been smashed and processed beyond recognition it still contains the phytic acid.

Remember that cooking emmer grains without soaking them didn't allow them to actually cook no matter how long they were left on the stove. The phytic acid acts as an irritant and decreases the potential to assimilate any potential nutrients.

A third theory is that what people are really suffering from is an intolerance to digesting and processing pure starch, which is what wheat flour becomes once it has been stripped, bleached, and processed into white flour. Once it has been stripped certain nutrients that aren't necessarily easy to assimilate are added back in to meet US Department of Agriculture requirements.

Yet another theory, also supported by various studies, is that it's the pesticides and herbicides used while growing and transporting the grain that people are really reacting to. Pesticides like Melathion, which is a neurotoxin, hormone disruptor, and carcinogen. Melathion has been found in approximately 50% of the conventional, domestic wheat flour making its way to the consumer. Remember that as a neurotoxin this means disruption of the gastrointestinal tract since the gut contains a high amount of neural tissue.

All of these reasons and more are why I caution people against simply jumping on the gluten-free bandwagon. To do so, without further investigation, simply turns a blind eye to the way our food is being manipulated, processed, and degraded. Rather it would be much more in the interest of the public good and our overall health to take a stand against these detrimental processes and recover our essential right to unadulterated and healthful food.... only sayin'.

DAY 207 – CHAMOMILE

The taste of nature; Chamomile is earthy, slightly bitter, with hints of sweet and a mouthfeel that is slightly astringent. It is growing wild everywhere in the fields right now and each afternoon as I wander through the landscape I am assailed with the scent of roman Chamomile on the wind. The name Chamomile derives from Greek and French and it translates into "earth or ground apple". For some reason I really love that and have even a greater affinity for this lovely little herb. Chamomile appears quite delicate with feathery and fernlike leaves and dainty white, daisy like flowers that smile up at the sun; however apparently it is quite hearty and seems to be growing everywhere among the crops and wild plants.

Chamomile is typically considered a medicinal herb commonly known as a remedy for stress and anxiety; however, it can also be a really interesting addition in the culinary realms. It is part of the flowering plant family that also includes the daisy, the Jerusalem Artichoke, and even the dandelion. The flowers, leaves, and roots can be used for various remedies and recipes.

But let's not forget it has a horticultural use too with carpets of it planted to make a Chamomile lawn. What a wonderful experience to walk across one kicking up that wonderful scent as you scuff the plant with your feet.

From a culinary perspective I have, personally, mostly used Chamomile as a tonic or medicinal remedy, yet recently have come across some really interesting culinary endeavors using Chamomile. For example, lemon and chamomile infused crème brulee. Or how about sea scallops with a Chamomile infused butter sauce?

From a health perspective Chamomile has a long, long history as a medicinal intervention. Its chemical properties are anti-inflammatory, antioxidant, astringent and antibacterial. Traditionally, it has been used as a treatment for wounds, ulcers, eczema, gout, skin irritations, bruises, burns, canker sores, neuralgia, sciatica, rheumatic pain, and hemorrhoids. Externally, chamomile has been used to treat things like diaper rash, chicken pox, ear and eye infections, and other issues of the eyes including blocked tear ducts, conjunctivitis, nasal inflammation and even as a remedy for poison ivy.

Chamomile is also widely used to treat inflammation mucous membranes and also for bacterial infections. Chamomile is also used as a mild sedative to calm nerves and reduce anxiety, to treat hysteria, insomnia and other sleep problems. It's also a digestive relaxant and has been used to treat a variety of gastrointestinal issues including indigestion, diarrhea, and nausea. So here's where I love when traditional medicine and science meet up in the middle... every traditional intervention listed above is also being demonstrated in the lab. Got to love that! So it may be worth sitting down to a cup of chamomile tea sometime soon.

DAY 208 – ANTICIPATION

My mouth begins to water as the aroma of fresh baked pies wafts through the air and swirls around my head. Inhaling deeply stimulates an automatic 'mmmmm' upon exhale. More saliva begins to build up in my mouth and my stomach begins to growl in anticipation of enjoying a bite of something delicious. Anticipation is a necessary part of digestion.

When we anticipate something it stimulates the para-sympathetic nervous system and begins to pave the way for health digestion and assimilation of nutrients. This is called the Cephalic Stage of digestion. It is a very important stage because there are particular enzymes, called ptyalin, that are released only in the mouth during this anticipatory stage.

These enzymes signal the body to begin preparing for what's to come. At the same time the gastric juices in the stomach begin pumping and preparing for the oncoming food. When you actually begin chewing the anticipated food the ptyalin mixes with the food and identifies the combination of nutrients, it then signals the body to begin releasing the appropriate enzymes for breaking down the protein, fat, carbohydrate combinations and any micronutrients. Without this critical stage, the digestive process is incomplete. This can result in digestive upset, and believe it or not malnourishment, as the nutrients in the food are unable to be properly digested and assimilated.

Think about the last time you allowed yourself to anticipate a meal? If you can't remember the last time you were able too, then I highly recommend beginning now. Those few moments of anticipation are critical to your overall health and wellbeing, not to mention your satisfaction and pleasure in life. I call it stimulating the "mmmm" factor.

DAY 209 – MUSTARD (DIJON)

Spicy, tangy, a hint of vinegar, and even sweet; Dijon Mustard is a tasty condiment. I have to admit I've grown addicted to having Dijon Mustard with my peas. Mustard is a condiment made from ground up mustard seed paste. Originally Mustard was made from ground up Mustard seed paste mixed with the unfermented but aged grape juice.

This juice is called "must", hence the name "Mustard". Being the research geek that I am, I needed to further investigate the origin of Mustard once I decided to use it as a flavor and have found a quite varied and interesting history. It appears Mustard as a condiment, actually first appeared as a grilling sauce for wild boar, was recorded in a Roman cookbook titled Apicius, and included an interesting array of herbs and spices. This seems to be how the ingredients for Dijon Mustard originated. This recipe was first recorded sometime around the 1st century in Rome then Mustard made its way to Gaul, and stayed on through history until the creation of France where, around the 1300's, Dijon Mustard became the popular "thing".

From a culinary perspective, Mustard is typically used as a condiment; however, it is also an ingredient in dressings, sauces, and even soup. I clearly like Mustard, especially Dijon, on peas.

From a health perspective, Mustard actually has interesting health properties. Mustard seed itself has good stuff going on but apparently, when vinegar is added to Mustard seed paste it boosts particular healthy qualities. Research demonstrates the Mustard seed is beneficial for gastrointestinal health. The glucosinolatic compounds inhibit the growth and spread of cancer cells. Mustard seeds also have anti-inflammatory properties and help reduce the risk of colon cancer and other gastrointestinal issues. Mustard is anti-oxidant, anti-bacterial, and anti-viral. It helps with cardiovascular issues and can balance metabolism and enhance glucose management.

I say what's not to love about mustard and peas.... okay, maybe just mustard, but peas are tasty too!

DAY 210 – MUNG BEAN SPROUT

Crisp and fresh with a slightly sweet, slightly nutty and very moist snappiness; the Mung Bean Sprout is an interesting addition to my morning eggs. Mung Bean Sprouts are...drum roll please... sprouts from Mung Beans, which are a type of legume. Mung Beans seem to have originated in India however they have made their way into hot and dry regions around the globe. The sprouts are made by soaking the dry beans in water for about four hours then letting them sit in a dark space for about four hours.

Sprouting beans at home is quite simple, but one must take great care not to end up with a breeding ground for bacteria. That being said, sprouts are a delicious addition to meals both sweet and savory. A common ingredient in Asian cuisine, most of the 'bean' sprouts found in stir-fries, spring rolls, and other delicious dishes are from the tasty Mung Bean. Sometimes though they are from soy beans so it's good to ask if you are concerned and avoiding soy. Personally, I like the fresh, young sprouts before they actually grow into the longer version that you find in most dishes. The young sprouts will still have a decent part of the bean attached making them quite fun to chew and imparting greater nutrient density.

From a health perspective, sprouts are typically a really great source of nutrients.

Sprouting is similar to cooking in that it decreases the lectin content in legumes, making the nutrients more available for assimilation. Mung Bean Sprouts are a great source of vitamin K, C, E and B. They have a significant amount of iron and potassium. The phytonutrients in sprouts make them anti-inflammatory, anti-bacterial, and anti-fungal.

Interestingly, researchers say the highest nutrient density is on day one of sprouting, decreasing with each day and amount of growth thereafter. The consumption of Mung Bean Sprouts can help balance blood sugar and increase metabolism of nutrients. Studies also show that the young sprouts have antimicrobial qualities that help fight Helicobacter pylori, which is a bacteria that contributes to ulcers and other gastrointestinal issues.

If you haven't tried sprouts, I highly recommend it, just be mindful to wash them well to avoid any bacterial mishaps.

DAY 211 – KEEVED CIDER

Bubbly and yeasty, Keeved Cider makes my nose twitch a little but it tastes interesting and refreshing. This particular cider comes from Somerset. Pilton Cider in the UK and has won the Great Taste of the West Awards for the past couple of years. I can see why, this cider is tasty and mellow. It's the first time I've tried a Keeved Cider, which is, of course, the reason I had to try it.

Keeving is an old traditional way of making hard apple cider. Ripe cider apples are collected, then pressed as is the usual practice. However the pulp is left to stand for about 24 hours so the pectin can be released from the oxidizing pulp. The next day the pulp is pressed and the result is thick, brown, rich juice. The juice is then allowed to continue to sit as wild yeast builds up and begins a natural, slow, sulfite free process of fermentation. This particular cider was fermented for about six months very slowly and then bottled. It can continue to age in the bottle and mature into a delicious and mellow cider.

From a culinary perspective, cider can be a great addition to various meals both sweet and savory. It not only can be a nice accompanying drink, especially on hot, sunny days, but it is great to cook with. I've used it in stews and to braise various meat dishes. I've also used it as a foundation for dressings and dips. Baked and cider basted pears with goat cheese and almonds are a stellar dessert.

From a health perspective, it's important to note that Keeved Cider is a hard cider, which means it contains an amount of alcohol, about 5.5% so there is that to keep in mind as you are thinking about health and wellness. That being said, believe it or not cider, especially Keeved Cider, packs some pretty decent nutrients. In fact, research at the Brewing Research International Institute demonstrates that a half pint of naturally fermented cider provides similar antioxidant content to that of a glass of red wine. Studies have shown that the phytonutrients in fermented cider can provide similar nutrients to eating a fresh apple.

Apparently with the process of keeving as the pulp oxidizes and the pectin gets released into the juice it is able to retain and develop new nutrients as it continues to ferment. Studies show that Keeved Cider contains a significant amount of polyphenols, which play a significant role in preventing cancer and degenerative diseases from systemic inflammation and oxidation.

The only downside of Cider? It can have a pretty high sugar content, so moderation is always best.

DAY 212 – MUTTON

Umami, with an almost gamey flavor, complex and rich; Mutton has a softer flavor than I anticipated. I've read about Mutton as a mainstay in early traditional diets. In various stories and readings, Mutton was the meat for the common man. There is some disagreement on what actually constituted "Mutton" from a traditional viewpoint.

Some historical writings suggest Mutton was a title reserved for castrated male sheep that had reached 5 years or older. There are other records that suggest that "Mutton" represented ewes, female sheep, past their breeding prime. Today's Mutton, however, is from sheep that has typically reached about two years of age and been raised in a natural lifestyle on a natural diet.

I was intrigued but also a little squeamish to try Mutton for the first time. I am an omnivore, so my diet does include meat, but I'm also very committed to traditional and sustainable forms of animal husbandry. This makes eating meat a little bit trickier, especially in the U.S. The Mutton I prepared for today's flavor came from locally grown sheep in Wiltshire, U.K. The area is scattered with sheep ranging over the pastureland, grazing happily on grasses, nettles and other wild growing plants.

I went to the local butcher and inquired about Mutton and he let me know that within a day or two he would have some in his shop. When I checked back, sure enough, Mutton. Now, let's be clear, the laws around the raising, butchering, transporting, and sale of meat tend to be kind of ridiculous in both European countries and the U.S. They are definitely not laws that favor the small, local, producers and conscious animal husbandry, which I feel committed to supporting.

From a culinary perspective, Mutton is best served up seasonally from the months October to March. It is a type of meat that lends itself well to being slow cooked and/or added to soups and stews. This particular meal was slow cooked with Garlic, Olive Oil and a few other herbs. It was tender and flavorful.

From a health perspective, Mutton is a good source of quality protein. It is also a great source of zinc and iron and B vitamins. Pasture raised sheep and lamb is an amazing source of Conjugated Linoleic Acid (CLA), which research demonstrates is a great source of improved immune function and decreased systemic inflammation. Mutton is a great option for quality protein and nutrient density. The only caveat, be sure you know where it comes from...especially in the U.S. Local, sustainable, humane, are the only way to go. Also, typically in Indian and Asian cuisine Mutton refers to goat, so you may want to ask questions if you haven't prepared the Mutton yourself.

CHAPTER 8 AUGUST

DAY 213 – SHIITAKE

Springy and chewy, with an earthy and very mildly pungent flavor; Shiitake mushrooms are versatile and interesting addition to your culinary endeavors. Shiitake mushrooms are also known as black forest mushrooms or oakwood mushrooms and though they still grow wild, they are also one of the most widely cultivated mushrooms in the world.

So, widely cultivated, in fact, that many of them no longer come from actual trees but are instead cultivated in sawdust, often with high amounts of pesticides and fungicides. This is one reason I tend to avoid conventionally cultivated fungi. However, if you can manage to get your hands on some naturally cultivated or wild, forest grown, then you are in for a real treat.

From a culinary perspective Shiitakes are desirable for a variety of reasons. First, they tend to be sturdier than their other fungi relatives and they can impart a variety of nuances to flavor depending on how they are preserved and prepared. Fresh Shiitakes have a lighter, earthy, almost sweet/nutty flavor. In contrast, dehydrated or dried and reconstituted Shiitakes can be almost smokey with a stronger muskier flavor. They are great additions to a wide variety of savory dishes; soups, stews, and stir-fries. They can be fried, steamed, baked, sautéed; my favorite way to eat them is thinly sliced and then sautéed in Olive Oil and Garlic.

From a health perspective, mushrooms have long had a history of medicinal properties. Shiitake mushrooms are no different. Like their counterparts they are high in a wide variety of nutrients, minerals and vitamins. Most notably, they are a great source of copper and also of vitamin D.

Interestingly, mushrooms produce more vitamin D if they are exposed to the sun for a few hours with their gills facing upward. Research demonstrates that eating one gram of sun treated Shiitake mushrooms provides the recommended daily dose of vitamin D. Studies also suggest the Shiitake mushroom contains other chemical components that inhibit tumor growth, cancer cell propagation, and systemic inflammation. They are restorative to the liver, with research showing beneficial results for people suffering from liver related ailments like hepatitis and fatty liver disease. Mushrooms, including Shiitake, are widely used in Traditional

Chinese and Indian medicine for a wide variety of ailments, from cardiovascular issues to suppressed immune function. It seems that conventional research is also supporting many of the amazing properties found in the Shiitake mushroom.

DAY 214 – MEAD

Sweet, earthy, and slightly astringent, with an emollient mouthfeel; the flavor of honey Mead depends on its fermentation process. The Mead I'm trying for today's flavor was small batch traditionally fermented with hops, which accounts for the earthier more astringent quality.

Honey mead is one of the oldest beverages in human culture; made by fermenting honey with water and sometimes other herbs and spices. Earliest archeological evidence of human consumption of a fermented honey beverage is as early as 7,000 BC. Mead was considered food of the gods because bees were considered their messengers; the pollen they gathered was watered by the dew from the breath of the gods and filled with prophetic messages. It was considered a sacred drink with magical properties and used for rituals. It was also considered a drink for healing depending again on how it was fermented and which herbs and spices were fermented with it.

From a culinary perspective, Mead can be used in a variety of ways with both sweet and savory meals. Baking, sautéing, veggie dressings, marinades... all will add an interesting back-note to your culinary endeavor.

From a health perspective, Mead has historically been a source for health and healing. They were fermented with specific herbs and used to address any number of ailments. For example, Mead made with lemon balm was thought to aid digestion and eliminate depression. Mead made with borage was used to revive hypochondriacs and the chronic illness. Traditionally, the name for these medicinal meads is Metheglin, which derives from the Welsh word "meddygol" meaning curative or medicine.

Whether or not Mead is "healthy" depends entirely on how it is fermented and processed. Conventional Meads are typically highly processed and ultra-filtered pretty much removing the potential for any "medicinal" quality. Mead is similar to cider in that respect. On the other hand traditionally fermented Meads, depending on the quality of the honey and herbs used, can still carry the same medicinal value they have for thousands of years. One downside of traditional fermentation is it can be challenging to predict the outcome. However, if the outcome is good, you may well have an aphrodisiac, immune boosting, cardiovascular supporting, mood balancing and soothing drink on your hands.

DAY 215 – PURSLANE

Purslane has a zesty, not quite bitter, but also not quite sweet and smooth, flavor to it. In a way, it reminds me of the bitter or peppery greens like dandelion, watercress, or arugula. It has an appearance similar to lamb's lettuce only with fatter leaves and stem. It is considered a succulent, which is why its leaves and stem are fat and juicy; they store water.

There are about 40 different varieties of Purslane, both winter and summer. Apparently, all can be eaten and each has its own flavor quality and texture. In the U.S., Purslane is typically considered a weed and an inordinate amount of energy and resource is expended trying to eradicate it from fields and gardens. It is, however, catching on in the culinary world and beginning to make its way into the market place and onto the dinner plate. In other parts of the world Purslane enjoys a place in a variety of cuisines and has done for centuries. It is also known by other names such as Qulfa, little hogweed, moss rose, and verdolaga. All parts of the plant are edible, seeds, leaves, and root.

From a culinary perspective Purslane can be eaten raw or cooked. It can be tossed into salads as a zingy and refreshing addition or it can be steamed or sautéed much like spinach. Some interesting combinations and uses from various other cultures are, combining it with tomato, feta cheese, Garlic, onion, and Olive Oil; or use it to stuff fish or as an ingredient in Tomatillo sauce. It also can be added to soups and stews or baked into casseroles.

From a health perspective Purslane is an amazing source of a wide variety of nutrients. Given that it has typically been considered a weed in the Western diet, there has been quite a significant amount of research on its healthful properties. It is packed with antioxidants and is a valuable resource for reducing systemic inflammation. Just one serving of Purslane supplies roughly 60% of recommended daily intake of Omega 3 fatty acids. It is also an excellent source of brain happy chemical compounds like glutathione and melatonin; both of which help reduce the risk of Alzheimer's and other brain related degenerative diseases.

They also help balance mood and cognitive function. The beta-carotene levels in Purslane make it a great resource for skin, tissue, and bone health.

Studies have shown that the chemical compounds in Purslane provide a wonderful nutritional support to the body for recovery from stress and stress related ailments. All this awesomeness means it could be worth a little foraging expedition to see if Purslane is in the natural environment around you or at the very least on the shelves in your neighborhood market.

DAY 216 – SALMON (RECIPE)

Flaky, dense, almost meaty, a tiny hint of fishiness; Salmon is a mild and flavorful fish. It is probably one of the most popular fish from a culinary perspective, having been pushed into the limelight for all of its healthful qualities. Due to its popularity, the demand for wild Salmon has resulted in many varieties being almost fished out. Sadly, this has led to the farming of Salmon, which has created a version of the fish that isn't anywhere near as healthful and has also been removed from its natural and very amazing lifestyle.

The natural lifestyle of the Salmon is actually pretty interesting. Most of them, depending on the variety, are able to live in both fresh and salt water. They are born in freshwater and over the next couple of years begin to chemically change, a process called smolting, so they can make their way from their freshwater habitat into the ocean. The changes they undergo are pretty fascinating; the fat redistributes in their body, their coloring changes to something that will keep them safer in the ocean, their behavior changes, as does their metabolism.

Once they make the journey to the ocean, they spend a year or more in that habitat and then at some point, when the timing is right, they make their way back to their original spawning stream or at least as close as they can get to it. Researchers have shown that most Salmon attempting to get back to freshwater to spawn, do indeed try to get back to their point of origin. It's pretty amazing really to think of their natural design.

From a culinary perspective, wild Salmon is a great choice for a variety of dishes because of its great texture and mild flavor. Like all fish, if Salmon is fresh, it tastes of the environment it came from rather than the sharp fishy flavor and smell that can accompany fish left too long before cooking. You can bake it, steam it, grill it, fry it... even make it into sausages (which I had for dinner last night). Salmon also preserves well. You can smoke it, salt cure it, and even pickle it.

From a health perspective Salmon is a quandary and a controversy. Wild

Salmon is amazingly good for you. Typically, when people think of the health benefits of Salmon the first one they list is the presence of Omega 3 fatty acids, which is indeed one of its healthful qualities. It is also, however, a great source of vitamin B12, Vitamin D, selenium, and higher quality protein (if it's wild). Research also demonstrates that wild Salmon contains specific types of protein molecules that can help repair cartilage, decreases systemic inflammation, and regulate insulin production. It is the combination of these protein molecules with the fatty acids that contribute to the healthful benefits of wild Salmon.

Notice that I keep emphasizing the word "wild"? That's because, no matter how you cut it, farmed Salmon doesn't hold a candle to the healthful qualities of their wild relatives. In fact, typically, farmed Salmon contain a high amount of Persistent Organic Pollutants (POPS) and other petrochemicals from their contained environment. They tend to be less muscular, lower in nutrient density, and higher in stress chemicals. Because of the type of food they are given, they tend to have a decreased amount of Omega 3's and an increased amount of Omega 6 fatty acid. I mean think about it, a relatively sedentary lifestyle in a confined net cage, and a diet of sub quality food doesn't make for a healthy body in any species. (this is also true of supplements made from farmed Salmon)

To feed farmed Salmon the type of diet they need to thrive well requires two to three times the amount of wild foraged fish than they themselves produce (Salmon are carnivores and eat other fish and insects). There has been a push to hybridize farmed Salmon so they will thrive on plant products like corn and soy; again, this produces a drastic change in the quality of the fish. To be fair, there are also initiatives that are trying to "ranch" Salmon in a more healthful or natural environment which seem to be making decent inroads on repopulating the overfished habitats and also meeting the public demand for Salmon. And then there's the question of the huge amounts of antibiotics and pesticides used to keep them lice free and 'healthy.' Not good for the environment at all.

The next time you're choosing Salmon, you may want to ask first where it came from and how it got to your table. If you are lucky enough to find wild Salmon on your plate, take a moment and think about the tenacity of this great fish and the gift of health it provides.

If you're feeling adventurous here's a recipe:

FENNEL & HONEY-CURED GRAVLAX

1/2 cup dill seeds
2 tablespoons peppercorns
2 tablespoons juniper berries
1 cup honey
1/2 cup molasses (optional)
1 cup sea salt
1 cup filtered (or boiled and cooled) water
4 pounds Salmon fillet, no thicker than 1-1/2 inches, skin on, pin-bones removed
1 fennel bulb, with stalks and leaves, thinly sliced

Toast the dill, peppercorns, and juniper berries over medium-high heat in a dry pan.
Allow the spices to cool and then crack with mortal and pestle or process briefly in a mill.
Mix spices with honey, molasses (if using), salt, and water, stirring until salt is dissolved. Pour 1 cup of cure into bottom of curing vessel.

Lay the Salmon fillets skin-side down on the cure and pour remaining cure over the Salmon. Cover the Salmon with sliced fennel, then fennel leaves. Cover the fish tightly with a piece of wax paper.

Place a dish or water-filled zip-top bag on top of the Salmon. Cure at 40-50F for 24 hours (fridge is fine for this, but if the weather's cool enough, I put it in a protected area outside), then turn the fish skin-side-up, replace the weight, and cure for another 24 hours. Fish is fully cured when it is uniformly firm to the touch. If there are still some mushy spots, return the fish to the brine and cure for another 12 hours or so and check it again.

Remove from the brine, rinse thoroughly and wipe off the seeds. Pat dry, wrap tightly in wax paper or a piece of plastic, then store in the fridge. Should keep for a week.

DAY 217 – OLIVE OIL

Hints of nut, earth, slight bitterness, and even salt with a mouthfeel that is smooth and dense; today's flavor, Olive Oil, is yet one more of those flavors that is infinitely challenging to describe, not least because the flavor is dependent upon its terroir and how it was processed.

The particular oil I have tasted today is a cold pressed, extra virgin, made from Coratina Olives and imported from Southern Italy. Olive Oil is basically the fat extracted from olives. What accounts for the variations in taste, mouthfeel, and even healthfulness is how/where the olives were grown, how it was extracted and to what degree it has been processed and filtered.

According to archeologists extracting the fat from olives and using it as oil has been part of the human dietary repertoire for over 8,000 years. If you use Olive Oil at all, I'm sure you've realized that it comes in different grades; Extra Virgin, Virgin, and refined (sometimes there are variations of these). Oil grade depends on processing. Initially, they all start out the same way; olives are crushed into a paste then churned up until the fat globules separate from liquid and can be extracted by pressing.

Extra Virgin and Virgin oil means that the oil was extracted without use of heat or chemicals and retain the flavor of the olive as well as the beneficial nutrients. Refined oils have been processed differently and tend to be devoid of any nutritional benefit as well as any identifying flavor. In short, unrefined Olive Oil is the best choice: whether Virgin or Extra Virgin is up to you.

From a culinary perspective Olive Oil is a really great option for a wide variety of dishes both sweet and savory. It is delicious as dipping oil; which can actually become its own taste and flavor extravaganza if you choose a variety of terroirs and "bouquets". It is great as a dressing or even to use for a quick sauté or braising. It can also be used in baking and roasting foods; however, you want to avoid using it in high heat situations. It has a lower smoke point and will burn much more quickly...besides in high heat situations you tend to lose all of the lovely flavor nuances.

From a health perspective the media has done a fantastic job over the past few decades proclaiming the benefits of Olive Oil. So much so that demand has increased between 8 - 10% each year over the past decade. Spain produces over 50% of the world's Olive Oil with Italy coming in a close second. The focus on Mediterranean diet as a more healthy way of eating has increased the interest in bringing Olive Oil to the table.

The polyphenols in Olive Oil are pretty rocking as far as nutritional benefits. Research suggests that they can help decrease systemic inflammation and oxidative stress both of which contribute to cardiovascular disease as well as a wide variety of degenerative diseases. They also provide protection for your liver, pancreas and colon all while decreasing your risk of a variety of cancers. Studies also suggest that the nutritive properties of Olive Oil contribute to brain health and balanced mood.

DAY 218 – PICKLED SEEDS

Plump, slippery, caviar like, too much fun to eat quickly...pickled seeds were an unexpected delight accompanying my meal. Just a teaspoon of them tucked unassumingly to the side of my plate, but truth be told, they stole the show. I'm not a foodie newbie and I've had pickled mustard seeds before but this particular combination was new to me and too much fun. I will be whipping up a batch myself in the not too distant future.

Assuming that quality ingredients were used to make them, pickled seeds are not only fun to eat but will also pack all the nutrient power that, whatever seeds you choose, will contain.

In this case, pickled mustard, coriander, and fennel seeds provide the taste entertainment and remember that coriander is on the A-List of nutrient rich foods with research demonstrating it helps with digestive issues, blood sugar issues, and cholesterol issues. It is anti-inflammatory and also helps with skin conditions like psoriasis and eczema.

Mustard seeds have a beneficial impact on the gastrointestinal tract and colon. They contain glucosinolatic compounds, which inhibit the growth and spread of cancer cells. Mustard seeds also have anti-inflammatory properties and are a digestive, while fennel seeds are great for relieving cramping and menstrual pain; they outperformed Non Steroidal Anti-Inflammatory Drugs in clinical trials.

If you're up for a culinary adventure you may want to give this a try:

PICKLED SEEDS
(Adapted from Bon Appetit magazine)
1 bay leaf
1 cup white wine or apple cider vinegar
2 tablespoons sea salt
2 tablespoons sugar
¼ cup mustard, coriander, nigella, cumin, fennel, or caraway seeds

Bring bay leaf, vinegar, salt, sugar, and 1 cup water to a simmer in a small saucepan, stirring to dissolve salt and sugar.

Meanwhile, toast seeds in a dry medium skillet over medium heat until fragrant, 1–2 minutes. Add seeds to pickling liquid and bring to a boil. Reduce heat and simmer until tender (they should yield easily between your front teeth), 30–45 minutes.

Let seeds cool in liquid; transfer to an airtight container, cover, and chill. Do Ahead: Store pickled seeds in their liquid in the refrigerator up to 3 months.

DAY 219 – CHILI SAUCE

Spicy, zesty, tangy...invigorating to my palate; Chili seasoning doesn't have to be hot to be tasty. Chili seasoning, like garam masala, is actually a blend of spices, varying in ingredients from region to region and individual to individual. That being said, there are some main ingredients typically found in southwestern blends of Chili, which is the kind I've doused liberally all over my morning eggs. First ingredient? Chili peppers. Mix that with some apple cider vinegar, Garlic, a touch of onion, cumin, cloves, coriander, oregano, a spot of honey, and we're in for an amazing flavor adventure.

I'd love to be able to write more about the origination of Chili as a sauce and meal but there is such a wide variety of information and definitely plenty of confusing facts that I think the safest bet is to stick with the flavor details of the sauce on my plate.

Red Chili Peppers are the main ingredient, which seem to have originated in the Americas. There is archeological data supporting their culinary use as early as 7500 B.C. They have since made their way around the globe and can be found in cuisine and medicinal interventions in a wide variety of cultures. Adding vinegar to the blend of Chili and spices helps preserve and also synergize the flavors. It also helps deliver the heat. How hot a pepper is depends on its variety and environment, apparently the hotter and drier the climate, the hotter the pepper. The combining of spices and herbs with the Chili helps moderate and enhance the flavorful qualities of the pepper, allowing it to be an actual flavor experience rather than simply flaming out your taste buds.

From a culinary perspective, Chili Sauce is a great as a condiment or a main flavor ingredient in your meal. I like to use it most as a condiment. Another way I love to use it is to make some healthy and flavorful snack options; soaking chickpeas in Chili sauce and then baking them until they are crisp makes for a tasty snack food.

From a health perspective, Chili Sauce, especially if home made with quality ingredients, imparts a number of healthful qualities. Capsicum is the main chemical compound in Chili peppers. It's what makes them hot. Capsicum can be used internally and externally in a variety of ways to promote health. Research demonstrates that it is anti-inflammatory and anti-oxidant; helping to relieve oxidative stress and systemic inflammation. It also works topically as a pain reliever. Just make sure you avoid any mucus gland or sensitive areas!!

Studies show capsicum can help relieve the pain of ulcers (seems counterintuitive in a way) and help the tissue begin to repair. It helps decrease the risk of a variety of cancers, most notably gastrointestinal mutations. It is a vasodilator, which means it enhances blood flow. Several studies have demonstrated that through improved vasodilation delivery of antioxidants is augmented resulting in a beneficial impact on tissue protein repair. Two studies in particular showed beneficial impact on DNA repair.

It could be worth dashing a few drops on a meal, here and there or maybe even try your hand at making your own.

DAY 220 - PARMIGIANO-REGGIANO

Salty, nutty, grainy and distinctly, indescribably umami; Parmigiano-Reggiano cheese is by far one of my favorites. Sometimes just called parmesan, the real deal stuff goes by its full name Parmigiano-Reggiano, signifying the area in which it is produced. It is one of the items protected under the designation of origin, meaning to have that name it must come from the appropriate region and have followed the traditional standards of production.

Parmesan is a blend of whole unpasteurized milk and milk that has been skimmed naturally. The two milks undergo a multi-step process that ultimately results in being transformed into a cheese wheel, where they then make their way to the aging shelf. They then are allowed to age for at least 12 months, after which they undergo inspection for perfection.

From a culinary perspective, Parmigiano can be an interesting addition to both sweet and savory dishes believe it or not. It is most often grated or shredded and sprinkled on pasta or in soups and stews. It can also be baked or broiled for a more intense flavor. I have fond memories of visiting friends in Italy where a wheel of Parmigiano was always sitting on the sideboard in the kitchen and we could just cut small slices off to nibble. One thing that makes Parmigiano so desirable is the intensity of 'umami' flavor. A little bit goes a long way and it stimulates the palate and brain. The umami flavor is also what lends it to pair well with sweeter dishes like fruits and jams.

From a health perspective, it's a cheese so it has all the qualities of cheese. It provides a good source of complete protein and minerals and vitamins, like calcium and vitamin B12. It satisfies the palate as well as stimulates digestion and nutrient uptake. Remember that you have umami taste receptors in your gut that appear to help regulate the digestive process as well as signal satiation, so it enhances that process. Research suggests that consuming a good quality cheese in moderation can also help regulate blood sugar and promote insulin balance.

Studies have also been conducted with Parmigiano-Reggiano cheese specifically and found that it can contribute to weight management. It's also lower in fat and lower in lactose, while being a nice source of lactobacilli, which can help balance your gut and make your belly happy. So, you can see there's lots of good stuff going on with Parmigiano-Reggiano cheese.

One important caveat: most of the cheese carrying name produced outside of Europe is not genuine Parmigiano and does not necessarily follow the traditional production. They can also contain additives that are not allowed in Europe. Why? Because in the U.S. we do not recognize designation of origin requirements or labels. If you want to be sure your cheese is high quality, traditionally processed, you will have to read your labels very carefully.

DAY 221 – CILANTRO (RECIPE)

Zesty, refreshing with a hint of pine or earthy citrus; fresh chopped Cilantro stimulates my palate with its 'exotic' and earthy back-notes. In my experience that people either love Cilantro or they hate it. There doesn't seem to be any in-between. What I describe as refreshing and zesty someone else describes as soapy and unappetizing. Cilantro is a Mediterranean herb that has managed to make its way all around the globe. It is actually the name for the leaves of a coriander plant and features frequently in Mediterranean, Mexican and Asian cooking. It's also sometimes called Chinese Parsley. It can be used in much the same way as parsley or other fresh herbs; just be aware that not all of your diners will be in agreement as to whether it adds to the meal or ruins it.

From a health perspective, Cilantro seems to have quite the reputation as a super-food. It is rich in vitamins, minerals, and phytonutrients. It is one of the best sources of vitamins K and A. It also packs in plenty of potassium, calcium, manganese, and iron. It is ridiculously prolific in the phytonutrient department; nutrients like quercitin, kaempferol, pinene and limonene just to name a few.

All of these phytonutrients are big in the anti-oxidant and systemic inflammation arena. The help reduce oxidative stress and inflammation, decreasing your risk for degenerative disease and ailments. They also help balance blood sugar and manage insulin production. They are antimicrobial, antibacterial, and antiviral.

Research suggests that eating the fresh leaves might help fight against food borne illnesses like Salmonella. The chemical compounds in Cilantro also possess antibiotic properties, so not only do they help boost immune function but also directly aid in fighting off any health sabotaging bugs. The most recently circulating news about Cilantro is its ability to eliminate heavy metal toxicity in the body. According to several studies Cilantro does indeed remove heavy metal deposits in the body as well as imparting an antibiotic effect to further eliminate any harmful bacteria that may be lingering as a result of toxicity.

So, why do some people think Cilantro tastes like soap while other people don't? Apparently, it's a genetic thing. Certain people have the heightened ability to detect aldehydes in their environment. Aldehydes are a common property in soap and fragrance. They are naturally occurring compounds in quite a few foods and essential/volatile oils.

If you love Cilantro, this is a quick and easy chutney recipe:

CILANTRO CHUTNEY
1 bunch of Cilantro
½ inch of ginger root
1 green/spicy Chili (optional)
1 tsp lemon juice
½ tsp of Cumin
salt to taste

Enough water, coconut oil or Olive Oil to emulsify (depending on which you choose the exact amount will vary; water will require a little less, either of the oils will require a little more, start small)

Mix all ingredients in blender until smooth. Store in a sealed jar in refrigerator and use as a condiment. This will last a couple of weeks if sealed and refrigerated.

DAY 222 - PU-EHR TEA

Bold and smoky, with a hint of tangy that fades into soft earthiness. My cup of Pu-ehr tea hints of the coming autumn. Pu-ehr Tea is more descriptive of a process than an actual type of tea; although it is definitely its own variety of tea. It is an aged and fermented tea that originates in the Yunnan province of China. The process for making authentic Pu-ehr Tea involves multiple steps that begin with green leaves and end with aged, fermented, dark leaves that have an appreciably distinct flavor. It is the process of fermentation rather than solely oxidation that imparts this tangy, earthy flavor.

Authentically processed Pu-ehr contains a minimum, if any, of the bitterness or astringent qualities that typical oxidized black teas contain. This allows the leaves to be steeped multiple times with lasting flavor. I love brewing a pot of Pu-ehr and refilling the water several times throughout the day, each pot has a slightly different nuance of flavor.

Tea is another amazing area to delve into if one is interested in exploring the nuances of taste and flavor. There are so many different types and styles of cultivating and brewing that it boggles the mind. According to tea aficionados (which I am not) the most appropriate way to brew Pu-ehr is to first remove a small amount of tea leaves, a teaspoon or two, from the "tea cake" or brick (also called 'bing cha'), place in your teapot and pour hot but not quite boiling water over the leaves. Then immediately dump, strain and dump that first pour. This first step is to rinse and then 'awaken' the leaves. Now you're ready to brew your tea. Pour more hot water over the tealeaves and let steep to your desired taste preference. I typically steep mine for about 5 to 10 minutes depending on the weather and the season. I like deeper, bolder tea in the fall and winter.

From a health perspective, Pu-ehr Tea has a variety of beneficial qualities from both a traditional medicine and westernized medicine approach. Traditional Chinese Medicine suggests that Pu-ehr Tea is good for opening the meridians, warming the 'middle burner' (which is part of the triple burner organ system and begins at the stomach and ends at the pyloric valve...without getting too technical). In TCM the middle burner is responsible for 'transformation', so if you are feeling stagnant and unable to transform your life, perhaps a pot or two of Pu-ehr Tea could feel invigorating. Western research demonstrates that Pu-ehr Tea aids in digestion, helping to process and appropriately utilize lipids and fatty acids, increases metabolic function, enhances cognition and memory, and lower blood pressure.

It also imparts many of the same benefits as Green Tea with the added bonus of fermentation. For more info on green tea check out DAY 251 – MATCHA. If you are in the U.K. or visiting the U.K., I am currently enjoying a delicious cup of Pu-ehr Chai, which I secured from the Hundred Monkeys Café in Glastonbury, which some say is the site of ancient Avalon.

DAY 223 – NIGELLA SATIVA (BLACK CUMIN)

Crunchy little seeds that pop when you chew them and taste like toasted onion, Nigella Sativa are an exotic addition to my morning breakfast. They are also known as black seeds, black cumin, and even Roman Coriander although, according to the plant specification, coriander, fennel, and cumin are in a different family from Nigella Sativa (very confusing, indeed).

Apparently Black Cumin has been recognized for its medicinal qualities for centuries upon centuries, especially in the area of the ancient Fertile Crescent. Egyptian Pharaohs were buried with Nigella Sativa seeds and archeologists have found remnants of Black Cumin seed mixed with honey, propolis, and beeswax in a "pilgrim" flask while excavating Boyali Hoyuk, a site dating back to 1650 BC. Black seed is also referenced in Biblical text suggesting it is a curative for a wide variety of ailments.

From a culinary perspective Black Cumin is really interesting. It tastes nothing like cumin or fennel or any of the other names that has been given. It is distinctly its own flavor experience. It features prominently in Middle Eastern and Indian cuisine, sprinkled on flatbreads, sautéed into curries and added to Tagines. I sprinkled it on my breakfast eggs and avocado and love the subtle flavor nuances.

From a health perspective, the amount of research conducted on Nigella Sativa is ridiculously amazing. Studies have demonstrated it is antibacterial, antimicrobial, anti-inflammatory and antiviral…the list goes on and on. It helps lower cholesterol and balance blood sugar, as well as, One of its more recently researched claims to fame has been as a remedy for high histamine response. In fact, studies have been so successful that Nestle attempted to patent the chemical properties in black seed and make it into a product to combat food allergies. Thankfully they were not granted the patent so you are free to extract thymoquinone from the nigella seed without the worry of jail time. (:

This is good, because apparently thymoquinone is quite the phytonutrient. In studies it has demonstrated pretty significant antioxidant qualities, protecting the heart, liver, and kidneys from damage due to oxidative stress. It has also demonstrated tumor-inhibiting and anti-cancer qualities. Apparently, it forces the mutated cells to blow themselves up while strengthening the surrounding healthy cells. Pretty cool.

Thymoquinone is not the only beneficial phytonutrient in Black Cumin; in fact it has quite a few others that are each showing up as health superstars in research. Needless to say, while the health benefits are amazing, it's also just a tasty addition to bump up your culinary adventures and stimulate your palate.

DAY 224 – KOHLRABI

Purple Kohlrabi feels smooth and dense to the touch with a shiny, bulb base and long green foliage. It has attracted my attention as I wander through the produce aisles. It looks slightly aquatic to me, the way the leaves grow out from the bulb. I've seen Kohlrabi on the shelves before

but never given it much thought, mostly because I realize I would have no idea what to do with it. I select one and bring it home and after a little research am on the way to making a meal.

Kohlrabi can be eaten raw or cooked. To me it has a mouthfeel similar to red cabbage or broccoli stem. The taste is refreshing, slightly sweet but also a little extra something similar to a radish. I like it. Kohlrabi is in the brassica family. It is also sometimes referred to as German Cabbage, and its name translates into "cabbage turnip." I'm guessing because it looks like a turnip but the taste and texture resemble red cabbage.

From a culinary perspective, you can eat Kohlrabi raw or cooked. It can be made into slaw or added to salads. It also fares well in soups and stews or even as a roasted veggie like many of its root brassica cousins. All parts of this veggie can be eaten, with the leaves making a great addition to sauté's or salads as well.

From a health perspective, being in the brassica family, Kohlrabi has a wealth of good stuff. Because it is newer on the scene and a hybrid of sorts, it doesn't quite have the nutrient density that its counterparts have but still has quite a bit to offer. It is rich in Vitamin C, B, and A. It's also a good source of minerals like potassium, copper, manganese and iron.

It contains many of the same phytonutrients that other brassicas contain and as such imparts similar health benefits. Research suggests that the isothiocyanates like sulforaphane help in the prevention of various cancers. They also support metabolic function, increasing the body's ability to process nutrients and eliminate toxins. This makes them highly beneficial for decreasing systemic inflammation and eliminating oxidative stress.
One caveat: as with all things, it is possible to get too much of a good thing. The glucosinolates in brassicas like Kohlrabi can contribute to thyroid issues and goiter if consumed in large amounts.

I'm making today's Kohlrabi into pancakes. I've shredded a cup of Kohlrabi, added an egg and some spices, with a pinch of baking soda and hey presto ... breakfast pancakes. (:

DAY 225 – HEN OF THE WOODS (GRIFOLA FRONDOSA)(RECIPE)

Dense, slightly spongy, springy and earthy; eating Hen of the Woods mushrooms brings a rustic and wholesome feel to my meal. Is it the name? Is it that I've rambled the forest in search of them? Either way, they are a 'romantic' addition to my urban breakfast. Hen of the Woods are also called Ram's Head mushrooms, however, you may also know them as Maitakes.

I am only just this past year or two beginning to appreciate the world of fungi. Prior to now, I have shunned any and all mushrooms regardless of accompanying ingredients, unless as a medicinal intervention in which case, I would plug my nose and just quickly down the ingredients.

However, I like to believe that my palate is 'growing up' and maturing, allowing me to branch out and try things I would not have tried in the past. I've learned that mushrooms when prepared 'right' are actually quite delicious and that I do, in fact, enjoy them or at least certain kinds of them when prepared well.

Hen of the Woods (Maitake) are well known in Asian cuisine and even more so in Traditional Asian Medicine. From a culinary perspective, they are a treat. Their texture lends well to pan or oven roasting, which is how I prepared them. They can be added to soups, stews, pastas, really anywhere that your creativity leads you. I love the shape of them so find preparing them as close to whole as possible the best option, just because they are so aesthetically pleasing.

From a health perspective, Maitakes are an amazing resource for good stuff, much like their fungi relatives. They are a great source of vitamins like B and D as well as minerals like potassium, calcium, and magnesium. They also have an abundance of phytonutrients making them extremely useful in boosting immune function and regulating blood glucose levels. Research has demonstrated that the chemical compounds in Hen of the Woods help stimulate not only the 'innate' immune function but also adaptive immune function; helping to boost natural killer cells in order to force mutated cells to self destruct while also fortifying surrounding healthy cells to inhibit further mutation. Other studies have shown that the compounds in Maitake help to regulate insulin production, exhibiting a hypoglycemic effect and decreasing blood sugar, making them a potential benefit for management of diabetes.

Caution: Hen of the Woods should not be confused with Chicken of the Woods, which is a similar in appearance but has very different properties. I would never recommend searching these things out without expert advice...unless you are foraging for them on an urban expedition to your local market.

Once you have secured the real deal, here's a tasty way to prepare them:

2 cups-ish Maitake mushrooms
5 sprigs thyme, minced
3 tablespoons Olive Oil
flaked sea salt (such as Maldon)
black pepper

Put the oven rack in the middle position and preheat the oven to 300 degrees F (150 C). If you have a convection oven, use the convection mode.

Trim any tough bits of stem or growing medium off the bottom and then shred the mushrooms into small clusters. Put them in a bowl and toss with the Olive Oil and thyme.

Line the clusters up in a single layer on a sheet pan and roast until the mushrooms are golden brown and crisp around the edges (50-60 minutes). Sprinkle with salt and pepper to taste and serve immediately.

DAY 226 – CHANTERELLE

Dense, meaty and chewy without being rubbery together with a flavor that is subtly earthy with a hint of sweet; this is my first taste of a Chanterelle. I decided to stick with the mushroom theme since it appears they are coming into season and the market shelves are beginning to brim with more variety. In my opinion Chanterelle's are among the prettiest in the mushroom family.

They are a lovely golden or apricot hue, with a satiny stalk and a cap that resembles an unfurling lily. With their softly fluted edges and gold tones, I can't help but ascribe a feminine quality to them. In truth, I'm also enamored of the Chanterelle because of the mushroom scene in the movie "Ratatouille". Remy the rat goes bonkers when he finds a Chanterelle and a bit of Tomme de Chevre cheese and creates a lightening generated gastronomic explosion. That rat has taste!

A couple of fascinating facts about Chanterelles; they grow almost exclusively in symbiotic relationship with trees. This is one reason they are hard to cultivate commercially. Also, research suggests that a chemical compound that is actually a type of insect repellent creates their golden hue. An insect repellent that is highly beneficial to them and the tree they are in relationship with but completely harmless to humans. Although there is written record of Chanterelles as part of culinary endeavors worldwide, it seems that it wasn't until around the 1700's that their fame as one of the most delectable mushrooms took off and they have since then been one of the most highly sought after fungi in the culinary world.

From a culinary perspective, they are another example of a dense, meaty mushroom so they fare well in a wide variety of dishes. That being said, they have a very subtle flavor, some describe it as almost fruity, I definitely found them to be slightly sweet but not quite too sweet. The Chanterelles I prepared today were roasted similarly to the Hen of the

Woods mushrooms that I roasted yesterday. This allowed me to taste the subtle flavor without distraction of other ingredients. You can guarantee I will be finishing them off with some Tomme de Chevre cheese later this evening. (:

From a health perspective, they have a very similar nutrient signature to the rest of their mushroom relatives. They are a great source of vitamins A, B, and D as well as minerals like potassium, copper, zinc, and calcium. Chanterelles also exhibit antibacterial and antifungal properties as well as being highly antioxidant. They can help decrease oxidative stress and systemic inflammation.

DAY 227 – HATCH CHILE

Zingy, earthy, pungent and subtly peppery with no heat just full Chili pepper flavor. It's Hatch Chile time! Mounds of shiny peppers are piled in open crates at the front of my local market. Their long, narrow bodies, all slick and wavy, tumbled together resemble the day's catch in a fish market. In every shade of green, with some already beginning to ease their way to red, they remind me that autumn is on its way. I love that we still have some food that is seasonal! For fresh Hatch Chilies the season is short, just a couple of weeks toward the end of summer. After that you can only get them frozen or canned.

Hatch Chilies are a specific type of Chile and are technically relatively new to the Chile scene. By "new" I mean about 150 years. They are a cultivar of the Chili pepper, created at New Mexico State University in the 1800's. These Chilies gets their name from Hatch, New Mexico, the town and surrounding region where they are grown and harvested. They do indeed have their own unique flavor and are one of the few members of the capsicum family that I really enjoy.

From a culinary perspective, Hatch Chilies are embedded in the cuisine of New Mexico, even though they are relatively new. The use of Chilies in Native cuisine is not and the Hatch Chile has been embraced fully into the heart of the kitchen in New Mexico. Because they are so flavorful and relatively mild, they make a great addition to dishes both sweet and savory believe it or not. They are typically roasted first, which is its own interesting process. That can be done in an oven, although fire roasting imparts really amazing flavor. Then they can be used in anything from Chile rellenos to enchiladas, Chili sauce, soups and stews and even pies and ice creams. I have yet to try Hatch Chile ice cream but I have had them in pumpkin pie and it is an interesting and very tasty experience.

From a health perspective, Hatch Chilies have all the benefits of their Chile relatives. They are a great source of vitamins and minerals like C, B and A as well as calcium, iron and potassium. The chemical compound that Chilies are most noted for includes capsaicin, which is notable in a variety of ways. The hotter the flavor the higher the capsaicin content which means the higher the endorphin release when you eat them. Of course, there is a threshold so the hatch peppers make a nice choice for just the right benefit. They are also great for immune function, increased digestion, and contain a wide variety of antioxidants.

If you are in an area that is lucky enough to get a batch of fresh Hatch Chilies delivered, I say grab a few and embark on a culinary adventure.

DAY 228 - SWEET CORN (RECIPE)

Sweet and succulent, each perfectly roasted, butter drenched kernel creating a small taste explosion in every bite. Sweet Corn is a variety of maize, which is biologically in the grass family. I rarely eat Corn, for a multitude of reasons; however, about once a year, in the summer or early autumn, I have a craving for its juicy goodness. Sweet Corn is different than field corn in that it has higher sugar content and the kernels are smaller and juicier. Part of what makes it so tender is that it is harvested during the early stages of maturation, called the milk stage. This ensures that the kernels are still packed with sugary sweetness.

To be clear, when I enjoy an ear of corn it is without a doubt an organic ear, mostly because otherwise chances are it is genetically engineered since as of 2015 about 93% of the U.S. conventional corn crop is genetically engineered.

From a culinary perspective, my favorite way to enjoy an ear of corn is on the cob either roasted or boiled in water with a little bit of milk. I always assumed the addition of milk to the boiling water was to bring out the sweetness of the corn, but actually, the addition of milk helps make some of the nutrients in the corn more bio-available. Sweet Corn, since it is harvested younger, is not as shelf sturdy and should be consumed or preserved very shortly after it has been harvested. Interesting, that this is seen as a downside when quite honestly, I prefer to eat food that is fresh and doesn't have some genetically extended lifespan. If you're wondering what to do with it once you get it into your kitchen, you can try roasting (either oven or grill), boiling, or you can cut it off the cob and add to soups, stews, salads, and puddings. It can also be made into baked goods. One of my absolute favorite corn dishes is Sweet Corn pudding...it is amazing and delicious! Really there's no end to the culinary possibilities of corn if you feel like being creative.

From a health perspective, corn has an interesting reputation.
Traditionally, corn is a staple food and has served humanity well as one that fortifies the body. I believe that heritage and unadulterated varieties of Corn still do provide more of a health benefit than not. Unfortunately, we are inundated with some variation of GMO Corn product in almost every kind of foodstuff so we get an over-abundance, most often without even realizing it, of Corn in our diets and it does take its toll. Fresh, unadulterated Corn is high in fiber, vitamins, and minerals. It is a good source of vitamins A and B and minerals like zinc, magnesium, copper and iron. It provides quite a variety of antioxidants that help eliminate oxidative stress and decrease risk of cell mutation that leads to degenerative disease and cancers.

SWEET CORN PUDDING
2 extra large eggs
1/4 c. raw honey
½ cup cream or full fat milk (if you use almond milk add 1 TBS of coconut oil)
3 TBS organic cornmeal
½ tsp salt
2 c Sweet Corn kernels

Preheat oven to 350. Whisk the eggs until blended and a little bit frothy. Add honey and cream and whisk until all blended and honey seems dissolved or dispersed. Add Cornmeal and salt and finally the corn kernels...whisk thoroughly. Pour into a greased pan and bake for about 30 minutes until set. Remove from oven and allow to 'rest' for a few minutes. Enjoy.

DAY 229 – YACON

Sweet, crispy, and juicy; Yacon is similar in texture to jicama or Jerusalem artichoke. I came across a recipe for pumpkin Yacon muffins and realized that while I've heard of Yacon and seen it in the store, it has always remained in my periphery. I chalked it up to one more media hyped "super-food" and just sort of ignored it. Shame on me...Yacon is really quite interesting for a variety of reasons.

Yacon is the tubular root of a daisy plant and is in the sunflower family. That's why it is similar in texture to the Jerusalem artichoke although its appearance is more like a sweet potato or Yam. Apparently it originates in the Andes but has made its way around the globe in climates that are suitable. It can be very easily cultivated under the right conditions.

From a culinary perspective, Yacon can be eaten raw as a tasty snack or it can be added to a variety of dishes both sweet and savory, even though it is mild and sweet in flavor. In that respect, I equate it to a carrot, I imagine that anywhere you might add young, sweet carrots you could add Yacon for an interesting twist. Because of its particular sweet qualities, Yacon has become wildly popular as a syrup or sweetener for foods as a low calorie replacement for other sweeteners. The pumpkin Yacon recipe that inspired my search for Yacon called for Yacon syrup as the sweetener.

From a health perspective, like so many other "super-foods" Yacon has been touted as an intervention for about a bazillion ailments, most of which have to do with lowering blood sugar and treating diabetes. This is due in part to the fact that the type of sugar/saccharide that makes Yacon taste so sweet, is not metabolized the same way that regular sugar is, therefore decreasing the impact on glucose production and other metabolic functions.

Research demonstrates that indeed when individuals consumed an infusion of tea made from the leaves of Yacon for 30 days, there was a decrease in plasma glucose and insulin levels. It may be important to note the results were based use of the leaves; most of what can be found in the market is the root. The other benefit of Yacon in its root form, seems to be its prebiotic impact, it has a significant level of oligosaccharides, which contribute to the beneficial bacteria in the gut. Yacon root also possesses a variety of antioxidants giving it the quality of decreasing oxidative stress and systemic inflammation.

I found Yacon to be quite tasty and if you are in the market browsing for something new and interesting to delight your palate, this could be a nice treat.

DAY 230 – AMOUR EN CAGE (PHYSALIS)

Mildly tart and juicy, with the sweet earthiness akin to that of a cherry tomato, Physalis Peruviana was an enjoyable little addition to my evening meal. They are tasty but honestly, I think I am more enamored with their French name; Amour en Cage – Love in a Cage. I would eat them every day if I could, just so I could say their name in French. (:

I first encountered these interesting little fruits last October in Salisbury, UK while on a Mojo mission. They were the garnish on my plate. I was so enraptured by their natural outer packaging that I didn't pay too much attention to their flavor; to be fair there was only one and we shared it among four of us so everyone could have a try. When I inquired further about them, I was told they were a type of gooseberry and left it at that. Then yesterday as I was wandering the produce section looking for something interesting and new, lo and behold, there was a very small stack of what I now know are called Physalis Peruviana or in French, if I may repeat, Amour en Cage. Of course, I had to get some.

Once home I set about my research. Perusing nutritional and botanical databases, I learned that these juicy little treats are indeed sometimes called a Cape Gooseberry although they are really no relation to the common gooseberry. Rather, they are related more closely to the Tomatillo and another plant called the Chinese Lantern; hence their slightly tomato-ey flavor. They actually look similar to a tiny tomato when cut in half, filled with tiny seeds and a similar cross section. I am completely in love with their delicate, papery outer covering and the way they reveal their inner golden goodness.

From a culinary perspective, once Physalis are divested of their outerwear, they can be used in much the same way as a small tomato or even a gooseberry for that matter. They can be eaten raw, in jams and jellies, salads, sautéed, stewed and even pies or other baked goods.

From a health perspective, Amour en Cage will make you feel better just saying the name with as much dramatic flare as possible. (: However there is the added benefit of it being a great source of vitamins, minerals and bioactive compounds that are highly antioxidant and anti-inflammatory. Studies suggest that the compounds found in Physalis Peruviana are highly beneficial to the liver, which corresponds with its use in Traditional Indian Medicine where it is a therapeutic intervention for Jaundice and other liver related ailments.

Other fascinating research suggests that a combination of bioactive compounds interact with cell mitochondria, resulting in two functions; healthy cells got healthier and malignant or mutated cells deconstructed. Pretty cool. Still further fascinating research demonstrates these dynamic little fruits are a superhero in the battle against radioactive pollution.

In fact, they fall into the "radioprotective" category. If that's not enough, they are also a significant source of melatonin, which is a key player in hormone regulation. Studies found in the database of International Atomic Energy Agency identify Amour en Cage as having these beneficial properties: antioxidant enzymes, nitroxides, and melatonin, antiemetic, anti-inflammatory, haemopoitic and immuno-stimulant compounds.

They forgot to add linguistically pleasing to the list.

DAY 231 – RED CURRANT

Tart and sweet at the same time, with an astringent quality that makes my mouth pucker slightly even though the juicy, red berries are visually delightful as well as tasty. These are another fruit just in the marketplace for a brief period even though, depending on climate and geography, they tend to have a longish growing season. Red Currants can be found as a culinary specialty in a wide variety of cultures around the globe.

Countries like Germany, Austria, France, the U.K., Russia and even Mexico all have specialty dishes featuring the jewel like Red Currant. Interestingly in the U.S. growing Red Currants (or any currant for that matter) was banned in the 1900's. Their leaves were perfect breeding ground for a fungal disease that attacks white pines. The Federal ban on cultivating them was lifted in 1966, however there are still States that prohibit their planting and cultivation. Maybe this is one reason it is challenging to find them in the U.S. marketplace.

From a culinary perspective Red Currants are tart and astringent, with a hint of sweet, especially if they are fully ripened. They can be eaten raw, tossed in salads and other dishes, turned into jams, jellies, spreads, syrups and liqueurs. They are delicious in baked goods, custards, and tarts.

From a health perspective Red Currants have a wealth of antioxidants and polyphenols. They are a good source of vitamin C and quercetin. Several studies have demonstrated that of all the berries (gooseberry, black currant, cranberry) Red Currant has the highest chlorogenic acid and anthocyanin content, making them highly beneficial for managing blood glucose levels, maintaining liver health, decreasing oxidative stress and systemic inflammation as well as contributing to vision and eye health.

DAY 232 – KIPPERS

Smoky, salty and, of course, a little fishy. It took me a while to get used to the flavor and mouthfeel of Kippers. Even now, that first bite is always accompanied by the slightest hesitation and hope that it's not going to go 'horribly wrong' once I've taken that bite. To date, each bite has been good enough to follow up with another and now I actually eat Kippers at least once a week. My favorite go to is Kippers on a bed of arugula with some avocado. If there is a really nice, crusty Sourdough hanging around that may be the foundation.

Salting or pickling and then cold smoking is the process involved in turning a herring into a Kipper. In fact, the process of salting and preserving food, especially fish is called 'kippering'.

From a culinary perspective Kippers can be eaten in any way you might eat any other smoked or cured fish. They fit in at breakfast, lunch, or dinner and even as a snack.

From a health perspective herring is a small, oily cold-water fish so it is an excellent source of healthy fatty acids and other good minerals and vitamins without being too impacted by heavy metals and other toxins that tend to be found in abundance in larger oily fish. Eating the whole Kipper (which is about 4-6 oz) including their small bones will provide you with more calcium than a cup of milk and also a nice, healthy dose of Vitamins D and B.

Enjoying a serving or two of cold, oily fish, like Kippers, at least twice a week will supply you with the recommended dose of essential fatty acids as well as ton of other nutrients that you can't get from a supplement. I recommend getting a scrumptious freshly baked loaf of hearty Sourdough bread, still warm if possible, layering it with arugula and avocado, then adding the Kippers and voila', you have a truly delicious palate satisfying meal.

The only caveat: choose sustainably harvested, naturally processed, in BPA free cans if you are eating Kipper snacks, otherwise, you end up with plenty of chemicals and additives that you didn't bargain for and the health benefits are decreased substantially.

DAY 233 – DURIAN

Sweet and creamy with hints of vanilla and almond, the inside of a Durian fruit is like custard. Today's flavor comes from the Asian market where end of season Durian fruit were on sale. Durian is a very interesting fruit and while there are actually many varieties native to various tropical habitats, there is typically only one variety that is exported to the U.S. That variety tends to be similar in size to a pineapple, sometimes larger, with very spiny skin and a moderate to mild odor. Which brings me to one of the main points that make the Durian so very interesting. It stinks. Literally.

My first encounter with a Durian fruit was while hiking through the Thai countryside. As I made my way down a small dirt road I was hit by the most nauseating smell of rotting meat. I was just sure something was lying dead on the roadside. One local noticed the look on my face and started laughing (not unkindly), he gestured to the trees and the giant hanging fruit, which to me looked like little sleeping porcupines.

After cutting one from the tree he brought it over and invited me to smell. Oh my, oh my...it was the fruit that smelled so bad. He proceeded to break it open and scoop out the custardy inside, taking a taste and then offering it to me. No way!!! After some friendly coercion, I gave it a try and it was absolutely one of the most delicious fruits I have ever tasted. It was like flan or custard, all creamy and deliciously sweet. Lesson learned. Never judge a book by its cover...or rather never judge a fruit by its stink.

I have since learnt the Durian fruit doesn't smell the same to everyone. Much like Cilantro it appears there is a particular chemical compound that some people smell and some do not. So to some individuals the Durian smells very similar to the inside fruit, while to others it smells, well... a little revolting. In one report by World AgroForestry Centre the smell is one way the tree ensures that it will propagate. It needs to have the seeds disseminated and they are much too big for birds or bees to carry, so it has created the ability to smell like something a foraging animal would want to eat. The seeds are then carried in the digestive tract until a later "release" at some other location in the forest. Nature is amazing!

From a culinary perspective obviously the Durian is an amazing sweet dish all by itself, either raw or steamed. In some ethnic cuisines, it is fermented and used as an accompanying condiment to savory dishes as well. The seeds can also be dried and eaten as a sweet treat. Whether you then release them back into the tropical forest is entirely up to you. (:

From a health perspective, Durian is interesting because it is a good source of starch without having a huge impact on your system. In fact, research has demonstrated the Durian fruit has the potential to balance blood glucose and decrease plasma lipids (involved in things like high cholesterol and other fatty related diseases).

It is also a great source of protein and Vitamins B and C as well as a wide variety of antioxidants. The Durian has high levels of quercetin, caffeic acid, and p-coumaric and cinnamic acids. What does all of that mean to you? Reduced oxidative stress and systemic inflammation! It also means the Durian is one more food that eliminates mutating cells at the mitochondrial level while encouraging healthy cells to grow and shine. I say if you are ever in an Asian market and see a pile of giant porcupine-looking fruits, get one and give it a try...even if it's stinky.

DAY 234 – MINERAL BROTH (RECIPE)

Sweet, savory with a little bit of zing from ginger and a little bit of salt from the seaweed, mineral broth is definitely an experience of "umami". It's also deeply nourishing. From time immemorial for cultures all around the world, soups and broths have been part of a foundation of nourishment, nutrition, and even social structure. Soups are a way to make ingredients go further for a frugal kitchen and also a way to whip up some health infusing remedies.

This particular mineral broth brings together all the goodness of mineral dense vegetables, herbs and spices. Squash, sweet potatoes, celery, juniper, kombu and more; all slow simmering their anti-inflammatory, immune boosting properties to fruition in the pot.

From a culinary perspective, I make up a batch of mineral broth a couple of times a year and then either can it or freeze it so I have it on hand. It is a good flavor dense base to soups, stews, sauces, and even for grains. When I'm feeling I need a little extra nourishment I just sip a cupful as a remedy for whatever is ailing me.

From a health perspective, this particular mineral broth is packed with all the building blocks for cellular health. If you check out the recipe you'll notice there are no nightshades or high histamine ingredients. This means your body can just soak up the natural goodness without the worry of being triggered or further inflamed. Even if you don't have trouble with histamines or nightshades, it can be good to just give your body a rest. This is a perfect broth for someone suffering from cold and flu, or someone needing to be on an elimination diet. It's also a deeply nourishing broth for stress.

Pile all these ingredients into your slow cooker or a stock pot and let them simmer for at least 6 hours. I simmer mine about 24 hours. Cool. Strain. Enjoy.

MINERAL BROTH

6 unpeeled carrots, cut into thirds
2 unpeeled yellow onions, cut into chunks
1 leek, white and green parts, cut into thirds
1 bunch celery, including the heart, cut into thirds
1 small kabocha squash unpeeled
2 unpeeled Japanese or regular sweet potatoes, quartered
1 unpeeled garnet yam,quartered
5 unpeeled cloves garlic, halved
1/2 bunch fresh flat-leaf parsley
1 8-inch strip of kombu (seaweed found in the asian food section of most markets)
12 black peppercorns
4 whole allspice or juniper berries
2 bay leaves
8 quarts water
2 inches ginger and turmeric; each (or more if you want more zing)

DAY 235 – BONE BROTH (CHICKEN)

Although bone broth is a clear broth it has a rich and almost creamy mouth feel with a hint of umami. From the first sip, it satisfies both my body and my spirit. Chicken Broth has long been a part of many folk remedies and the main go to for feeling under the weather. Throughout time in almost every culture, there is reference to the healing quality of good Bone Broth. Science now validates the claims with empirical data showing the gelatin and mineral content in Bone Broths absolutely provides the body with the

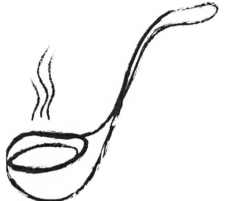

necessary components for self-repair. Today's Bone Broth was made from a heritage, pasture raised, slow-growth chicken and several feet, necks, and backs. It sounds crazy to have to specially seek out a chicken that led a normal life and even pay more for it but the truth is that's what modern day animal practices have led us to.

Most, if not all, conventional chickens have been bred to have the highest quantity of breast meat and fat, which has decreased the length of their legs and wings significantly. This change has increased their bulk so much that it makes it almost impossible for many of them to actually walk around or move in any significant way. The bones and cartilage from a "heritage" chicken were twice the length and amount as that of a conventional chicken. So, if you want the healthiest broth for you and for the planet, invest and get the chicken that got to actually be a chicken.

From a culinary perspective, Chicken Broth is rich and complex, so it makes a really delicious base to any number of culinary endeavors; not to mention a tasty treat all by itself in a mug full. One of my favorite ways to enjoy Bone Broth is for breakfast, heating it slowly on the stove, then dropping two eggs into it, slowly stirring to blend the whites without breaking the yolks. Then once I am ready to eat it, I stir the yolks in quickly and it provides an even creamier broth. Super delicious!

I just can't rave enough about the health benefits of a good bone broth. Of course, the nutrient density will vary from batch to batch depending on the quality of your ingredients. Again, because you are making a food that will really permeate all of your cells and tissues it is worth going the little extra and making a good quality base from organic or sustainably raised chickens. The recipe that I'm sharing actually ends up making several quarts, so you will have an amount to stockpile that will make it just that much more worth the investment.

Current studies are demonstrating that just a cup of broth a day, whether on its own or as a base to a meal, has a significant impact on skin disorders, osteo and rheumatoid arthritis and digestive disorders (including Crohn's disease and IBS.) It reduces systemic inflammation quite dramatically and improves immune function. So, yes, chicken soup really does cure what ails you...but only if it is soul nourishing Chicken Bone Broth.

DAY 236 – ACORN SQUASH

To me Acorn Squash tastes slightly sweet and even more slightly earthy, with a dense almost grainy mouthfeel. It is very light in flavor so adds more of a texture influence to the meal it is part of rather than a flavor impact. Acorn Squash is part of the Cucurbita Pepo family. The Cucurbitas are gourds, winter, and summer squashes. The Pepo subspecies signifies that it is also closely related to the zucchini and summer squash. Earliest recorded domestic cultivation of the Curcubita Pepo variety is in Oaxaco, Mexico as early as 5,000 B.C. It made it's way down into Central America and up through Texas and the Mississippi valley until finally they can now be found cultivated all around the globe in appropriate climates.

From a culinary perspective, Acorn Squash is one of the more popular kitchen squashes. Typically they are baked or stuffed with something delicious and then baked. But you can also steam, fry, sauté, or any number of other methods. Today I pureed my squash added two eggs and some pecans and turned them into pancakes. They were delicious. They have a mild flavor that allows spices and whatever else you are preparing with them to take the stage.

From a health perspective, one shouldn't be fooled by Acorn Squash's unassuming flavor. It packs a significant nutrient punch; vitamins C, B, and A, as well as a wide variety of minerals including potassium, magnesium, manganese, iron, copper, phosphorous, and calcium. Studies have shown significant benefit to eye and vision problems including degenerative diseases.

The fiber and phytonutrients are beneficial to digestive health and immune function. Research has demonstrated a beneficial impact on blood glucose maintenance, making it a valuable resource for insulin resistance and diabetes. So, as you can see, health benefits abound, not to mention palate-pleasing possibilities. Autumn is coming and the time is getting ripe for delicious additions like squash and root veggies.

DAY 237 – SOURDOUGH

Sourdough is tangy and piquant, which means pleasantly sharp with enjoyable zing. This perfectly describes how a slice of Sourdough bread tastes to me, especially if it is warm and buttery. The sensation of creamy, sweet butter with warm crusty bread that tastes pleasantly zingy is an experience not to be missed.

Sourdough is exactly that; sour dough, or rather sour flour. It can be made from a variety of flours although it is most commonly made from wheat or rye. To make Sourdough, a small amount of flour is mixed with water and left to "sour" for a few days. Each day more flour and water is "fed" to the base as it sours so that the lactobacilli and yeast cultures colonizing the mixture can grow, mature, and create more. Basically, Sourdough is fermented flour and water.

Once you have a batch of Sourdough base, if you treat it well it can last forever. In fact, there is an Italian pizza place in Stroud, U.K. whose claim to fame is a Sourdough culture that is over 200 years old. Each generation of bakers has committed to keeping the culture alive, passing it down from family member to family member. I have tried their Sourdough crust pizza and I must admit it is completely delicious.

From a culinary perspective the base can be used for a multitude of things, you dip a little out, add back in a little fresh flour and water and just keep on going. The fermented mixture acts as a natural leavening agent, giving bread or other baked goods a delicious tangy quality. It can be used in bread, cakes, cookies, and muffins. Sourdough pancakes and waffles are to die for and even you can make tortillas and flat breads. Really anywhere that you use flour you can use Sourdough for an added flavor bump.

From a health perspective, Sourdough is a fermented entity... a little happy village of beneficial bacteria just waiting to make your belly happy. Many people avoid bread these days because they are either worried about the gluten (unless it's rye bread) or they are worried about the glycemic spike that can accompany eating regular bread. Research demonstrates that the nutrients generated by the fermentation process actually help decrease impact on blood glucose levels and allow the bread to be metabolized at a slower rate.

The fermentation also helps your gastrointestinal tract better utilize the proteins that are present, so Sourdough bread is usually better tolerated by people who may have less tolerance for regular flour breads. Of course, if you suffer from Celiac's disease then even Sourdough should be avoided. Fermenting the flour also neutralizes the phytic acid that can be irritating to gut lining and completely decimates any potential for ergot poisoning.

Ergot is a fungus that grows on grains, especially Rye. Consuming grain infected with ergot causes what has historically been called St. Anthony's Fire or ergotism; it results in hallucinations, aggression and ultimately convulsions and gangrene of the limbs. Ugh! Fermenting the grain saves the day, which is why the Anglo-Saxons never suffered ergotism; they only ate Sourdough.

Another beneficial quality of the fermentation process is that it helps populate your gut with good bacteria. Studies show that having a balanced gut microbiome (community) increases cognitive function, moderates serotonin and dopamine levels, which stabilize mood and energy; increases nutrient assimilation and boosts immune function. What's not to love about keeping the beneficial bacteria in your belly very, very happy...especially when it tastes pleasingly zingy and it's oozing buttery goodness!

One caveat: Sadly most, if not all, factory-baked breads found on conventional shelves do not actually use a Sourdough starter. Instead, they add a packet of dry Sourdough, which is sort of like dry yeast, to complete the "Sourdough" process. Unfortunately, this does not impart the same health benefits, since it actually requires a slow fermentation process to build the bacteria necessary for true Sourdough. So, do be sure to read labels and know where your bread is coming from, chances are if it was manufactured then it is not genuine Sourdough.

DAY 238 – HONEYCRISP APPLE

Juicy, tart and tangy with just enough sweet in each crisp bite; Honeycrisp Apples are here! These are indeed my favorite kind of apple and they are seasonal, so it's always a treat and sign of impending autumn when they find their way to the market. Honeycrisps have an interesting history, albeit a rather brief history since they're a relative newcomer on the apple scene. They started out as a test cultivar from the University of Minnesota.

Initially, they weren't passing the mustard as far as the desired apple results and were almost cut from the list of continued testing. Then someone noticed that they were juicy beyond any other type of apple juiciness that they have ever experienced. Sure enough, it turns out their cellular structure is different, larger, moister and more juice filled when the cells are ruptured by chewing. Bite into a Honeycrisp and your mouth is flooded with tangy, sweet goodness like no other apple can provide.

From a culinary perspective, Honeycrisp apples are best eaten raw. They don't really lend themselves well to cooking or processing in other ways, so enjoy the whole apple and all of its juicy richness.

From a health perspective the Honeycrisp is a hybrid of an already cultivated pair of apples. Apples are an amazing wealth of nutrients, fiber, and moisture content. Quercetin, Malic Acid, Boron, Potassium; all helping your body do things like balance blood sugar, boost immune function, and even whiten your teeth.

DAY 239 – SHISHITO PEPPERS (ROASTED)

Umami, salty, piquant, and pungent all at the same time; fire roasting adds a dimension of flavor to these mild green peppers that makes them out of this world. The Shishito pepper is a member of the Capsicum annum family originating in East Asia. They are for the most part mild although growing conditions impact the level of heat and sometimes one pepper in a batch will be hot while the others will remain mild and pleasantly piquant.

From a culinary perspective, Shishitos are delicious when roasted, sautéed, or grilled. I've tried them raw and was only mildly impressed, but roast them and add a little sea salt to the mix and they are almost impossible to stop eating...until you hit a random hot one. Shishitos are popular in Japanese cuisine and are typically served as tempura or added to dishes like yakitori. They can typically be found in season, which is late summer to early fall, in International or Asian markets. If you can find them, I highly recommend giving them a try.

From a health perspective, like their Chili relatives, Shishitos are rich in antioxidants, vitamins C, B-6, and A and a variety of minerals. Research suggests that these little peppers provide the benefits of capsicum without the heat of capsaicin (which is what makes peppers hot). Super interesting studies on the Shishito pepper, and a few other Japanese vegetables, found that a heated extract was highly beneficial in the destruction of tumors and as a free radical scavenger with particular success in the elimination of the Epstein-Barr virus. So, heating up these little peppers before you indulge is the way to go if you want to reap the benefits of all of their nutrient goodness.

DAY 240 – GALANGAL

Pungent and expansive on the palate, Galangal is a zesty addition to any culinary endeavor. It is a member of the ginger family and has all the peppery, spicy zip that gingerroot has but also has its own unique twist, similar to camphor or pine. Galangal is native to Asian cuisine but has made its way into cultural foods and herbal remedies around the world. The most delightful cup of Galangal and ginger tea inspires today's flavor of the day. Galangal resembles ginger very closely but has smoother skin and is lighter in color.

From a culinary perspective, Galangal is a common ingredient in Thai, Malaysian, and Indonesian food. It adds an earthy almost citrus quality due to its volatile oils so ginger and Galangal together make an awesome combination. Galangal can add well to savory and sweet dishes alike. It can be steeped in teas, soups, stir-fries, and grated into curries and other stews. I've enjoyed Galangal brulee, which was delicious and it is definitely a favorite addition to curries.

From a health perspective Galangal has a long tradition as a medicinal herb. It has similar properties to ginger. It has long been used as a digestive stimulant and carminative (which means anti-flatulence). It is anti-inflammatory and anti-spasmodic, as well as antiviral, antifungal, and antimicrobial. Research demonstrates that Galangal like ginger is beneficial internally and topically for things like arthritis, ulcers, and other inflammatory based diseases and ailments. Studies show that it is also highly beneficial for managing and eliminating oxidative stress.

DAY 241 - AIOLI (GREEN GODDESS)

Creamy and rich, with herby goodness that causes my taste buds to dance; green goddess Aioli is definitely fit for a goddess. Aioli is a type of 'sauce' traditionally made from egg yolks, Garlic, Olive Oil and lemon juice. It appears to have originated in French cuisine, however, variations of Aioli sauces can be found in cuisines around the world. The creamy goodness comes from emulsifying the fat of the oil with the egg yolk and the lemon juice and whatever else is being added; in the case of green goddess Aioli, herbs like tarragon, chives, parsley were combined with the Garlic for a deliciously creamy effect.

From a culinary perspective, traditional recipes call for making Aioli in a mortar and pestle, first crushing the Garlic, then adding the egg yolk and finally drizzling in the oil while mixing and thickening. The consistency can then be adjusted with the lemon juice. Most Aioli sauces these days are prepared with a food processor or are simply flavors added to mayonnaise.

The green goddess Aioli, that I enjoyed with my dinner, last night was hand prepared in the traditional style with mortar and pestle and it was absolutely amazing. I can't wait to get home and try to recreate it. Aioli can be served with fish, meats, veggies, as a sauce, a dip, or a spread. It can also be featured as a main entrée as it is in Provence on Christmas Eve.

From a health perspective, one might think that with all that fat and oil Aioli can't possibly be good for you. One would actually be wrong. If prepared with fresh ingredients, and eaten as a condiment, Aioli is actually quite a nice and even healthful addition to your dietary repertoire. The health benefits of Olive Oil can be found on Day-147, Garlic on Day 260, Egg Yolks on Day 308. But if you don't feel like tracking those down, not to worry; trust me, these are all great ingredients.

Basically, the Garlic is an immune boosting, inflammation fighting, antiviral, antibacterial, antimicrobial, pro-digestion, super food. The Olive Oil provides a significant amount of healthy fatty acids and also works to decrease systemic inflammation and oxidative stress. The egg yolks are little treasure chests of goodness, providing healthy fats, minerals, and vitamins like A, B, and D.

DAY 242 – LINGONBERRY

Tart, sweet, slightly earthy, with a little bit of astringent zip; Lingonberries are a hearty and delicious relative of the cranberry and the blueberry. They are native to colder climates, like Scandinavia, Alaska, and Northern Canada, although they can also be found in limited quantity in some of the more northern states in the U.S. My first introduction to the lovely Lingonberry was on a Swedish pancake smothered in Lingonberry jam. Oh so very delicious!

Lingonberries are a mainstay in Scandinavian cooking; in fact Lingonberry jam is a common accompaniment for dishes both sweet and savory. Lingonberries tend to have a two-crop season, with the first fruit arriving some time in July and the second arriving later in the fall.

From a culinary perspective, if you can get your hands on some Lingonberries, they are similar enough to cranberries that you can use them anywhere you might use a cranberry and vice versa. They are tart, with a hint of sweetness, and a very astringent quality like the cranberry so be prepared to have a wide variety of experiences on your palate if you eat them au naturel.

From a health perspective, Lingonberries are closely related to cranberries, so they do have similar nutritional properties. They are an excellent source of Vitamin C and other vitamins and minerals. They have a similar quality to the cranberry in that the chemical compound, D-Mannose, acts as a bacterial deterrent for the urinary tract, kidneys, and bladder. D-Mannose basically makes it very difficult for bacteria to hang around and propagate so in a sense it has antibiotic qualities without the negative side effects of taking an antibiotic.

Lingonberries also contribute to beneficial gut flora, increasing pre and probiotic colonies, which in turn helps you with digestive function, immune response, and mood regulation. As if that's not enough to love them Lingonberries also possess a good supply of anthocyanin, about 100 milligrams per three and a half ounces berries. Anthocyanins, a member of the flavonoid family, are a really potent antioxidant. They help decrease systemic inflammation and oxidative stress. Research suggests that Anthocyanins can help reduce the risk of heart disease, heart attack and cancer.

DAY 243 – GARLIC

Pungent and zesty, fresh raw Garlic is a tasty addition to the list of ingredients that will make up my lunch today. Garlic is part of the allium  family, which includes foods like onions and leeks. According to the Food and Nutrition encyclopedia, Garlic is originally native to middle Asia but has made its way around the world. First recorded use of Garlic as a medicinal intervention can be found in China, India, and Sumeria around 2700 BC, although archeologists have found remnants of Garlic use as early as 7,000 BC.

From a culinary perspective, Garlic is a much-loved addition to dishes in almost every culture. I have grown to love adding Garlic right at the end of cooking so that the zip found in the raw state is still available as a distinctive flavor. Crushing Garlic and allowing it to sit for a few moments in the air releases it sulfuric properties, which is what gives it the strong odor and flavor.

From a health perspective, Garlic is truly a "super-food" and has been recognized for thousands of years in various cultures as such. Garlic is considered a heating and stimulating herb and has been used to stimulate both physical and emotional function. As early as 2700 in several ancient medicinal texts, Garlic is utilized as a remedy against depression, starvation sickness, tuberculosis, fungal infections, colds, flu and a general health stimulator.

The Egyptians made sure it was a mainstay in the diet of their builders, recognizing that without it their poor diet did not allow them to maintain the strength and balance necessary to work.

Chemical compounds like allicin and allinase are what make Garlic so amazing; providing it with antibacterial, antibiotic, antimycotic, tumor blasting, free radical eliminating goodness. It is antithrombotic, which means no blood clots. It balances and decreases serum lipids making it a great intervention for cholesterol issues. This is what makes Garlic such a heart friendly food. It is also anti-carcinogenic, demonstrating some pretty awesome effects against cell mutation and tumor growth. Several studies indicate that high doses of Garlic have a beneficial impact on the body, assisting it in fighting a wide variety of disease.

So, if you're feeling a little moody or under the weather, it could be worth chopping up some Garlic and tossing it in your soup.

CHAPTER 9 - SEPTEMBER

DAY 244 – SORREL

Palatably bitter with an almost citrusy back-note, Sorrel is a delicious green that is making a comeback to the culinary scene. It was a tasty accompaniment to my dinner of fresh baked trout and Purslane. Sorrel is in the same family as spinach, chard, and even beets.

The beautiful arrow-shaped leaves transform in taste from spring to fall, starting off slightly sweeter and increasing in bitterness as they mature. The bitterness is due to the high oxalic acid content, so while it is fine to eat them raw as an addition to salads or other fresh dishes, if they are mature, it is best to cook them up a little bit to break down the acid and make them more palatable.

From a culinary perspective, Sorrel has a long history of use in a variety of cultural cuisines across Europe and into Asia and Africa. The Greek dish spanakopita (one of my absolute favorites) traditionally contains a blend of Sorrel, chard, spinach and leeks. It is a common ingredient in many recipes in Nigeria; even drink recipes. And it's found in culinary endeavors all across Northern Europe either as a stand-alone or an ingredient in soups and stews. Its the citrusy back-note gives it a distinct flavor, making it well worth experimenting with.

From a health perspective, Sorrel, is a great source of Vitamins C, A, and B. It has a nice variety of minerals like magnesium, potassium, and calcium. It is high in fiber and the bitter quality acts as a digestive, enhancing peristalsis. It also sports some pretty awesome phytonutrients like flavonoids, anthocyanin and polyphenolic acid.

All of that adds up to improved immune function and cardiovascular health, decreased systemic inflammation and elimination of oxidative stress. Research demonstrates that Sorrel leaves contain chemical compounds that decrease the potential for tumor growth and cell mutation. Sorrel was once upon a time a common kitchen ingredient but these days it's a little harder to find, however, if you do come across it, I highly recommend giving it a taste.

DAY 245 – TRUFFLES

The scent of truffles is packed with heady, earthiness that makes my salivary glands stand up and take notice. Just the smallest drop of Black Truffle oil on my morning eggs turns my simple breakfast into an exotic feast. With a flavor that gives fleeting hints of forests primeval, there's just something about the tiniest taste that feels so right as the feel of autumn begins to slip into the air. For me Truffles are indeed a seasonal food.

I love them in the fall and winter and don't love them quite as much in the spring and summer. Interestingly, that just happens to fall right in line with when White and Black Truffles are actually in season. White Truffle season runs from roughly October to December (depending of course on the climate) and Black truffle season begins in December and runs until March-ish.

Truffles are, according to multiple culinary resources, the most sought after and the most expensive edible fungus in the culinary world. They are challenging to find without the help of a truffle sniffing pig or dog. Truffles create symbiotic relationships with trees, so they are typically found a couple of inches below the detritus/soil amongst tree roots. Interestingly Truffles cannot reproduce from their own mating spores so need to find a way to get in contact with non-related Truffles in order to proliferate. This is where the Truffle snuffling wild boars come into play; they eat the Truffles that they love so much and carry the spores to another location, ahem, "depositing" them in the vicinity of better Truffle reproductive potential.

From a culinary perspective, Truffles are the *"diamonds of the kitchen"* according to Jean Anthelme Brillat-Savarin. It's important to keep in mind that a little bit goes a long way; not just because of the price but also because the smell and flavor can become so intensely overpowering that it is no longer inviting. White Truffles tend to lighten in scent and flavor once added to heat, while Black Truffles appear to do the opposite. Just the right amount will enhance the flavor of meats, veggies, whatever you are preparing with an earthy, woodsy quality that is almost beyond description.

From a health perspective, one reason the scent and flavor of Truffles can tend to defy description is because Truffles elicit a sensation as much as a flavor. Their scent is molecularly similar to human male pheromones (and pig pheromones), which stimulates a more complex neurochemical response. In a way you could say that indeed Truffles are a bona-fide aphrodisiac.

Nutritionally Truffles contain a high concentration of protein and a lovely combination of amino acids making them a heart healthy tidbit. As a fungus, they contain many of the same properties as the Reishi or Maitake mushrooms, however, chances are you wouldn't eat enough of them to reap the full nutrient potential. They are immune boosting, heart friendly, belly friendly, and above all palate friendly! Try a Truffle and see if it makes you swoon. (:

DAY 246 – SHEEP'S CHEESE (FRESH)

Sweet and creamy, creamier than the richest butter, with hints of sweet grass and sunshine; fresh sheep's milk cheese from Black Sheep Creamery is indescribably delicious!

Being a lover of all things cheese, and finding myself in a new region with local delicacies I had never tried, I felt like a kid in a candy store; or even better, me in a cheese store!! The cheese counter guy (sorry if there's a more official title that I'm unaware of) began discussing the local artisan cheese options and handing out samples, all of which were delicious, and then, whammo, he handed over a tiny scoop of fresh Sheep's Cheese. Just brought in that morning from the creamery, in limited supply and huge demand, he had only two small crocks left. This stuff was divine creamy, buttery goodness.

Yes, please I'll take a crock of that. I would have taken both but didn't want to deprive anyone else of experiencing that flavor phenomenon. Fresh sheep's cheese is made within days of milking, according to Black Sheep Creamery's website, it is made within three days to be exact.

From a culinary perspective, this cheese is creamy and lovely. I imagine it could be used anywhere you might typically use a cream or ricotta cheese. In fact, I'd love to get my hands on another crock and make a Sheep's Milk Cheesecake. The flavor is creamy, sweet and savory all at the same time; creamier than either goat or cow's milk. I ended up spreading it on toast (homemade Sourdough), eating it with apple slices, enjoying it on eggs, and even stirring it into a bowl of bone broth.... divine and divine.

From a health perspective, Sheep's Milk supplies different nutrients than cow or goat. It is higher in iron, zinc, phosphorous and calcium as well as, vitamins A, B, D, E. It also is a significant source of Omega 3 fatty acid based mostly on the sheep's diet of grass. Sheep's Milk also tends to be easier to digest and assimilate than other dairy. It is much higher in protein and good fat; possessing a significant amount of medium chain fatty acid.

Remember that research suggests consumption of medium chain fatty acids helps reduce fat deposits and increase satiation, while also boosting cognitive function. Some studies are also demonstrating that the chemical composition of Sheep's Milk provides the body with an enhanced ability to absorb the nutrients more efficiently. Individual's who drank Sheep's Milk had demonstrated an increase in calcium absorption, which decreased their risk of osteoporosis and other calcium deficient related ailments.

All in all, it's definitely worth keeping an eye out for some Sheep's Milk products, especially fresh cheese!

DAY 247 – YAM

Starchy and sweet, the Yam has its own unique mouthfeel and flavor even though it is so often confused with the sweet potato. Typically, when you peruse the produce market shelves, you will find sweet potatoes and Yams all piled together and sometimes the Yam is indeed called a sweet potato and vice versa. However, the Yam and sweet potato are not botanically related.

Yams are more closely related to lilies and grasses, technically, they would be more closely related to a grain than they are to the potato. Yams are the tuberous root part of a very interesting spade-leaved plant. To me, a Yam feels almost stringier when chewing, as if I can feel the starch fibers. True Yams seem to be native to Africa and Asia, although they have made their way around the world into appropriate climates and cultivated agriculture.

From a culinary perspective, Yams, while often interchangeable with the sweet potato, have their own unique properties. They tend to be higher in starch and have less moisture content, if you're working with a recipe that might be impacted by these differences then you will want to adjust. Otherwise Yams can pretty much be enjoyed anyway that a sweet potato can, except raw. Most Yams have a significant amount of naturally occurring toxins and so require cooking to make them more palatable and easier to digest with no repercussions. The Japanese Yam is one of the few true Yams that can be eaten raw.

From a nutritional perspective, Yams possess different nutritional properties to sweet potatoes. There has been quite a bit of interesting research conducted on the Yam Tuber Mucilage (YTM) which is basically the liquid that rises to the surface when you cut a Yam open and let it sit out for a few minutes. If you slice a Yam and let it sit, you will see a milky looking substance bead to the surface. That substance contains some pretty amazing qualities.

One of the first is allantoin; which is a featured ingredient in medications that fight the herpes virus. Applying the YTM milk to ulcers, cold sores, and other virus related skin issues has been a common practice in traditional medicine for centuries and now we know why. Allantoin wipes out the virus while at the same time stimulating the healthy part of the cell to regenerate. There are other chemical compounds found in YTM that inhibit the angiotensin enzyme. Angiotensin contributes to vasoconstriction, which can, if out of balance, elevate blood pressure and increase the potential for blood clots and heart issues.

Yams are a good source of vitamin C and B and a wide variety of minerals like potassium, iron and manganese. They are also high in fiber and belly friendly fructo-oligosaccharides (lovingly known as 'olies'). Eating your olies helps your gut friendly bacteria stay strong and healthy, giving them the edge over any invaders that might want to take over and cause your gastrointestinal tract distress.

The next time you're in the produce section sorting through the tubers, it could be worth asking specifically for a real Yam, just to see if you can notice the difference, and also to reap the benefits of this often misidentified food.

DAY 248 – GOJI BERRY

Plump and juicy, not too sweet with just a hint of earthiness, fresh Boji Berries are a treat. Until yesterday, I'd only experienced dried Goji Berries, which are chewy and tasty without being too sweet or too sour. Goji Berries are a member of the nightshade family and have been known by a wide variety of other names throughout history; boxthorn, wolf-berry, desert thorn. They have a long history in folk medicines around the globe and in recent years have been swept up by pop culture media and whipped into a super-food frenzy. While Goji Berries do have a number of nutrient dense properties, they are potentially over represented as a miracle cure-all for whatever ails you.

From a culinary perspective, Goji Berries have a unique taste and make an interesting addition to both sweet and savory meals. I have been known to toss them into soups and stews and also use them in desserts or sweet treats. They make a great snack just straight out of the jar or off the bush and, apparently, in the right regions are pretty easy to cultivate and grow. They make quite a lovely addition to a container herb garden if you live in limited space.

From a health perspective, not wanting to just propagate the media hype I went straight to the peer reviewed journals and medical databases to see what I could discover about the wonder-fruit Goji Berry. They are indeed a wealth of nutritional goodness! That being said, they have very similar properties to the gooseberries, cranberries, lingonberries and just berries in general. All of which are packed with polyphenols, flavonoids, and other chemical compounds that inhibit oxidative stress and systemic inflammation while also increasing immune function and boosting cardiovascular and gastrointestinal health.

So, here are my thoughts... Goji Berries are delicious. If you can locate some fresh ones they are definitely worth a try but not because they are a miracle food, simply because they are palate pleasing and interesting. Definitely don't get caught up by the hype that has you spending major amounts of money. If you are looking for foods that will help heal your body, mind and spirit, the Goji Berry can be a nice addition, along with a wide variety of other real fruits and veggies. Eat real food, not too much and not too little...

DAY 249 – TOMATILLO

Juicy and tart, almost citrusy, the Tomatillo has a surprisingly refreshing flavor and dense mouthfeel. Tomatillos are a member of the nightshade family and although, they are sometimes referred to as green tomatoes they are in fact distinctively different from the tomato. They are also called husk tomatoes because, like the cape gooseberry, they have a paper-like type of husk surrounding the outside. Tomatillos apparently originated in Central America and then made their way to appropriate climates around the globe. They have been part of human cuisine for thousands of years. Interestingly, while the Tomatillo is relatively easy to grow, once underway, it is the type of plant that requires several other plants for cross-pollination in order to reproduce and thrive.

From a culinary perspective, the Tomatillo is a key ingredient in Mexican and Guatemalan cuisine. It is high in pectin, making it an awesome ingredient for sauces, stews, jams, jellies or other culinary endeavors that could use thickening. They are delicious eaten raw or added to raw to salads, salsas or Pico de Gallo's. I smashed up some Tomatillo, lime and avocado with Cilantro and made a delicious Tomatillo/avocado 'salsa'.

From a health perspective, Tomatillos are an interesting source of nutrients. They are almost nutritionally closer to a berry than a tomato. High in minerals like potassium, iron, copper and manganese, Tomatillos help balance cellular fluid; assisting in the regulation of blood pressure and cardiovascular health. They are also a good source of Vitamins A and C.

Research demonstrates that Tomatillos contain a chemical compound that is cancer preventive, especially in colon cancers. Studies also suggest that the bioactive compounds in Tomatillos are effective in the prevention of diabetes and hypercholesterolemia. They also appear to aid in the repair of tissue in the gastrointestinal tract.

Seems to me that mixing up a nice little batch of Tomatillo salsa, with some fresh Garlic, onions and Cilantro can be a delicious way to support your health and well-being. Eat real food; not too much and not too little...

DAY 250 - PERSIMMON (FUYU)

Sweet, juicy, crunchy, oh I wait all year for the small seasonal window that includes the Fuyu Persimmon. They look like squat little pumpkins but they are full of sweet delicious flavor. I have a bazillion recipes that call for persimmon but they never seem to last long enough to be made into anything other than a snack.

Fuyu Persimmons are non-astringent so unlike their relatives the Hachiya Persimmon Fuyus do not make your mouth feel like you've just eaten a barrel of alum powder.

From a culinary perspective non-astringent persimmons are best for eating raw for a wider variety of uses while still in various stages of ripening. Astringent persimmons can be used for cooking and some eating but they must be very ripe. Fuyu Persimmons make a great addition to meals both sweet and savory adding an exotic autumnal quality to your dish.

From a health perspective Persimmons are a nice addition to diversify your dietary repertoire. They are a pretty good source of vitamins and minerals; especially vitamin C and A. They are a great source of fiber, so even though they are a little higher in sugar content, they still provide significant benefit. Fuyu Persimmons also have a significant load of phytonutrients. They contain chemical compounds that make them antiviral, antifungal, anti-inflammatory and antioxidant. They promote tissue repair at a cellular level and inhibit tumor growth and spread. The astringent quality even in the non-astringent varieties can help inhibit bleeding and is useful for drying out wounds, infections (the catechins help fight infection) and even things like cold sores.

Lots of good stuff going on with the Fuyu Persimmon but mostly I just think they are an amazingly delicious seasonal treat, well worth keeping an eye out for them.

DAY 251 – HAWTHORN BERRIES

Earthy, soft and dense; Hawthorn Berries are another sign that autumn is underway. They are figuring prominently in my foraging efforts (right up there with Rosehips) this year. I have typically thought of Hawthorn berries as a medicinal intervention until I recently came across a recipe for Hawthorn Berry ketchup, which piqued my curiosity. Now, I'm excited to discover other Hawthorn recipes, like Hawthorn pie and jam.

Hawthorn Berries are the fruit of the white thorn tree, also called the Mayflower. They grace the forest path and tracks quite beautifully. I find them unassuming yet majestic all at the same time. Their white flowers of spring give way to the autumn red of their berries as they cycle through the seasons.

From a culinary perspective, Hawthorn Berries are apparently more versatile than I originally thought. They can be eaten raw or added to salads, soups and stews; even made into jams, pies and the infamous ketchup. The only warning is to be sure to remove the seeds as they contain cyanide and while it might take quite a few to cause an issue, it's probably best not even entertained.

From a health perspective, Hawthorn berries are about as heart friendly as it gets. I use them in tea as a replenishing drink during the summer and a digestive aid. Research demonstrates that Hawthorn berries are beneficial for issues like angina, cardiac arrhythmia, congestive heart failure, high blood pressure and other nervous system related disorders that specifically involve the circulation and heart. They contribute to strengthening the

walls, vessels, and veins of the heart and circulatory system.
They also have some pretty great liver protective qualities, benefiting individuals who suffer from hepatitis and other liver related disorders and they assist in the elimination of oxidative stress.

Hawthorn berries have an astringent quality as well as antispasmodic, diuretic and they are sedating so assist with anxiety. They are a good source of Vitamin C and B as well as a wide variety of phytonutrients like flavonoids and bioflavonoids.

As a Bach Flower Remedy; Hawthorn helps ease emotional turmoil, soothing the heart and clarifying confusing thoughts.

DAY 252 – LEMON CURD

Tangy, zesty, sweetness that makes you pucker and salivate all at the same time; that's a Lemon Curd experience. Today's taste of Lemon Curd was part of the after meal pudding for end of harvest dinner; a wonderful way to finish a delightful meal. Lemon Curd is basically a finessed mixture of lemon juice, zest, egg yolks and sugar. The ingredients are cooked slowly and gently until they become thick and creamy. Fruit curd can really be made from almost any fruit or berry, however, lemon is by far my favorite. Curds are different from pie fillings, custards or jams because they tend to retain a higher amount of the actual fruit flavor.

From a culinary perspective, fruit curds are amazing and versatile for sweet and even savory dishes. I have to admit that the very best Lemon Curd I have ever had in my life is made by my dad from the lemons off the Meyer lemon tree in my brother's back yard. Nothing compares, although, tonight's pudding was very close. Lemon Curd is an amazing filling for pies or puddings; topping for scones or biscuits or even just toast and it even goes well on a baked sweet potato!

From a health perspective, okay let's face it, this is a dessert (for the most part). However, because it is slow cooked, it does retain some of its lemony goodness, not to mention the nutrients found in the egg yolks. Remember that adding lemon to foods can help the flavors brighten and become more complex. If your dish is missing a little something, reach for a little lemon before you reach for the salt and it can add just the right notes...even better reach for a little Lemon Curd and you can also include some healthy fats and creamy mouthfeel to complete the experience.

Research suggests that adding fresh citrus to foods can help people with difficulty tasting and smelling enjoy their food again. I think Lemon Curd would be a nice surprise for someone with muted taste buds, both for the mouthfeel and for the increased flavor from the volatile oils.

Lemon has a long list of benefits. It aids in digestion and stimulates peristalsis. It is antiseptic, antimicrobial, and antibacterial, so it helps with wound care and can help tissue heal without scarring. Lemon is a great addition to ginger and honey to make an awesome tonic for cold and flu...or slow cooked into a curd it can brighten someone's palate if they are feeling a bit under the weather. (:

DAY 253 – ELDERBERRY

Tart and earthy, black Elderberries are in abundance right now as summer gives way to Fall. Technically, even though the black Elderberry appears to be non-toxic, it's best to eat them cooked, even if only slightly. They have an earthy taste that hints of sweetness but doesn't quite get there, which is in a way, refreshing. They also lose any bitterness they have once they are cooked; leaving you with an earthy, complex flavor that is neither sweet nor sour.

Black Elderberry is also called Sambucus Nigra. They are native to temperate climates in both Europe and the North American continent. The only variety that isn't toxic when raw is the Sambucus Nigra, so be sure you know what you are picking and then cooking in order to stay well. The Elder tree actually has many phases of culinary influence. The flowers can be made into cordials and added to salads or other foods and the berries make a great wine, jam, pie filling or addition to soups and stews.

From a health perspective Elderberries are a great source of vitamins and minerals. It is high in vitamin C, B, and A and has an amazing variety of phytonutrients that contribute to the decrease of both systemic inflammation and oxidative stress. Sambucus Nigra has long been a folk remedy. It has been used for colds and flu, both as a relief for chest congestion but also for immune boosting.

Research suggests that it is indeed good for quite a number of ailments. It stimulates the immune system so it helps to decrease colds and flu as well as yeast infections and other bacterial/viral infections. It is tumor inhibiting and also helps healthy cells get healthier while mutating cells deconstruct. It has also been found beneficial in managing blood sugar and helping with weight loss.

DAY 254 – SLOE (BLACKTHORN)

Tart and astringent, tasting almost salty, the Sloe fruit are bursting onto the hedgerow with abundance. They look like overlarge blueberries although they are actually in the plum family; Prunus spinosa. I have been excitedly watching them ripen over the past weeks waiting for the day they can be foraged and while they are still not quite ready, I couldn't resist plucking a few and giving them a try. I anticipated they would be fruity since they look like a berry. They absolutely were not, instead their heavy astringency gave them a salty quality that actually made them a little refreshing.

Prunus spinosa, also known as Blackthorn is native to Europe and some parts of Asia and has now been introduced in suitable temperate climates around the world. It is a deciduous tree that has strong, flexible branches filled with thorns, hence the name Blackthorn. It is often used as a hedge or barrier because of its formidably sharp thorns and dense countenance.

From a culinary perspective, the Sloe fruits claim to fame is none other than Sloe gin. Sloe gin is traditional liqueur made from fermenting the Sloe fruit in gin for a number of months until it's a lovely bright reddish purple. Once the fruit have soaked long enough the liqueur can be poured off and stored in airtight containers and the fruit can be made into other things. They can be dipped in chocolate, made into a chutney, or even a pie filling (make sure you remove the seeds). If you're not into gin, you can still use the Sloe fruit to make jams, jellies, pie filling, or add to soups and stews for a unique twist. Just be sure that you either freeze the briefly first or wait to pick them until after first frost.

From a health perspective, the Sloe fruit is AMAZING! Initially, I thought it might be challenging to find anything healthy about the Sloe. (Although, I've been discovering this year that just about everything that exists in nature has some health property.) But, lo and behold, a search through the pharmacological database revealed some pretty great stuff about blackthorn in general; the fruit, the flower, and the leaves and small stems.

The fruit are packed with phytonutrients; most notably several variations of quercetin and kaempferol. Quercetin is beneficial for conditions of the heart and lungs, it is also useful to eliminate histamine overproduction or processing so is useful in allergies and congestive issues. Kaempferol is also beneficial in heart and circulatory issues and works synergistically with quercetin to help eliminate cancer cells in the body.

Historically, folk remedies have recognized that blackthorn (including the Sloe fruit) are astringent, antioxidant, diaphoretic (inducing perspiration), depurative (elimination of impurities), febrifuge (minimizing fever), laxative, stomachic, and diuretic. Research demonstrates that they are immune boosting, increasing digestive properties, beneficial for systemic inflammation and decreasing oxidative stress. They also possess the potential to stimulate cellular health in already healthy and growing cells while causing mutated or unhealthy cells to deconstruct (that will be the kaempferol and quercetin working together).

DAY 255 – UMEBOSHI PLUM

Puckery, astringent and strangely satisfying after the initial impact on my palate; Umeboshi plums are a type of pickled/salted Japanese plum. The Ume plum (before preserving) is a particular variety of plum, actually more closely related to the apricot, that is native to Japan. It can now, however, be found in appropriate climates around the world. The plums are typically harvested in summer and then packed in salt and salt cured for several months. They are tangy and tart and definitely enliven the palate.

From a culinary perspective, Umeboshi plums are typically eaten as a condiment or an accompaniment to a meal or tea. They can also be added to soups, stews and other dishes to provide a more complex flavor. I like to eat a small amount of Umeboshi plum with scrambled eggs or even on toast. It jazzes everything up and wakes up my taste buds and my tummy.

From a health perspective Umeboshi plums are considered stimulating in traditional medicine. They stimulate digestion and gastrointestinal motility and help remove toxins from the body. They are a decent source of vitamins and minerals; providing vitamins C and A, and minerals like iron and potassium. Studies on the Umeboshi plum suggest that they are antioxidant helping to decrease oxidative stress in the body.
They are anti-inflammatory, helping to decrease systemic inflammation and ailments that result for inflammation. Umeboshis are also antibacterial, with research suggesting they can help significantly in eliminating candida. They contribute to gastrointestinal health and in turn

increase immune function. Umeboshis are proof that good things come in small packages with a little bit going a long way.

Caveat: be sure to read the ingredients, newer ways of processing Umeboshi include preservatives and food coloring that are better left alone. Traditional salt curing ingredients are just plums and salt; they are the ones you want to go for. They will be faded in color.

DAY 256 – STILTON CHEESE

Sharp and pungent with a creamy earthiness; Stilton cheese is traditionally enjoyed with a nice glass of port. Tonight's cheese is actually accompanying dinner so no port is on the scene, although a nice glass of shiraz seems to be holding its own with the strong Stilton flavors.

Stilton is a protected designation of origin cheese and in order to be called Stilton must be from one of three counties; Derbyshire, Leicestershire, or Nottinghamshire in the U.K. Stilton is a particular strain of blue cheese, which gives it the strong and pungent flavor. First recorded written history referencing Stilton cheese is around 1720. Stilton is a much-revered cheese, even having a sonnet written in its honor by G.K. Chesterton:

SONNET TO A STILTON CHEESE
Stilton, thou shouldst be living at this hour
And so thou art. Nor losest grace thereby;
England has need of thee, and so have I—
She is a Fen. Far as the eye can scour,
League after grassy league from Lincoln tower
To Stilton in the fields, she is a Fen.
Yet this high cheese, by choice of fenland men,
Like a tall green volcano rose in power.
Plain living and long drinking are no more,
And pure religion reading "Household Words",
And sturdy manhood sitting still all day
Shrink, like this cheese that crumbles to its core;
While my digestion, like the House of Lords,
The heaviest burdens on herself doth lay.

From a culinary perspective, Stilton is amazing. I love it on its own with fruit or in a heavier meal that features game or earthier flavors. It can also be turned into some pretty amazing sauces for pasta, veggies or meat. Blue cheese, including Stilton, is created by adding the mold *Penicillium* as it ferments. This creates a blue, green or gray vein of mold through the cheese. Sounds a bit off-putting when you read about it but trust me, it's absolutely delicious on your plate. Blue cheese is actually a very heart healthy food.

Research demonstrates that blue cheese in particular has a very anti-inflammatory impact, so it helps relieve oxidative stress, systemic inflammation and increases cardiovascular health. Side note and total bonus: The research also indicates that pairing the blue cheese with a good red wine increases the heart healthy potential and the yum factor incrementally. I'm sure it's all about moderation but really, could there be a better pairing for your health? (:

DAY 257 – BLACK PUDDING

Umami, earthy, slightly sweet and salty with a cake like mouthfeel, Black Pudding is an accompaniment to a "traditional" English breakfast. Initially, I was indeed squeamish about eating Black Pudding, also known as blood sausage, but in light of sustainable and "no waste" consciousness, I felt it was important to give it a try. To my surprise, I found it quite enjoyable.

There are various recipes for Black Pudding depending on the region or even the country, however, they all tend to have a foundation of ingredients which include, onions, a grain (I prefer oats), pork fat and blood. These ingredients are mixed together then put into a casing of some type so they can be sliced and grilled, fried, baked, or otherwise cooked for a meal. Almost every culture that consumes meat has a variation of blood sausage, this from the days of valuing and consuming every part of the animal. It's only in recent history that we've had the luxury of picking and choosing and ultimately wasting parts of the animals that we've chosen to eat.

From a culinary perspective, it might be easier to find a reputable, sustainable source for your Black Pudding rather than trying to make it yourself. Then you can fry it up for breakfast, bake some up for dinner, or serve it up as a small plate option. If you wanted to try to make your own, the most challenging part would be to get a hold of some blood. Short of having to find your own pig and do the deed yourself, there are options, believe it or not, to purchase dried blood and reconstitute it. I'm sort of on the fence about all of this, on the one hand, I don't want to be a hypocrite and shy away from the process, however, on the other hand, the thought of stirring up some blood and oats in the kitchen seems a bit daunting. Trust that I will keep you all posted if I end up giving it a try.

From a health perspective, believe it or not, Black Pudding is really good for you. It is high in protein and minerals, like zinc and iron, and also possesses all the nutritional qualities of the added ingredients like oats. Remember that oats are little rock stars. As with any food, the closer they are to their natural state, the better they are for you.

They are a great source of fiber and various vitamins and minerals. Studies demonstrate that the inclusion of oats in your diet can help with cholesterol, decrease the potential for colorectal cancer, and help balance blood sugar. Oats are also a great prebiotic, increasing the production of short chain fatty acids that aid in helping you have a happy belly. Add that to the power of nutrient dense blood and Black Pudding becomes quite a powerhouse of nutritional goodness.

Caveat: Make sure you are eating quality ingredients, from animals that have been sustainably raised with conscious animal husbandry practices. I've seen some recipes that use corn meal as the filler rather than oats, avoid those at all costs. Traditionally made, organic/sustainable, quality ingredients are the only way to go.

DAY 258 - KIWI BERRY

Sweet and juicy with a pleasantly plump squishiness that refreshes the palate, I can see why Kiwi Berries are called baby Kiwis. They are related to the larger Kiwi, however the Kiwi berry can be eaten whole without peeling or worrying about seeds. In fact, from just an eating perspective they have a mouthfeel quite similar to a grape. Kiwi Berries (Actunidia arguta) are native to Northern climates and do quite well in an environment with varying temperatures, this is one reason they are referred to as Hardy Kiwi. They are making their way to market now with a season that typically lasts September through November.

From a culinary perspective Kiwi Berries are seriously juicy and delicious, which makes them a great option for just munching as is. They are great anywhere their larger relative is used, salads, smoothies, desserts, dressings, really anywhere a sweeter fruit like Kiwi would work.

From a health perspective, Kiwi Berries are, you guessed it, an amazing source of nutrient density. They have five times as much vitamin C as an orange. They are rich in Vitamin A, B, and E, with 60% more vitamin E than a serving of avocado. They are an excellent source of minerals like potassium, magnesium, manganese and iron.

In Traditional Chinese Medicine Kiwi Berries are used for issues of digestion, systemic inflammation, and kidney and urinary tract problems. They are also used to correct systemic imbalances that contribute to various kinds of cancer. Research has, in the past few years, begun to support claims made for their beneficial impact.

Studies show that a combination of chemical compounds found in the Kiwi family, and in higher degree in the Kiwi Berry, generate an impact similar to other berries and "super" fruits, when it comes to influencing cellular health. To be specific, these particular compounds support the healthy cells, helping them grow even stronger, and cause the mutated cells to blow themselves up (a process known as apoptosis). Kiwi Berries also aid in gastrointestinal health, calming inflamed tissue in the intestinal tract and contributing to its potential to heal and renew.

I found Kiwi Berries to be altogether delicious and delightful; a refreshing snack for a warm autumn day.

DAY 259 – DAMSON PLUMS (RECIPE)

Tart and tangy, I've been waiting all year to try a Damson Plum. I first was acquainted with them last year but only vicariously, so was determined this year to experience them firsthand as they ripened on the trees waiting to be picked.

Damson plums are abundant in the English countryside and according to genetic testing, they seem to be particular to the region where they grow, even though there are theories that suggest otherwise. The Damson can also be found in very small areas of the U.S. where they were introduced by the English colonists, although, there are many rival varieties that give them a run for their money.

From a culinary perspective, the Damson is a great fruit for making jams, jellies, pies, or other backed goods. It is not too sweet and it has a strong texture with a good amount of pectin to help give it a thick texture. Because it is tangy as well as sweet, it pairs well with game and other meat dishes. I have a batch of damsons that are going to find their way into a baked crisp. Damsons are also used to make gin and wine, something I haven't tried yet, but you can bet it's on my list. Apparently, they make a good cloth dye as well.

From a health perspective Damson plums are right up there with other plum relatives providing vitamins, minerals and phytonutrients that fight cancer, oxidative stress and systemic inflammation. They are high in fiber, pectin, as well as vitamins and minerals that contribute significantly to gastrointestinal health, including inhibiting colon cancer. Damsons are high in potassium and magnesium, making them great for heart health. They also have a significant amount of copper and iron, contributing to endocrine balance and increasing red blood cell counts.

Damson cobbler here I come....

DAMSON AND VANILLA COBBLER
(Adapted from Galton Blackiston)
For the filling:
700 g damsons, halved and stones removed
300 g light soft brown sugar
1 vanilla pod, halved lengthways
4 tbsp amaretto (almond liqueur)
50 g butter, diced, plus extra for greasing

For the cobbler topping
200 g oats
4 tbsp caster sugar (I actually used2 tbs of dates processed in the food processor instead of sugar, it was divine!)
50 g ground almonds
250 ml double cream, lightly whipped to very soft peaks
Preheat the oven to 375, 190C/Gas 5. For the filling: butter a 20 x 30 cm shallow ovenproof dish with plenty of softened butter. Scatter the damsons over the bottom of the dish, packing them in quite tightly. Sprinkle over the sugar and tuck in the vanilla pod halves. Drizzle over the amaretto and dot with the butter.

For the cobbler topping: tip the oats, sugar (or dates) and almonds into a bowl and mix together. Fold in the whipped cream to make a sticky dough. Gently tear off pieces of the dough and arrange on top of the damsons, covering as much of the fruit as possible.

Bake in the oven for about 45 minutes, or until the top is golden and the damsons are bubbling. Serve with ice cream or cream.

DAY 260-POMEGRANATE

Tangy, sour and sweet, all at the same time, the Pomegranate seed is the true harbinger of autumn. It is because of the Pomegranate seed that we have Fall and winter, according to mythology. A brief overview of the myth goes something like this; Hades took Persephone, the daughter of Zeus and Demeter, to the Underworld. She didn't want to stay but, unfortunately, while there she ate several Pomegranate seeds. Some myths say three and others say six. Whichever the number, by consuming food from the underworld Persephone was doomed to spend one month for every seed eaten. Persephone is a vegetation goddess and the consequence of the time she spends underground is the death of vegetation; demonstrated by the change in vegetation from autumn to winter. As Persephone rises again to the surface, vegetation awakens and spring begins.

So, here we are in autumn and the Pomegranates are in season and ripening for harvest. They are tangy and tart and sweeten as they ripen. They are an interesting fruit, containing anywhere from 200 – 1400 seeds per fruit, with a thick skin that can be challenging to peel. Pomegranates originate in the area of the Middle East known as the "Fertile Crescent" but have since made their way around the world to appropriate climates.

From a culinary perspective, Pomegranates are delicious raw, although sometimes challenging to eat. It's a common ingredient in Middle Eastern and Persian cuisine both as syrup or the seeds, or both. One of my favorites is a dish called Fesenjan, which is basically a stew made with chicken, walnuts and pomegranate.

From a health perspective, Pomegranates are yet one more of those super-foods. There is ample research demonstrating they are highly antioxidant, eliminating oxidative stress and systemic inflammation. They are also amazing in the cardiovascular department, helping to reduce the risk of cardiovascular disease. Studies also demonstrate that pomegranate is anti-carcinogenic, reducing the risk of a wide variety of cancers by, you guessed it, helping keep the healthy cells healthy and encouraging the mutated cells to blow themselves up (apoptosis).

Pomegranates are fun to eat and even more fun to share, so keep an eye out in your market, they should be arriving on the scene soon and you can celebrate the onset of autumn.

DAY 261 – SPELT

Nutty, with a slight hint of sweetness, Spelt has its own subtle flavor, unique from its other wheat relatives. Spelt is a grain in the wheat family; however, it is sort of in its own class. While it is considered an ancient grain, it is a "newer" hybrid from the truly ancient grains such as emmer and einkorn. Several things make Spelt unique. First, it seems to be a natural hybrid between a 'hulled' variety wheat grain and what is considered a 'free-threshing' wheat grain (all to do with the presence and density of the coating of the grain).

It also appears to have popped-up of its own accord in a variety of landscapes as a natural cross between the hulled and free threshing varieties. It was initially believed that Spelt hybridization gave rise to what we currently understand as bread wheat (T.aesivitum), however archeo-botanists no longer believe this is necessarily the case. In some areas, early man was cultivating variations of bread wheat before Spelt came into their landscape. So, it appears the most accurate identification would be that Spelt is a naturalized hybrid of various wheat varieties. It appears Spelt first emerged on the domesticated grain scene around 2200 B.C., in several different locations across Europe and the areas known as the Fertile Crescent.

From a culinary perspective Spelt is a delicious addition to your dietary repertoire. It has a distinctive flavor, sweet, nutty and chewy; quite similar to barley but still unique. It cooks relatively quickly and is great for sweet and savory dishes. It can be a breakfast grain, added to a salad, tossed in soups and stews. As flour, it is a great replacement for bread flour, being slightly lower in gluten/gliadin ratio. It still possesses enough to make a good pliable bread dough and give some lift to other baked goods.

From a health perspective Spelt is a good choice because it contains a significant amount of protein and vitamins and minerals, while containing lower amount of tannins and about 40% less phytic acid than other common wheat varieties. This makes Spelt easier to digest and the nutrients easier to assimilate. Spelt is a great source of glutamine, lysine, methionine, and proline; all of which are amino acids critical to our health.

Spelt also contains a significant amount of vitamins A, E, D, and B.

Studies have indicated the inclusion of Spelt in the diet can help decrease the occurrence of ailments like colitis, high blood cholesterol, dermatitis, systemic inflammation and oxidative stress. It's important to remember Spelt does contain gluten so individuals suffering from Celiac Disease or genuine gluten allergy/intolerance should avoid consumption.

DAY 262 – CATSUP (KETCHUP)

Savory, sweet, salty, earthy, in short, very umami; a good Catsup seems to hit all the flavor notes in the palate. Today's Catsup comes straight from the kitchen of the Red Lion Free House in East Chisenbury, UK. It's home made from fresh, wholesome ingredients and is quite a treat.

Catsup is a well-loved condiment in most of the world and especially in the U.S. It is one that seems to transcend almost all potential culinary, cultural, or socio-economic boundaries; finding its way into roughly 97% of American kitchens, according to recent polls. Even though Catsup is considered as American as apple pie and hot dogs, it isn't an American creation. It made its way to the States before they were even States, via British culinary migration but originally it hails from Asia.

Ke-tsiap is a type of pickled fish sauce that caught the attention of British travelers and found its way to British tables in the 1700's and from there continued on to the American colonies. Initially, recipes for Catsup did not contain tomatoes rather they were more of a brown sauce with a mushroom, walnut or even an anchovy base. Tomatoes weren't introduced as an ingredient in Catsup until 1812 when James Mease, a scientist and horticulturalist with a penchant for tomatoes published a recipe for tomato Catsup.

Since that time Catsup has undergone any number of variations, with initial commercial recipes containing alarming chemicals and harsh preservatives. In 1876 Henry Heinz and Dr. Harvey Washington Wiley teamed up to create a Catsup that was preservative free, while still possessing all of its flavor and extended shelf life. Catsup quickly became an American icon, with billions of gallons consumed every year.

From a culinary perspective, making your own Catsup can be quite the undertaking. It can be as labor intensive and creative if you are following the general idea of Catsup as a pickled condiment. If you are trying to recreate a bottle of Heinz then it may be a bit more challenging. Catsup is a condiment and can accompany any number of foods to bump up the flavor spectrum of a meal.

From a health perspective, unfortunately, although Mr. Heinz began his commercial product with the intention of creating something worthy of the public health, it has not remained that way. Most commercial ketchups are made from tomato concentrates and contain dubious ingredients like High Fructose Corn Syrup. However, if you can get your hands on some good old-fashioned Catsup, it can be quite the find, containing healthy ingredients like cooked tomatoes, vinegar, herbs and spices, and happy belly probiotics.

Research indicates that cooked tomatoes are indeed a wealth of nutrient goodness. Not only are they high in various vitamins and minerals, but also supply phytonutrients that inhibit and even destroy mutated cells that contribute to cancers like prostate, colon, and pancreatic. Cooked tomatoes are also anti-inflammatory and anti-oxidant, as well as being highly beneficial for lowering blood pressure and keeping cholesterol levels in healthy balance. If you're a Catsup user, you will want to check the ingredients and if they're all natural, from real foods, pour it on.

DAY 263 - COCONUT WATER

Sweet, salty, slightly earthy, and then back to sweet; Coconut Water is refreshing and tastes almost umami with its complex nuances of flavor. Coconut Water is the liquid from young, green coconuts. In its natural state straight from the coconut, it is quite delicious and nutritious. Coconut Water has been getting quite the critical acclaim over the past few years as yet another super-food. The marketing tactics touting the health benefits of Coconut Water have been so successful that the production and sales are now a billion dollar industry.

From a culinary perspective, Coconut Water is most delicious in its most natural state; either straight from the coconut or at least as unprocessed as possible. It is a great addition to raw soups and stews or as a refreshing drink. I love to get the whole young coconut, drain off the water, then scoop out the fresh inner meat and use it to make various raw food dishes.

From a health perspective, Coconut Water gets very interesting. If you pay attention to the marketing, you can't help but be amazed at the health benefits you will receive from drinking that carton of Coconut Water from the refrigerator section in the market. It's better than any sports drink, provides you with more energy that a cup of coffee, boosts your immune function, perks up your cognitive function and increases your digestion...what's not to love??? Too good to be true? Maybe...

Fresh, young Coconut Water is indeed packed with vitamins, minerals and other phytonutrients. One claim to fame is that it is full of the electrolytes necessary to replenish athletes during workouts. Historically, marketing has suggested that it is better than any other sport drink on the market and supplies all the nutrients necessary to keep the body in balance while working out or playing hard. Research suggests that this may indeed be true to some degree.

Fresh Coconut Water does possess an admirable amount of electrolyte and in combination that works very well for balancing the human body. Unfortunately, not quite enough to serve as the replenishing super drink that marketing was suggesting. Several Coconut Water companies have had to remove those claims and pay out several million to settle a class action suit.

To be fair, the initial impetus for those types of health claims was grounded in some truth. Coconut Water from young coconuts is pretty close to our optimal balance. In fact, close enough that in some tropical regions in situations of extreme emergency, Coconut Water has been used successfully in plasma transfusions. Yep, that's right, intravenous Coconut Water with no reported adverse effects.

When news of these studies hit the public market, the word soon spread that Coconut Water was the same chemical makeup as human plasma and therefore could be useful for all sorts of miraculous health interventions. Unfortunately, this is not the case; Coconut Water is not the same as human plasma. That being said, it does absolutely possess an amazing amount of minerals; potassium, calcium, magnesium and sodium and an amazing array of vitamins like B and C.

This wide variety of nutrients can indeed help boost immune function, increase digestive quality, lower cholesterol, and any number of other health benefits. So, what's the catch? The key word is "fresh" Coconut Water. Unless you are getting it straight from the coconut or shortly thereafter in its raw state, you aren't drinking fresh Coconut Water. Chances are, what you are drinking is heat pasteurized Coconut Water with additives, including sugar and preservatives...which all adds up to pretty significant sugar consumption.

A typical 330ml container of Coconut Water contains the equivalent of 6 teaspoons of table sugar (yep, 6 teaspoons) and that doesn't include the sugar that is often added to enhance flavor. Also, once processed, while Coconut Water does still contain minerals and some vitamins, the heating process not only destroys the taste but also kills off almost all of the other ingredients like enzymes that contribute to health. This is typically why sugar and other flavor enhancers are added back in with some preservatives.

The downside of drinking sugary Coconut Water? It increases candida in the gut, contributes to an imbalance in energy, decreases immune function (studies show up to 40% decrease lasting several hours after sugar is consumed), and contributes to "brain fog". Notice that the pasteurized results are almost the exact opposite of the benefits of fresh Coconut Water? Pretty crazy how just one little process, and a few additives, can completely adulterate something.

The bottom line? Read labels and don't fall for the hype. Fresh young Coconut Water does indeed possess health benefits, is refreshing, and thirst quenching. It also possesses some great bioactive components that help soothe digestion and boost metabolism, however, once it's processed and packaged for the store shelves it no longer resembles what you get straight from the coconut and while it is definitely better than picking up a soft drink, it isn't maybe your best option if you're avoiding sugar in your diet.

DAY 264 – KIDNEY BEAN (RED)

Smooshy and dense, with a flavor that is earthy and slightly sweet, the red Kidney Bean has found its way to my plate; or rather to my small foldout table, 10,000 feet in the air. I have to be honest and say the Kidney Beans are probably one of my least favorite things to chew, being a person who is predominantly texture and mouthfeel based with actual flavor composition coming in on a close second. Kidney Beans tend to feel just a little bit weird to chew. However, they have made an appearance and I have taken a moment to slow down and really find an appreciation for the bean.

The red Kidney Bean is so named because the outer skin is red in color and it is shaped, you guessed it, like a kidney. What we called them before we knew what kidneys are shaped like, I don't know. The Kidney Bean is considered a 'common bean' and according to archeo-horticultural sources, it was first called the Kidney Bean in about 1551 to distinguish it from the 'old world beans' from Europe. Apparently, the Kidney Bean is native to the Americas, Peru to be exact, but has since made its way around the world and is indeed common in many cultural cuisines. For centuries, beans have played an important role in the human diet, providing a complementary nutrient offering when combined with grains and/or other starches.

Native American tradition understood the importance of dietary balance and exemplified it with their cultivation of "The Three Sisters", squash, beans, and corn. The planting of the 'three sister's gardens" allowed for an agricultural balance with the maize providing stalks for the beans to cling to, the beans providing nitrogen for the soil, and the squash providing ground cover that helped reduce weeds. Interestingly, it also allowed for a nutritional balance with the combination of foods providing the necessary amino acids to form a relatively complete protein (B12)

From a culinary perspective, Kidney Beans are found in any variety of dietary/culinary endeavors from savory to sweet. It is a foundational ingredient in soups, stews, casseroles, curries, chili, and dishes like red beans and rice. Red beans can also be made into a paste or flour that can be used in baking or as a filling. How about some red bean brownies? Yes, please. Just be sure to soak the beans well before using or cooking. This opens up their cell wall and makes the nutrients more bio-available. There is also research demonstrating that the high concentration of lectins in red Kidney Beans is toxic, soaking and cooking eliminates this problem.

From a health perspective, red Kidney Beans are a highly useful and healthful ingredient. They are a fiber superstar, which helps to regulate things like blood sugar, cholesterol levels, and metabolic function. They are a great source of vitamins and minerals, like iron, magnesium, folate, copper and potassium. Kidney Beans also contain isoflavones and anthocyanins, which are antioxidants that protect against systemic inflammation and oxidative stress, reducing the risk of a variety of ailments. Research suggests that the fiber content combined with the variety of phytonutrients makes Kidney Beans a significant game changer in things like colon cancer, cardiovascular disease, and diabetes, just to name a few.

DAY 265 – KABOCHA SQUASH

Moist, dense, sweet, earthy, and almost nutty in flavor, Kabocha Squash is actually one of my absolute favorite foods (even more favored than

Pumpkin, if I may be so bold). Since we are now in the lovely season of autumn, one of my absolute favorite seasons, I thought it only fitting to celebrate the onset of winter squashes. Kabocha Squash is a cucurbita maxima variety of winter squash. It is also referred to as Japanese Pumpkin, not least because it is such a common ingredient in Japanese cuisine. In fact, it is a common ingredient in many Asian dishes, if you've ever ordered Pumpkin Curry in your local Thai restaurant you were actually eating Kabocha Squash.

From a culinary perspective Kabocha Squash is versatile, delicious, and nutritious. It is great in both savory and sweet recipes, partly because it has a more complex and slightly stronger flavor palate than other squashes. Its density makes it great to cook and bake with. I tend to use it in recipes that traditionally call for Pumpkin just because it is yummier and denser. It makes delicious soup, stew, Pumpkin bread, cookies, curry, stir-fry, and on and on. It's even delicious in raw recipes and you can leave the skin on, since it's edible too. Another little tip for using Kabocha Squash? As a puree, it makes a great thickener. For example, it makes a great base to tomato free chili, oh yes.

From a health perspective, Kabocha Squash is full of good stuff. It's lower in carbohydrate content than other winter squashes but higher in fiber. It is also lower in calorie than its winter counterparts. It is packed with beta-carotene, which helps reduce the risk of certain cancers and other ailments like macular degeneration. It is a good source of vitamins B and C as well as A. Kabocha also contains a significant amount of pectin, hence the thickening quality.

Pectin helps your body in a variety of ways; it contributes to lower cholesterol levels, helps to clear the body of heavy metals, contributes to tissue repair in the gastrointestinal tract, and is useful in glucose regulation. Studies have demonstrated that consuming foods high in pectin can also help reduce the risk and occurrence of prostate cancer. It's another one of those foods that induces apoptosis in mutated cells while helping the healthy cells get healthier.
Sounds like the perfect reason to celebrate the onset of Autumn with some delicious Kabocha Squash.

Not sure how to get more squash in your diet? Here's a super simple way to get started:

Take one small Kabocha Squash, wash it well because you will leave the skin on, then cut it into cubes, chunks, or thin long slices, toss them in olive oil (or coconut oil), cumin and a pinch of sea salt. Bake at 375 degrees until soft. Sprinkle with roasted hazelnuts and Enjoy!

DAY 266 – TOFFEE (RECIPE)

Sweet with a delicious hint of savory because of the Maillard Reaction, Toffee is one of those sweet treats that is definitely "more-ish". Toffee is basically sugar and butter (or sometimes molasses or golden syrup) cooked to either a particular temperature or, to what is referred to in the candy-making world, as a "hard crack" stage. The length of time cooked and/or the heat applied will elicit different textures, flavors and solidity. Today's inspiration for Toffee as the Flavor of the Day came from some left over sticky Toffee pudding topping that found its way to the table with some apple slices. Oh yes, it's that time of year for Toffee apples and Pumpkin.

Toffee and Taffy are apparently derived from the same ingredients; one is a result of pouring and the other a result of pulling. Toffee puddings, Toffee apples, and Toffee sweets to savor are all signs that fall and winter are settling in. I tend to think of Toffee as autumn flavor especially with reference to Halloween, however, it is also apparently part of other holiday traditions; according to the National Museum of Wales on Christmas in North Wales people would celebrate with an evening of Toffee pulling called 'Noson Gyflaith'.

From a culinary perspective, what's not to love about the delicious sweetness of Toffee? It has everything our brain loves to nosh on; sweet, fat, and the umami flavor of the Maillard Reaction.

You can make Toffee pretty easily with just some Butter, sugar (or molasses) and if you're going to pull it, some lemon. If you would just like a little creamy pot of Toffee, akin to sticky Toffee topping, you cook it slightly less. If you are going to pull then cook it longer until it actually begins to pull from the sides of the pan. Pour it out onto a cookie sheet or clean countertop, butter your hands and begin pulling. Be very careful because initially it will be hot. As you pull and twist it will change color and become easier to turn into different shapes. If you just want to pour it into a pan after you've cooked it to the desired density that works too. Pour it into a buttered pan and then slice it into pieces. If you cook it to the hard crack stage you can just break it into pieces and enjoy it as little hard candies.

From a health perspective, well let's get real; it's candy we're talking about, straight sugar with Buttery goodness. How good can that be for you??? In moderation, if it's made from quality ingredients it isn't going to do much damage. The impact it has on your body will be totally dependent upon the ingredients used and how much is consumed. It's unfortunate that we've become such a sugar laden culture so it is not really possible to enjoy sweet treats as much as they must have been enjoyed back in the day when you really only got to eat something sugary and sweet maybe a few times a year.

Each year as the holidays come around I think how fun it would be to prepare a basked of delicious goodies as gifts for friends and family. Then I just as quickly realize, it's not really a treat. As a populace, we consume so much sugar every day, both apparent and hidden, that to give baskets of more sugar is probably not the best or kindest thing to do.
Imagine what a treat it must have been to wait all year for Toffee time! Salivating with anticipation as the ingredients began to bubble and brown and become pliable; the smell must have been completely fantastic and titillating. What a treat to savor.

TOFFEE
8 cups dark brown sugar (I use muscovado...you can also use ½ molasses and ½ sugar)
2/3 cup boiling water
3 tablespoons fresh lemon juice, pulp strained out
½ lb softened salted butter

Using an enameled or stainless steel saucepan over low heat, gradually dissolve the sugar in the boiling water. Stir it continuously with a wooden spoon until the sugar is thoroughly dissolved. This usually takes from 20 to 30 minutes.
Remove the saucepan from the heat, add the lemon juice and the softened butter, and stir them into the sugar. Boil this mixture fairly briskly, WITHOUT STIRRING it, for 15 minutes.

Gently drop a teaspoonful of the mixture into a cupful of cold water; if it hardens at once, it has reached the required consistency (soft-crack stage).
Pour the mixture slowly onto a buttered marble slab or large flat dish. Do not scrape the saucepan clean as the scraping might turn the Toffee back into sugar.
Use extra butter to butter your hands. Pull the taffy into long golden

strands while it is still hot. Cut the taffy in smaller pieces. This makes about 3 pounds of Toffee.

DAY 267 – SAUERKRAUT (RECIPE)

Tangy, sour, crunchy and refreshing, sauerkraut makes a delicious accompaniment to any meal. Fermented and pickled foods have been part of the human diet for thousands of years. In fact, just about every culture has some type of fermented food with Sauerkraut being one of the most popular and well known. It is definitely one of my favorites, especially when it's homemade. Sauerkraut basically means "sour Cabbage" and that's exactly what it is. You take some Cabbage, spices, salt and sometimes whey and you smash it all up together then set it aside for a few days while it ferments.

From a culinary perspective, making your own Sauerkraut is actually pretty easy, fun and well worth it since raw sauerkraut is so much more flavorful and healthful than cooked and pasteurized. Once you've got a batch ready to eat, you can enjoy it as a condiment or as a zippy replacement for sauces or dressings.

From a health perspective raw Sauerkraut is seriously amazing stuff. Research demonstrates that eating four or more servings of Sauerkraut a week has a pretty significant impact on your immune system. In fact, one study revealed that when subjects consumed a half a cup a day of raw sauerkraut a day it significantly reduced the risk of viral infections like avian flu. For decades, if not centuries, Sauerkraut has been recognized as a digestive aid and treatment for gastrointestinal issues, including ulcers and ulcerative colitis.

Sauerkraut is a great source of Vitamins C, B, and K to name a few and it also has a significant amount of calcium, magnesium, iron and other minerals. If you're feeling adventurous it's worth trying your hand a batch of Sauerkraut, especially with flu season on the way. It will last a while once fermented.

Here's a basic recipe to begin with but once you get the hang of it you can switch it up and create your own unique options.

2 heads of Cabbage (green or red or both)
1/2 cup of Whey   (if whey is not available you can use more sea salt)
1 Tbsp of Sea Salt
1 Tbsp Caraway Seeds

Core the Cabbage heads, cut into wedges and then slice/chop into small strips. Place Cabbage in a large bowl and add whey and sea salt.

Here comes the fun part. Begin squishing and massaging the Cabbage into the whey and sea salt. Keep this up until the Cabbage is softened and enough liquid has formed in the bowl to cover the Cabbage easily.

Now add the caraway seeds and mix well. Place the Sauerkraut in glass jars with lids, canning jars are perfect. Fill almost to the top but make sure there is enough liquid in each jar for the Cabbage to be completely covered. This is very important because we want fermentation not mold and if the Cabbage is above the liquid, it will mold. Now put the lids on your jars and place them on a shelf or somewhere that they can rest and ferment.

Depending on the time of year this process can take anywhere from a week to 10 days (also depending on how fermented you want it to taste). Check on them every day or so to make sure that the Cabbage is below the liquid line. If it isn't just open the jars and push the Cabbage down under the juice. Make sure you have clean hands first!

If you'd like to experiment with different flavors and spices you can try these:
Use Curry instead of Caraway seeds, it may sound frightening but it is fantastic!
Add mustard seeds with the Caraway seeds
Chinese Five Spice is also interesting instead of Caraway seeds
For a spicier version of fermented goodness, try adding this to your Cabbage:
1 cup of grated carrots and 2 medium onions, finely sliced. Replace the caraway seeds with 1 tablespoon of oregano and some red pepper flakes.

Hints: Just so I can easily tell the difference between the Sauerkrauts I make I use different colored Cabbages for different spices. I use purple and green Cabbage for the spicy mixture (which is a modified Cortido). It turns a lovely pink/red color. I use just green Cabbage for the others, the caraway version will stay nicely green and white and looks lovely and the curry version turns a spectacular yellow.

Make sure you store your Sauerkraut in the refrigerator after it has fermented to your taste. It will last for a couple of months technically.

Although it never lasts that long in my kitchen because I love it and eat a little bit of it with just about everything. If your Sauerkraut does grow mold, which will more than likely be either black or pink, don't eat it. You'll have to throw it away and start over.

DAY 268 – CELERY SALT

Savory and slightly earthy, salty and a little something extra akin to umami, Celery Salt adds an interesting complexity to my morning meal. Celery Salt is something that has always confused me. Is it salt flavored with celery? Is it salt made out of celery? What exactly does it do and where does it come from? I've seen it as an ingredient on meat labels claiming to be naturally cured (the meat, not the labels). And recently I had a conversation with a chef who uses it as an in-house preservative. Here I thought it was just interesting to sprinkle on my lentil patties.

In researching Celery Salt I've found a mix of information and articles identifying what it actually is and how to use it. This sort of added to my confusion (apparently I'm not the only one confused, so that's good). Some articles say it is a mixture of sea salt and ground celery seed, while others have suggested it is actually a mixture of ground celery seed and dried/powdered celery juice. The Celery Salt that I used this morning was a finely powdered blend of sea salt and celery seed. Now that I've researched it more thoroughly I am interested to try making my own Celery Salt just from the seeds and juice.

So, it turns out Celery Salt /powder is a naturally occurring preservative due to the sodium content and the fact that it contains naturally occurring sodium nitrates. But wait! Aren't nitrates bad for you? Well, here's where it gets interesting. Nitrates and nitrites are both naturally occurring in many fruits, veggies, and even meats once they are cooked. So, it's virtually impossible to avoid them if you are eating real food. And believe or not, nitrites and nitrates in the right amount are helpful to the body. Who knew???

The nitrate/nitrite combination in the form of nitric oxide helps the nutrients in our food assimilate by assisting in crossing the blood/tissue barrier. Now when these naturally occurring substances end up in a too high of an amount and our body is very acidic, they then can become dangerous and carcinogenic because the convert to something called a nitrosamine. So, why do nitrates/nitrites get such a bad rap? Well, according to independent studies, non-naturally occurring preservatives, meaning those formulated in a lab somewhere, do not have the same helpful impact on the body that naturally occurring ones do. According to two recent studies, the 'frankennitrates' convert immediately to nitrosamines.

Back to our Celery Salt discussion... so, Celery Salt is indeed a natural preservative, one that is apparently beneficial to the body in the right conditions and right amounts. According to the data, your best bet is to consume Celery Salt that is actually just from celery, without the addition of sea salt. This provides a better mineral balance of not only sodium, but also potassium and magnesium.

From a culinary perspective, I would absolutely avoid purchasing Celery Salt unless you have full disclosure of ingredients. They often include anti-caking agents and other things that are better left out of your real food pantry. You can make celery powder or Celery Salt several ways; grind some celery seeds to a fine powder and mix in with sea salt; definitely, a delicious option. You can also dehydrate parts of celery, then grind them to a powder, and even add some finely ground seed. If you add celery powder or salt to things that you are pickling or curing, it will preserve the color. This is one reason meats that are preserved naturally with Celery Salt keep their pink color and look so "fresh".

From a health perspective, well, I think we've already pretty much covered that... Celery Salt or powder can be a healthful addition to your dietary repertoire when consumed in moderation.

DAY 269 – PUMPKIN

Sweet, savory, earthy, almost nutty with a mouthfeel that is dense but smooth and creamy, I love Pumpkin!! It is one of my absolute favorite foods. Today in honor of fall and the Supermoon (as if I really need a reason) it has made its way into my latte, and also into some deliciously easy Pumpkin pancakes.

The Pumpkin is a member of the Curcubito pepo squash family. It's a winter squash, so is typically, when left to its own devices a seasonal food. It's one that sort of sums up the onset of fall and symbolizes abundance and harvest in many cultures and it also calls to mind the mystical, magical world and  have been part of Samhain celebrations for hundreds of years. Pumpkins and winter squash relatives can be found all over the world, although it appears they originated on the North American continent.

From a culinary perspective, Pumpkin is awesome and easy to add to both sweet and savory dishes or drinks. I love Pumpkin in my coffee but I am not a fan of sweet, flavored syrups, so instead I add the real thing. A teaspoon or two of Pumpkin mixed with a tiny bit of coconut oil and cream... makes a to-die-for latte that is also good for you. Next easy peasy way to use Pumpkin?? You guessed it, pancakes. This morning I took one half cup of Pumpkin, one egg, ¼ c. chestnut flour and a pinch of baking soda...mixed them all up and griddled some delicious Pumpkin pancakes for breakfast.

Pumpkin is delicious in soups, stews, casseroles, on its own, as a side, as a main, in baked goods and puddings; you name it, you can probably add Pumpkin to it.

From a nutritional perspective, Pumpkin has all the same great benefits as other winter squash. It is very similar to the Kabocha Squash, although just slightly less nutrient dense. It is high in fiber and a great source of vitamins and minerals. It is especially rich in vitamin A. It is also full of phytonutrients that help lower cholesterol, manage blood sugar, and inhibit the oxidative stressors that contribute to cancer. It is packed with beta-carotene and zea-xanthine, which helps reduce the risk of certain cancers and other ailments like macular degeneration. It is another one of those foods that induces apoptosis in mutated cells while helping the healthy cells get even healthier.

DAY 270– PORTOBELLO MUSHROOM

Earthy, dense and almost meaty, Portobello Mushrooms can be a really delectable substitute for other less nutritious foods. Take for example the Portobello Mushroom fries that are the inspiration for today's flavor. Their texture and size actually makes them perfect for this substitution, providing a dense and inviting texture and complex flavor, with hints of umami.

Portobello Mushrooms are actually a grown up version of the common or button mushroom also called the Crimini. Mushrooms have been part of the human diet for thousands of years. Interestingly, "The first evidence that mushrooms were used as human food in prehistoric Europe is the recent find of a bowl of field mushrooms in a Bronze Age house near Nola in Italy."(Dalby, 2003).

From a culinary perspective, Portobello Mushrooms are great. They are great grilled, baked, sliced up and stir-fried, used in a sandwich, a replacement for burgers, you name it. The inspiration for this flavor was Portobello fries, seasoned and then baked to a crispy deliciousness and lastly, sprinkled with some Parmesan cheese. Yum.

From a health perspective, Portobellos have a very similar nutrient signature to the rest of their mushroom relatives. They are a great source of vitamins A, B, and D as well as minerals like potassium, copper, zinc, and calcium. Crimini mushrooms also exhibit antibacterial and antifungal properties as well as being highly antioxidant. They can help decrease oxidative stress and systemic inflammation. They're a great addition to your dietary repertoire.

DAY 271 – WILD GRAPES

Tangy, juicy, sweet and sour all at the same time; Wild Grapes pack a lot of flavor into a tiny package. Today's Wild Grapes were a delightful surprise found in quite the most unexpected place while trekking through the desert canyon.

Wild Grapes are actually pretty tenacious, it seems, so long as a water source is present and can be found in a variety of environments. According to the Department of Forestry, the grapes I found while hiking were likely Vitis californica, which can be found in shady canyons on the west side of the ridge, near a water source. Check! A little delving into plant lore of the Sierra Nevada's reveals that all parts of this particular wild grape are edible, with the grapes themselves being small, dark, and tart in flavor. Yep, that's them. The grape leaves and tendrils can also be eaten. I didn't know this so I didn't try them. I may have to go back and forage some.

From a health perspective, Wild Grapes are more nutrient dense than their conventional/hybrid counterpart. Their thick, dark skin is a good source for resveratrol, which decreases the incidence and risk of cardiovascular disease as well as balances cholesterol and reduces the formation of blood clots. Resveratrol also protects against cell damage and mental decline.

The ellargic acid found in dark grapes also contributes to an increase in metabolic function revving up the body's fat burning potential. This happens mostly by decreasing the body's ability to produce new fat cells and delaying the growth of fat cells already present. Because Wild Grapes have a large seed, they have increased antioxidant potential, decreasing oxidative stress and systemic inflammation. Research suggests that the phytonutrients found in grape seeds provide excellent support for the pancreas, kidneys, and liver, helping repair damage to DNA caused by oxidative stress.

DAY 272 – NORI

Weird, crinkly, salty, this particular Nori is marinated in wasabi, which is the only thing that gets me past the mouthfeel. I've eaten Nori before as an accompaniment to sushi, (which is a challenging cuisine for someone so highly sensitive to mouthfeel) but I've not really ever tried it by itself. A friend handed a wasabi flavored Nori sheet to me and I had to try it. First impression, crinkly and weird but I kept chewing and then it became more interesting. Obviously, there was the flavor of the wasabi but the texture changed as my saliva moistened the seaweed fibers and underneath the flavoring I could taste the sea, salty, fishy, and mineral rich. I was hooked and ended up eating the whole bag (which in the world of Nori sheets is not as lethal as it sounds).

Nori is seaweed; specifically a type of red algae. The use of Nori as sheets comes from Japan where the seaweed is made into a paste and then undergoes a process very similar to paper making to become the edible sheets commonly seen in the market.

Interesting tidbit: While Nori has been a big part of Japanese cultural cuisine and even their export market, it appears that in the early 1900's there began to be a decline due to the loss of traditional knowledge around the growth process of the algae. Then in the 1949, a female phycologist (which means algae expert, not psychologist) name Kathleen Drew, published a paper on the life span and cycle of *Porphyra umbilicalis*, the information was further studied and developed by researchers in Japan and the Nori industry was saved. Hooray! In Japan, Kathleen Drew is known as the "Mother of the Sea" and each year on April 14th she is honored.

From a culinary perspective Nori is, well, seaweed so actually you can use it anywhere you would like to impart a salty sea complexity, rich with nutrients, to your meal. It is commonly used as a wrap in sushi and clearly, it can be eaten just as the sheets. Nori is the same seaweed used in other cultural cuisines like Welsh Laver Bread.

From a health perspective Porphyra umbilicalis is an amazing source of nutrients. It is after all seaweed, which makes it rich in minerals and vitamins; especially Vitamins b12, iron, calcium and iodine. Seaweed is considered a "superfood". It is a powerful anti-oxidant and anti-inflammatory, which can help reduce the risk of inflammation related ailments like rheumatoid arthritis and autoimmune disorders. Research also suggests that consuming seaweed can help eliminate mood and mental imbalances like depression and anxiety. Seaweed also helps regulate estrogen and estradiol which helps manage PMS and other hormonal imbalances. It is also beneficial for gastrointestinal repair, helping with ailments like IBS or Crohn's Disease.

So, maybe it's time to expand your palate and try some Nori, if you haven't already, and while you do say a little thanks to Kathleen Drew.

DAY 273 – RAISINS

Sweet and chewy, with a hint of earthiness, there's a reason they're called "nature's candy". Raisins are dried grapes. Contrary to the ideas of Joon raisins are much more than just "humiliated grapes" (even though that is indeed one of my favorite scenes in the movie Benny and Joon). The drying process gives them an amazingly high concentration of fruit sugars making them sweet and delicious. If they are dried naturally without chemical processing, they also still get to maintain many of their healthful qualities.

It appears that raisins have been a cultivated part of the human diet since about 3000 BC. I imagine dried fruit was eaten well before that but the first references to actually created a cultivated dried "product" can be found in ancient writings from that time frame. Raisins that are naturally dried or sun dried without chemicals taste delicious and amazing. The mechanical drying process to me results in less deliciousness as well as added chemicals in the form of preservatives to maintain color and texture.

From a culinary perspective, raisins are awesome additions to dishes both savory and sweet. They can be added to soups, stews, casseroles, meat and veggie dishes; as well as baked goods, pies, and other sweet treats. Of course, they can also be eaten au natural as a satisfying snack.

From a health perspective people often think that the sugar content of raisins makes them unhealthy. However, this is not necessarily the case. Raisins are high in fiber and all the good stuff that grapes contain. Remember grapes are a good source of resveratrol, which is beneficial for things like cardiovascular health, including decreasing the risk of issues with cholesterol and blood lipid levels.

Believe it or not, despite the sugar content, research demonstrates a significant amount of protocatechuic and cinnamic acids, which are beneficial for managing insulin response as well as balancing the chemistry of satiety (leptin and ghrelin). Next time you've got a sugar-craving grab a few raisins and satisfy your body.

Full quote from movie, Benny and Joon, "It's a shame about raisins...They used to be fat and juicy and now they're twisted. They had their lives stolen. Well, they taste sweet, but really they're just humiliated grapes."

CHAPTER 10 - OCTOBER

DAY 274 – RED PALM OIL

Earthy, with a musky sweetness, tasting red Palm Oil is an interesting experience. Something about the way it tastes and smells reminds me of wet leaves. Because I have a stubborn streak a mile wide, I have to admit that up to this point I have avoided trying red Palm Oil because of all of the "superfood" hype. Today, however, there it was, right in front of me, ready to try. So, try I did. My response? Myeh! Then I proceeded to cook my hazelnut, sweet potato pancakes in it. It worked well as a cooking fat, although it is not meant for high heat.

Red Palm Oil is supposedly not to be confused with the "Palm Oil" that you find in every ingredient under the sun. Although, they come from the same source, the Palm Oil tree, it appears to be a matter of processing that decides whether or not it is something healthful or something very harmful. The unrefined Palm Oil is red in color because it contains beta carotenes and other phytonutrients that contribute to health.

Okay so why don't I love the Red Palm Oil situation? Well, first of all, while there is a moderate amount of data supporting unrefined red Palm Oil as beneficial to the body, it isn't really any better than any of the other fat you can eat to support your health, and in fact, in some cases definitely offers less benefit.

However, since it has been touted as a miracle superfood, the consumer demand has skyrocketed contributing the absolute decimation of the environments that naturally produce Palm Oil trees. That, in turn, results in the absolute decimation of homes for other beings like the Orangutans, Sumatran Tiger, Rhinoceros, and Pygmy Elephant, and this is by all means the short list. If you want to know more about all of that, you can check out "Just say no to Palm Oil" and now I will just continue on with the culinary perspectives.

In the kitchen, unrefined Red Palm Oil can be used as a cooking oil for things that require medium heat or less. It can also be added as a baking ingredient or an accompaniment to dressings and sauces. It is often used in African and Asian cuisine and gives a lovely red tinge to the foods cooked with it. It is quite mild in flavor so doesn't really impact the overall taste of whatever it is added to, which could be exactly what you're looking for if you have a lot of flavors going on that need to be synergized but not altered.

From a health perspective, as I said, I was reluctant to get on the superfood bandwagon until I had a chance to do my own research. I've now had that chance and found there is really no abundance of data that suggests it's worth the deforestation that is occurring to secure it for consumption. It does indeed have many beneficial properties when unrefined.

It has a particular configuration of fatty acids that allows it to contribute to absorption and assimilation of the other nutrients you eat. It also, when unrefined, rich in Medium Chain Triglycerides, which if you remember from coconut oil, can help boost metabolic function and regulate insulin production. Studies suggest that Red Palm Oil has a high concentration phytonutrients like beta-carotene, tocopherols, and vitamin E, which contribute to the reduction of cardiovascular disease, oxidative stress, and the increase of metabolic and immune function.

Caveat: Be aware that refined and hydrogenated Palm Oils, the kind you find in most foods, does exactly the opposite and contributes to systemic inflammation as well as dysregulation of insulin production, among other things.

My thoughts? It's not often that I am troubled by the flavors I research for this daily blog, however, I have to say, this is one that truly impacted me. There is so much damage being done to supply this product to the world at large, when truly there are so many other ways to get these nutrients from other foods.

DAY 275 – PARTRIDGE

Light, slightly herby, with a firm texture, fresh partridge is indeed a treat of the season. Today's meal comes almost entirely from the surrounding landscape. Partridge from the surrounding hedgerows, runner beans from the garden, cauliflower from a local farm, butter from a local dairy. The flavor of the partridge meat reflects the herbs and flowers found in the surrounding landscape and is entirely complemented by the accompanying vegetables.

From a culinary perspective, I imagine partridge is quite a versatile meat simply because it is so light in flavor and has a good firm texture. I love simply pan frying it in butter, sometimes accompanied by leeks. It can also be pounded out and wrapped around prosciutto and cheese, then baked for a more dramatic culinary endeavor.

From a health perspective, research suggests that eating game birds like partridge and pheasant is as good for your mental/emotional as it is for your body. The secret? Selenium. Selenium helps improve overall mood and eliminate depression. Selenium also plays a role in boosting the immune system and some studies suggest it reduces the risk of cancer by acting as an anti-oxidant or boosting immune activity. Selenium is especially important in today's modern diet, as research demonstrates that many people consuming the standard westernized diet are deficient in this and other nutrients.

DAY 276 – CELERIAC

Eaten raw I find celeriac slightly astringent, a little bit salty and tangy, with a juicy crunch similar to its topside stems. Celeriac is a variety of celery grown specifically for its large root bulb. It is sometimes called the turnip-rooted celery, giving an idea of what you might find once it is uprooted. Before I became a fan of the celery root, I was quite daunted by their appearance; a giant brown ball of knobby crags, packed with dirt and bits of root. How could that possibly be turned into something edible?

Then I had the singularly pleasurable experience of Celeriac soup. I was hooked, quickly cultivating a lovely culinary relationship with this crazy looking root.
It appears that Celeriac cultivation originated in the "Fertile Crescent" and managed to makes its way quite well throughout the rest of the world in areas with appropriate climates. It is quite popular in European and Mediterranean cuisine and over the past decade has been making its way into American cuisine quite well.

From a culinary perspective Celeriac can be used any number of ways. It can be a substitute for things like mashed potatoes. It can be roasted, mashed, baked, fried, turned into pancakes, soups, and stews. It can also be grated and eaten raw in salads or snacks, making it a really versatile addition to your winter pantry. It's a root veggie so it also keeps well and so long as the tops are left on, can store in a cool dark area for several months with no problem.

From a health perspective, Celeriac is really a wealth of nutrients and healthful properties. It's packed with vitamins like B, C, and K. It's a great source of Calcium, Magnesium, Phosphorous and Zinc. It is high in fiber and low in starch, making it a great choice for people dealing with insulin imbalance and dysregulation. First hand research has demonstrated that eating ½ cup of Celeriac can help regulate insulin production and blood lipid levels.

Because of its specific mineral combination, celeriac has demonstrated in studies, that it provides significant support for bone density and connective tissue health. It is also, like its relatives the carrot, packed with antioxidants. All of which contribute to the reduction of systemic inflammation and oxidative stress, while also increasing intracellular health and eliminating mutating cells that can become cancerous.

My favorite way to prepare Celeriac in the fall and winter? Boil it like potatoes, however add a little bit of milk to help soften the fibers, once it has boiled to desirable softness, drain it and mash it up with some ghee (or butter). It's a delicious, nutrient dense replacement for mashed potatoes.

DAY 277 – RYE

Nutty and pungent Rye has a sharper, more astringent impact on my palate than other grains. Rye is a grass or cereal grain and as a member of the triticeae family it is related to other grains like wheat and barley. Rye has an interesting history and has potentially contributed to some very interesting historical events.

Initially, Archeological research suggests that wild Rye originated in Anatolia, with first documented domestication of it being around 1800 B.C. It appeared to grow in popularity during the Bronze Age and in time made its way to appropriate climates around the globe. It is a much hardier grain than wheat, withstanding varying degrees of temperature, soil content, and climate; however, it does require a hard frost to trigger sprouting.

According to historians when Rye reached its domesticated peak, in the Middle Ages, it was considered a "poor man's" grain with wheat being the coveted cereal. Interesting that today Rye is prized over wheat as a result of the gluten free movement, even though Rye does contain some gluten. Another interesting fact about Rye is its potential to develop ergot poisoning. Ergot is a fungus that grows on grains, especially Rye.

Consuming grain infected with ergot causes what has historically been called St. Anthony's Fire or ergotism; it results in hallucinations, aggression and ultimately convulsions and gangrene of the limbs. Throughout history, there is reference to communities being struck by the "Holy Fire" and devastated by ergot poisoning. In 1988 several researchers released the hypothesis that the impetus for not only the Salem

Witch Trials but many others across Europe was actually an epidemic of ergot poisoning. One way to eliminate ergot is to ferment the grain, as in sourdough or alcohol like whiskey.

From a culinary perspective, Rye is a cereal grain and can be consumed in its whole state as a Rye berry, which is quite delicious, or it can be ground into flour and used in baked goods. Just remember to soak the grain before consuming to decrease the potential for phytic acid. Once soaked and cooked the berries can be added to soups and stews, or salads and sides. In flour form Rye can be used in much the same way as wheat flour, it does however, have a more pungent taste giving foods a distinctive flavor.

From a health perspective, does contain gluten, albeit less than wheat but still for someone who has Celiac Disease, Rye would not be a good option. It is a good source of minerals, vitamins and phytonutrients. Research demonstrates that the type of fiber found in Rye combined with its specific chemical composition make it a great resource to help minimize erratic blood sugar. It also appears to signal the satiation triggers in the gut, helping you feel satisfied and fed longer than other grains. Studies also show that Rye has a significant impact on intracellular metabolism, contributing the repair and optimal functioning of mitochondria and genetic function. That means, healthy genes stay active and healthy and damaged ones get shut down.

My favorite way to eat Rye? Sourdough Rye bread...oh yes. Fresh baked with lots of fresh butter.

DAY 278 – ABSINTHE

Aaack! Black licorice with the burn of high alcohol content, Absinthe must for sure be an acquired taste. It's hard to believe that this sharp and heady alcohol was the chosen indulgence of so many great artists and writers in the 19th and 20th centuries. Supposedly, Van Gogh removed his ear under the influence of Absinthe and for a time it was banned in the U.S. and much of Europe because it was believed to have such a negative influence on behavior. Perhaps if I had tasted it in a Sazerac, which is a type of cocktail featuring Absinthe, it would be more palatable.

Absinthe, also known as the "green fairy", is a grain alcohol, typically derived from a blend of grains (corn, Rye, wheat) and then distilled with herbs like anise, fennel, and wormwood. It is sometimes referred to as a liqueur; however, the absence of sugar in the distilling process keeps it firmly in the 'spirits' world. It's the addition of wormwood, specifically

Artemisia absinthium, that seems to have created the notorious reputation for Absinthe. Wormwood, is an herb historically used for its medicinal properties, it has been used as a stimulant, tonic, restorative for things like digestive issues, parasites, arthritis, anemia, even jaundice.

In ancient Greece, wormwood was added to wine and later in the 1400's it was also found in Europe and England in ales and wines. It seems today's version of Absinthe can be credited to a French doctor who happened upon the herb during his travels between France and Switzerland and began experimenting with it. Ultimately, he concocted what we know as Absinthe today, or at least the original Absinthe that captured the hearts and minds of so many artists and writers.

It is believed that the combination of alcohol with the thujone compounds of the wormwood, created a hallucinatory effect, which enabled one to think very clearly and 'follow' thoughts into the future. Research has since revealed that while wormwood can, in fact, impact cognitive function, it takes a very high amount to do so, much more than would have been found in the average glass of Absinthe, and researchers are now theorizing that it was actually the toxic chemicals used to process cheap alcohol that had a bigger impact. Crazy, huh?

From a culinary perspective, Absinthe is actually a nice ingredient to have around the kitchen. It makes a nice simmering sauce, especially for seafood and veggies. It adds its own distinct flavor note while still blending with whatever else you have going on in the pan. I have used Absinthe to cook mussels in and it was absolutely delicious. Oysters Rockefeller is a classic dish that calls for Absinthe as an ingredient. It can also be used in desserts like custards and soufflés.

From a health perspective, well, it's a hard grain alcohol, so a little bit goes a long way. Also, today's version of Absinthe is typically made with quality ingredients, including wormwood, which is no longer banned, so the hallucinatory cognitive influence would mostly come from the alcohol...which you would have to drink a lot of, which would result in a really bad hangover to say the least. I don't recommend it. That being said, if the Absinthe is made from quality ingredients, anise, fennel, coriander, even wormwood, all have their distinct properties. At the very least when combined, they make a great bitter and digestive aid. Current research has also demonstrated that wormwood is antimicrobial and anti-inflammatory. It has been found to be beneficial in the treatment of liver damage caused by overconsumption of acetaminophen.

It is also antioxidant, scavenging those nasty free radicals and oxidative stressors from your system. Wormwood extract also has an anti-malarial effect according to recent studies and is useful in decreasing the risk of malaria as well as helping the body recover from malaria. Of course, I'm guessing that's all in the extract form and not really in the Absinthe form. (:

DAY 279 – MILLET

Crunchy, nutty, with a sweet earthy taste, Millet is a delicious and versatile grain. Today's Millet was roasted, soaked overnight and then cooked until soft and chewy. According to archeologists Millet has been a cultivated part of the human diet for about 10,000 years. It is a small seeded grain, which grows well in a variety of terrains, making it more versatile as a crop than more temperamental grains like wheat or barley.

There are about 6,000 different varieties of Millet so it can be tricky to pin down where it came from and all of its nutritional benefits. Proso Millet is one of the more popular and nutrient dense Millets, which is the kind I used today.

From a culinary perspective, Millet can be added to both sweet and savory dishes. It can be mixed with cauliflower into a delicious mash that is nutrient dense and protein rich. It can be roasted and boiled, baked into breads and other baked goods. It can also be ground into flour and used that way. It can be eaten as a breakfast cereal or a side to a meal. It has a great texture and a rich, nutty flavor.

From a health perspective Proso Millet is a great source of protein and other nutrients. It is low in phytic acid, although I still soak mine just to make it more palatable. It is a good source of minerals like Calcium, vitamins like B complex and other phytonutrients like polyphenols.

Research is demonstrating that Millet is anti-diabetic, anti-tumerogenic, and atherosclerogenic. In other words, it helps manage blood glucose levels, decreases the risk of and helps eliminate tumors, and is beneficial against cardiovascular disease. It is also antioxidant and antimicrobial. Mostly, I just think it's fun to eat and a delicious addition to a varied and healthy diet.

DAY 280 – CABBAGE

Depending on how it is prepared, Cabbage can be either crisp and refreshing, or disgustingly slimy. Personally, I prefer the crisp and refreshing and really only enjoy Cabbage, either raw or as sauerkraut. Cabbage is a member of the brassica family and has a variety of cultivars. The impetus for today's flavor is the purple and green variants, which are the kind I use to make sauerkraut. Cabbage is for all of its variable palatability is actually one of the most widely used vegetables throughout Europe and Asia, with over 69 million tons a year produced and consumed.

Although where the Cabbage originally hails from is sketchy to pin down. Archeologists seem to agree that the forward moment of cultivation of the green and purple version can be attributed to the Celts and then the Romans. It has since made its way around the world into any number of cultures and their cuisines. Of course, different varieties of Cabbage have a little bit of a different historical trajectory.

From a culinary perspective cabbage is actually a pretty versatile veggie. It can be added to soups, stews, casseroles, and salads or featured as a main component of a meal, like stuffed cabbage rolls. (ugh!) Personally, as I've already stated, I like to make my cabbage into sauerkraut, which is a satisfyingly simple kitchen endeavor. (check out Day 268 for a sauerkraut recipe)

From a health perspective, as a brassica Cabbage has a wide variety of nutrient value. Things like Vitamin C, lutein, and other phytonutrients that support full health can be found in all the varieties of Cabbage, varying with color density and the environment they were grown in. Current studies suggest that phytochemicals found in Cabbage help lower cholesterol, manage blood glucose levels, repair damage to the gastrointestinal tract, as well as boost immune function.

The glucosinolates in Cabbage play a very important role in prevention of various cancers, including colon, pancreatic, prostate, and bladder. How you prepare your Cabbage has a huge impact on the availability and viability of the nutrients. Studies demonstrate the microwaving it in particular damages pretty much any of the beneficial enzymes and nutrients. The two best ways to maintain the vibrant, health-giving qualities of Cabbage? Steaming or fermenting, with other methods of preparation close behind.

DAY 281 – TEFF

Nutty and earthy Teff is one of those foods that is fun to eat if you are into the texture of foods. It is a tiny little grass grain filled with delicious flavor and texture. Archeological studies suggest Teff originated in the area that is now Ethiopia and because it is such a small grain, was easily spread via semi-nomadic travelers. It is a hardy grain that grows well in a variety of climates, especially in places with more sun through the day.

My first encounter with Teff was as the bread Injera, an accompaniment to my Ethiopian meal. Injera is very thin and spongy bread used as a scoop to eat the accompanying ingredients. It has the nutty, slightly sweet flavor of the grain and makes a delicious and filling staple. I became enamored with the flavor of Teff and started experimenting with using it in other ways.

From a culinary perspective, the grain is very tiny, smaller than quinoa and even amaranth, that's one thing that makes it interesting to eat as far as I'm concerned. It is delicious as porridge or added to soups and stews, lending a unique complexity to both the flavor and the texture. Teff flour can be used in baked goods and the grains can be used as a thickening agent or in just about any recipe that calls for other grain. Recently, Teff has gotten critical acclaim as a gluten free grain option for beer making.

Teff has in the past few years become a darling of the health food world, touted as the next superfood. While I'm not really a fan of the 'superfood' craze, thinking that really all, whole foods are superfoods in their own right; I have to admit that Teff is a really great addition to your dietary repertoire. It is gluten free so suitable for individuals with celiac disease or other gluten issues. It is high in vitamins, minerals like calcium, protein, fiber and phytonutrients.

Teff is comprised of a fair amount of dietary fiber in the form of resistant starch, which enables it to contribute to blood glucose management, weight management and gastrointestinal health. Other studies demonstrate the Teff helps decrease bone loss and support bone and tissue growth. If you're in for a culinary adventure, Teff is a fun way to branch out.

DAY 282 – MISO

Salty, sweet, savory, earthy, Miso is a veritable explosion of taste and flavor. If you've eaten Japanese food or sushi, chances are you've had a small bowl of Miso soup somewhere during the course of the meal.

Miso is a paste made from fermented grains and legumes; most typically, soybeans but it can also include barley, rice, or beans like the azuki bean. The beans and grains are prepared and then mixed with a fermented culture, called koji, which consists of rice and a particular kind of mold (aspergillus). Traditional preparation calls for these ingredients to then be placed in wooden barrels and fermented for a couple of years. Current day practices have become mechanized in a factory setting and can now produce Miso within a matter of months. Of course, I feel compelled to wonder what is lost, with respect to flavor and nutrient complexity, in the new conventional production methods.

From a culinary perspective, Miso is part of traditional Japanese cuisine that has become more globally popular over the last decade or two. It is typically used as a seasoning or a main ingredient in things like Miso soup. While its main initial flavor is salty, there are a multitude of other nuances that cascade over the palate after the first bite. I have always loved Miso soup but began really investigating the nuances of Miso when I started using it as a healthy replacement for vegemite. (Yes, I used to be a huge fan of vegemite until I started reading ingredient labels.)

I wondered what else could impart similar umami, savory, sweet, earthy flavor nuances but also still be actually good for me. One day I decided to try some Miso paste on a piece of toast with avocado and I've never looked back. It's absolutely delicious. Now I use Miso to add a complex flavor combination to dressings and sauces as well as enjoying it in soups and on toast.

From a health perspective, Miso is a fermented food packed with beneficial bacteria, especially if it produced following guidelines that are more traditional. Unfortunately, many of the quick conventional types of Miso deliver more sodium than beneficial bacterial and are best avoided. However, if you do get your hands on quality Miso, you are in for some belly loving health benefits.

The fermentation delivers pre and probiotics contributing to the health of your gut and boosting immune function. Because it's legume and grain based Miso can deliver the vitamin and mineral benefits of those particular ingredients, of course the caveat being, make sure you've chosen a non-GMO variety. For the moment, if you choose organic then you can be assured that it is non-GMO. One other interesting side note; much of the research concerning the health properties of soy comes from fermented soy products like Miso rather than just plain soy (more on that in tomorrow's flavor of the day).

So, if you're looking for a way to get upgrade your gut microbiome and increase your flavor potential, Miso could be a great option.

DAY 283 – TURBINADO SUGAR

Sweet, with caramel, earthy undertones, hinting of molasses, Turbinado Sugar is made from sugar cane. Today's flavor comes from a close call with my hummingbird feeder. Turbinado Sugar is not a good option if you make your own hummingbird food (which I recommend).

If you've ever seen a packet of "sugar in the raw" then you have seen Turbinado Sugar. It is often touted as healthier, even unprocessed 'raw' sugar, however these claims aren't really true. It is neither, raw nor especially healthier than other cane sugar options. Turbinado is made by juicing sugar cane and then spinning the liquid in turbines to process the liquid into sugar crystals. Because no other bleaching agents or cleaners are being used, the sugar crystals maintain their darker color and a hint of molasses flavoring. During the process of spinning the minerals and vitamins are removed, which is one reason it is not any more healthful than white cane sugar.

From a culinary perspective it can be used much the same way as any other granulated or brown sugar. It is, of course, sugar, so it is sweet; how and where it can be used, is sort of self-evident.

From a health perspective sugar is a very controversial topic for a wide variety of reasons. First of all, research demonstrates that consuming 100 grams of sugar, which is about the amount that is in a liter of soda, decreases your immune function by about 40 percent for roughly six hours. One way sugar consumption contributes to immune distress is that sugar and Vitamin C are molecularly very similar; sugar competes with Vitamin C and typically wins.

Studies show that sugar also significantly contributes to belly fat and dysregulated appetite. Consuming excessive amounts of sugar impairs cognition, contributes to heart disease, and chronic liver issues. Sugar also contributes to disruption and damage in the DNA and mitochondria creating long lasting ill effects, that can even be handed down to future generations.

There are other less degraded types of sugar with supposedly higher nutrient value, although truthfully the amount of nutritional value in sugar cane is negligible. That being said, the occasional use of Turbinado Sugar in small amounts is not going to make or break your health. The problem is that almost every single manufactured food item, from spaghetti sauce to sodas, has some amount of sugar (or worse yet corn syrup) in it. Which means, most people who eat manufactured food are getting a huge amount of hidden sugar in their diet. Also, to be clear, Turbinado Sugar and other processed granulated sugars should not be confused with natural fruit or real food based sugars.

One other side-note: Cane sugar and beet sugar have a little bit different structure but impact the body in much the same way, the only difference is that most sugar made from beets is GMO, unless it's organic. If you're consuming processed food with sugar, you want to make sure it says either cane sugar or it's organic.

DAY 284 – SAUERBRATEN

Tangy and tart, with sweet and earthy notes; Sauerbraten is one of those lovely meals that feels perfectly satisfying for the onset of autumn. Sauerbraten means "sour" or pickled meat and while it is typically attributed to German cuisine, its creation has also been credited to the Romans. Historical records suggest that Julius Caesar fed his troops by packing meat in large terra cotta amphora filled with wine, as they traveled through the Alps. The meat would pickle, while the alcohol preserved it and made it available for extended journeys.

Current day Sauerbraten is much less labor intensive, even though it does involve either some wine or vinegar and marinating for 4 or 5 days. The culinary region dictates the types of herbs that are used with the wine or vinegar during the pickling or marinating process; including flavors like juniper, mustard seed, cloves, mustard and more. Historically, the type of meat used could be beef, horse, or game meats like venison.

Sauerbraten is a tangy, flavorful stew. The meat is marinated and then slow cooked in its own juices. Once it cooks, the liquid is drained off and combined with gingerbread or gingersnaps to make a thick, brown flavorful gravy. Sauerbraten is typically also served with red Cabbage (called Rotkohl) and either a potato dumpling called a Knodle, or a particular type of egg noodle called Spaetzle.

From a health perspective, well, we're talking about wine pickled meat in gingersnap gravy. Though that might at the onset seem counter to a healthful meal, there are actually some very healthful components if it's prepared from scratch with quality ingredients. For example, the pickling process makes the protein and any collagen in the meat more easily assimilated. It is also higher in minerals, and it is more easily digested.

DAY 285 – PEA SHOOTS

A delightful combination of sweet and earthy, juicy and crisp and all in the same mouthful. Pea Shoots are a more mature version of the pea sprout. Pea Shoots are a really great addition to any meal that is in need of the green vitality of nature. They are an interesting addition to sweet and savory dishes alike.

Toss them on a salad, throw them in a stir -fry, you can even add them to dessert. I've resorted to using them most places where I use fresh spinach. They are crisp and refreshing and provide a delicious complexity that fresh spinach just doesn't have. (sorry spinach, no offense).

From a health perspective Pea Shoots are packed with Vitamin A and Vitamin C. They are also, as a microgreen, filled with phytonutrients and antioxidants. Research shows that they have seven times the amount of Vitamin C and A as a cup of blueberries and are an amazing addition to your heart health repertoire. Pea sprouts are also a great anti-inflammatory and detoxifier at the cellular level. And the good stuff doesn't stop there, research demonstrates that they are also a great intervention for insulin resistance and help with glucose balance in the fight against diabetes.

DAY 286 – BACON

Mmmmm bacon... salty, savory, and everything in between; basically bacon is the epitome of a food on the umami spectrum. True bacon is made from either the pork belly or the pork loin. Pork belly is the fatty portion of meat under the pig belly and the loin is a leaner cut from the back end or even "fatback" which is higher up into the back and shoulder region. Historically, bacon is a type of cured pork. There are a multitude of variations depending on culture, region and country...but even so bacon remains a beloved addition to any number of meals.

Love bacon? You're not alone... in today's world you can find bacon everything. Bacon donuts, lotion, chap-stick, lollipops, car fresheners, you name it. Believe it or not there is even bacon attire; swimsuits, socks, dresses, undergarments. The bacon craze is HUGE. Interestingly, the flavor quality of bacon actually generates a very specific neurobiological reaction. In short, it lights up the brain and signals deep food satisfaction in a way that not very many other cooked foods do.

There are so many different ways of curing and preparing bacon that it is impossible to cover them all in this short article, suffices to say that a naturally cured, or cold smoked bacon with naturally occurring preservatives, like Celery Salts, will always be your best choice for flavor and for wellness. One other great thing about naturally cured bacon? It comes from one single source. It's not some random piece of meat mixed up with various other pieces of meat and then shoved into a sausage casing. Single source meats are easier to track if there's an issue and they definitely pose less of a health hazard.

From a culinary perspective, seriously the bacon crazy is outrageous. I mean, what doesn't go with bacon??? Salted caramel bacon ice cream? Yes, please. Bacon and dark chocolate fondue? Yep, I'll have some of that. If you want to keep it simple and savory, how about frying up some cubed bacon and then throwing in some Brussels spouts or peas or Cabbage or anything else for that matter. Then, of course, there's the good old go to; bacon and eggs. So, really from a culinary perspective, there isn't much that you can't add bacon to.

From a health perspective... well, it's bacon. It is fried, fatty meat. However, depending on the type of fried fatty meat, it actually can be better for you than other options. For example, single source, cold smoked, naturally preserved (no artificial nitrates), cuts of pork from a pig that has led a happy natural pig life are better choices for eating then even many conventionally processed steaks or other cuts of meat. So, bacon in moderation? Sure, if it's from a good source, naturally grown and processed with naturally occurring nitrates like Celery Salt or if it's cold smoked... it's delicious and provides a good quality source of protein.

Fun little side-note: The phrase "bringing home the bacon" doesn't have anything to do with a paycheck. While there is a bit of disagreement about exactly how and why the Flitch trials began, earliest recorded history is 1104AD in the village of Dunmore in the UK. The trials continued each year since the first claimed occurrence until they began in earnest around 1400 AD. If a man would present himself to the church and prove that he had been forthright, patient, and steadfast for a year and day, with no arguments or disagreements with his wife, he would be sent home with a flitch of bacon. These trials still continue to this day! Every four years in the town of Great Dunmore, UK, a trial is held and couples can compete for the flitch of bacon to bring home.

DAY 287 – POTATO (PURPLE)

Satisfyingly starchy, with a soft but firm fibrous texture; purple potatoes are probably my favorite kind of potato. If you've never had a Purple Potato, it's worth hunting one down. Not only are they tasty, but also so beautiful with their purple and indigo hues.
Purple Potatoes are originally from South America. There are a few different varieties, each with its own lovely shade of purple. My favorites are the Peruvian Purple. They have a striated purple interior with a deep purple outer skin and make a beautiful shade of lavender when creamed or mashed.

From a culinary perspective, purple potatoes, while delightful in color, are really much the same as regular potatoes so can be used anywhere that a potato can be used. That being said, the Peruvians are a little bit starchier with a similar texture to a sweet potato and actually make a great ingredient in baked goods as well. Purple Potato muffins are delicious and eye catching.

From a health perspective, the Purple Potato is an aesthetically pleasing, nutrient dense addition to your dietary repertoire. They have all the basic nutrients of a regular potato, high in potassium and fiber. But it's the color density that gives them the extra health kick. The purple coloring signifies a high level of antioxidants; anthocyanins to be specific. The anthocyanin is a beneficial chemical compound that acts as a preventative measure against oxidative stress. This includes protecting against the development of different types of cancer and also diseases like heart disease, and autoimmune dysfunction. It is also the compound responsible for relieving the potential for muscle strain after a workout, which is especially true of potatoes due to their mineral content.

DAY 288 - BARBERA

To my palate Barbera is smooth, semi-fruity, with notes of honey and light earthy tannins. Barbera grapes originate in the Piedmont region of Italy. In the 19th century Italian immigrants brought the vines to California and Argentina and Barbera has now made its way to other vineyard regions around the globe. Over the last few decades Barbera grapes have become the third most widely planted grape in Italy.

From a culinary perspective Barbera is an interesting wine to pair. It has the singular ability to taste both rich and complex and light and fruity all at the same time. In my mind, this allows for a wider pairing repertoire, although rich, hearty flavored foods seem to match the best. A thick and hearty root vegetable stew with game meat and a glass of Barbera could be a great autumn evening meal.

From a health perspective Barbera grapes are similar in DNA structure to Mourvedre (which is probably why I like them). They are a rich source of antioxidants and other phytonutrients. Resveratrol is among the most popular being in the limelight of pop culture health and fitness.

Research suggests that resveratrol decreases incidence and potential of cardiovascular disease as well as balancing cholesterol and reducing the formation of blood clots. Resveratrol also protects against cell damage and mental decline. The ellargic acid found in red grapes also contributes to metabolic increase and increases the body's fat burning potential, mostly by decreasing the body's ability to produce new fat cells and delaying the growth of fat cells already present.

Of course, all this good stuff about red wine is dependent on moderation and type of wine. So, if you're going to have a glass, make it just a glass or two tops, and make sure it is a consciously produced wine. Old world wines from France, Italy, and Spain tend to have more stringent fermentation guidelines, otherwise, I say go for the organic, or better yet the sustainable and/or biodynamic wines.

DAY 289 – GNOCCHI (PUMPKIN)

A foodie mouthfeel extravaganza; Pumpkin Gnocchi are soft and chewy, but also dense and doughy, with the nutty, buttery, earthy flavor of Pumpkin. The gnocchi that are inspiring today's flavor are like little Pumpkin pillows of goodness. Gnocchi are basically very small dumplings. There are as many variations as there are varieties of cuisine, it seems that most cultures have some type of small dumpling.

These particular dumplings are Italian gnocchi made from semolina flour, eggs, ricotta cheese and Pumpkin with a few amazing spices tossed in. They are then boiled lightly until they are firm and dense, then drained and sautéed in butter and sage. Oh yes.
The word gnocchi is derived from the Italian word "nocchio", which basically means a gnarl or knot of wood. (Remember Pinocchio? He was made from a knot of wood.) The good thing is these little dumplings, while they may look like little knots of wood, are anything but woody or hard. If they are made right, they are chewy deliciousness.

From a culinary perspective, gnocchi are versatile; they can be just flour, egg and water or just flour and water, or veggie, egg and water. Some gnocchi are made from mashed potatoes and egg, with no or very little flour. They can be sweet or savory. They can be served as a main dish or piled up beside some other entrée. They also can be tossed on soup or part of a stew or casserole. One thing is sure; no matter how they are prepared, they are typically really scrumptious.

From a health perspective, well, they are flour, water and eggs; so potentially not the best thing on your plate in large quantity. That being said, in moderation, if they are made from quality ingredients, they can be made into a pretty healthful addition to a meal. Using non-bleached or processed Italian flours, or using organic or heritage potatoes or other vegetables, will make all the difference to the nutrient value. As an occasional mealtime treat, especially with the onset of colder weather, they are a great way to fill your tummy with hearty goodness.

DAY 290 – BALSAMIC VINEGAR

Tangy, with earthy hints of sweet almost caramel notes; Balsamic Vinegar is the perfect accompaniment to my baked fig and goat cheese tartine. Genuine Balsamic Vinegar is made from a reduction of white Trebbiano grapes. There are several grades of Balsamic Vinegar, with the real-deal stuff being produced in the Modena and Reggio Emilia regions of Italy.

Traditional Balsamic Vinegar is protected origin and has a long and esteemed history as a restorative tonic/digestive. The traditional, good stuff is actually quite expensive and takes many years to produce. It begins with a smashed concoction of white grapes, skin, seeds, and all, called a "must". The must is fermented and then allowed to mature for about 12 years. This traditional production is called Aceto Balsamico Tradizionale and chances are if you've enjoyed Balsamic Vinegar at a meal, it wasn't this version. The other more common and affordable version is called Balsamic Vinegar Modena. The production process for this version of Balsamic Vinegar is much less labor and time intensive; however, it isn't fermented.

From a culinary perspective, Balsamic Vinegar is a really delicious and complex addition to dishes both savory and sweet. It is typically considered a condiment. Just a few drops can change the entire structure of a dish. Drizzle it over cheese, vegetables or even meat dishes. Use it as a dip with some exceptional olive oil and fresh bread and you are in for a treat. If you have a chance to try the traditional stuff, I highly recommend it. The flavor is exquisitely different and delightful.

From a health perspective, traditional Balsamic Vinegar has some pretty great properties. It has a similar phenolic acid content to red wines and the fermentation process adds in some probiotic qualities that help balance your gut health. The bitter quality of the vinegar also acts as a digestive aid. The common version of Balsamic Vinegar does still have some health and digestive properties, however, not near as much as the traditional. Research demonstrates that traditional Balsamic helps moderate blood lipid levels and decreases oxidative stress.

DAY 291 – SUMAC

Smoky and slightly astringent with hints of citrus and earthiness; Sumac hints of exotic ports or cigars bars with sultry music or, if too much is used, furniture polish. I know it's hard to imagine all of that in one little flavor, but once you try it (if you haven't already) you will know what I mean. Of course, part of the flavor influence is how it is processed and made ready for culinary use.

Sumac is derived from the drupes, sort of like date stones or berries, of the Suma tree. For culinary use they are dried and then ground into a powder. Sometimes they are also smoked and then ground into a powder, hence the smoky flavor in the meal I was enjoying this evening. Sumac is a common ingredient in Middle Eastern food, as a main ingredient in Za'atar, which is delicious, and it's also used in Italian food.

Culinary Sumac, while in the same family, is not the same as the poison Sumac that gives you an itchy rash. Culinary Sumac can be added to any number of culinary endeavors, sweet and savory alike. As the main spice in quite a few Middle Eastern dishes, to a dusting powder for grilled meats, and on to Sumac meringue followed up with a nice cup of Sumac tea.

From a health perspective Sumac is, you guessed it, a good source of quite a few vitamins, minerals and phytonutrients. I'm hoping you are beginning to see the trend; real food equals real nutrients. Back to the Sumac… it is high in quercetin and vitamin C. Research demonstrates that it is effective in metabolizing carbohydrates effectively and balancing blood lipid levels. Studies also show that it is effective against cardiovascular disease and systemic inflammation. It is amazingly high in its antioxidant properties, contributing to the decrease and elimination of oxidative stress. Sumac is also antimicrobial, antifungal, and antibacterial.

In Native American tradition Sumac is often used as a tea for digestive issues, high cholesterol, heart disease, and also fungal infections.

DAY 292 - FILE GUMBO

File Gumbo has a bright and almost citrusy flavor, tempered with hints of earthiness. It's a flavor that is incredibly hard to describe, not least because much of its flavor comes from the mouthfeel. File is a spice that is a main ingredient in Creole and Cajun cooking. It is made from dried and powdered Sassafras leaves. Sassafras is a type of tree, of which there are several different varieties. Sassafras albidum is the tree typically used for culinary and medicinal purposes. They are native to North America and some parts of eastern Asia. While all the parts of the tree can be used for a variety of things like cooking and tonics; File Gumbo is made specifically from the young leaves.

From a culinary perspective File Gumbo is a spice that can be added to a variety of dishes. It has a distinct flavor and mouthfeel. It can be used to thicken soups and stews, imparting a kind of slippery and soothing feeling. Many sources claim that File became popular in Cajun and Creole cooking because the Choctaw Indians showed settlers where to find it and how to use it.

From a health perspective, it's important to note that while all parts of the Sassafras tree have been used in the culinary and medicinal world, the leaves are the only parts that do not contain Safrole. Safrole is a chemical compound natural to the tree, which has been used in perfumes, alcohols, flavorings, but has been banned by the FDA because it contributes to liver damage and is highly carcinogenic. The leaves do not contain the levels of Safrole found in the rest of the tree.

In traditional Native American medicine Sassafras has been used to treat abdominal pain, digestive issues, urinary tract disorders, throat issues, and high blood pressure to name a few. There is some data suggesting Sassafras as a remedy to these issues could be a viable option. Definitely, there is just as much evidence suggesting that too much could be a real problem, so taking Sassafras leaves or making large amounts of File into a tea could be a really bad idea. Sprinkling it on your eggs, mixing it into your Gumbo? Completely different story.

DAY 293 – PEPPERMINT

Cool, refreshing, with a little bit of zing; fresh Peppermint is a zippy way to wake up your palate. Peppermint is a hybrid of spearmint and water mint. It was originally most widely cultivated in Europe and the Middle East but now has made its way around the globe. The Peppermint plant is a hardy hybrid and often spreads quickly due to the prolific growth of the main root, especially in moist soil. Interestingly, because it is a hybrid, it doesn't produce seeds, so doesn't really produce "new" plants, however the root system is industrious and continues to sprout off new additions even if cut and transplanted.

From a culinary perspective, Peppermint is a common ingredient in quite a few cultural cuisines. In the U.S. it seems to make its presence known especially around the holidays. Peppermint has a high menthol content, giving it a much stronger flavor, which is why it is such a good option in the culinary world. Peppermint tea, Peppermint candy, Peppermint cake, even Peppermint Toffee; it provides a refreshing and invigorating flavor.

Peppermint isn't only reserved for sweet dishes, it can be a really interesting addition to savory as well; roll it into fresh spring rolls, throw it in soups (spring pea and mint is delicious), toss it into a salad, mix it into some yogurt as a dip, even mince it up to sprinkle over entrees.

From a health perspective, as part of the mint family, Peppermint has all the good stuff that its mint relatives have and then some due to the higher menthol content. It is an excellent digestive tonic; useful for nausea and stomachache. Research is demonstrating that it is highly effective in calming the gastrointestinal tract in cases of Irritable Bowel or Crohn's Disease. Studies also demonstrate that inhaling mint is enhances cognitive function and elevates mood. It also helps stimulate memory. Sipping mint tea and inhaling the aroma can be a great way to boost your energy and focus when you hit those afternoon slumps. This happens because the olfactory system plugs directly into the limbic system, which is responsible for emotional responses and memory. Inhaling and sipping creates a nice retro nasal effect; while also calming the nerves and soothing digestion.

Peppermint is also full of antioxidants and other phytonutrients that help alleviate oxidative stress and systemic inflammation. The chemical compounds in the volatile oils like menthone also give it an antimicrobial, antifungal, and antibiotic quality. I keep a bottle of Peppermint essential oil handy as part of my herbal medicine cabinet. Peppermint also makes a really great pest repellent, ants, spiders, even small rodents. Planted in your garden it can help manage the pests that bother your other plants.

DAY 294 – BUTTER

Creamy and sweet with a hint of saltiness, everything tastes better with Butter. More specifically, small batch Jersey cow Butter; even more rich and creamy than regular Butters. Butter is made by 'agitating' or churning fresh milk until the fat separates from the liquid, leaving Butter and Buttermilk. The Butterfat can then be used as a spread, to cook or bake with, or as a melted topping. Butter or some very close variation of Butter can be found in almost every culture that produces some type of animal dairy. Although, it is typically produced from cow's milk, you can also make Butter from sheep, goat, buffalo, really any milk that has fat in it. I recently purchased some buffalo Butter and found it to be wonderful in flavor and mouthfeel.

From a culinary perspective, Butter can be made from non-homogenized dairy. I thought it would be a challenge to make but through a simply trial and error found the best way was simply to place it in a jar and shake it until the fat became a little round golden ball and the Buttermilk poured off. You can then add a touch of salt if desired, however, I found that, especially with raw milk from grass fed cows, there was already a delightful balance of sweet and salt. Once you have your Butter it can be made into any number of things, even browned into a delicious caramel.

From a health perspective, it's unfortunate that the media and poorly orchestrated studies created such a trend towards the avoidance of fat. After more thorough scrutiny of the data, and with the introduction of new data, we now know that saturated fats are not quite the culprit they've been identified as with reference to heart disease and cholesterol levels. There is now ample research specific to some of the properties that are found in quality Butter demonstrating that it can be a healthful addition to your dietary repertoire.

For example, butter, especially butter from pasture raised, grass fed animals, contains medium chain fatty acid much like coconut oil; making it a more desirable choice for consumption. Remember that medium chain triglycerides are actually some of the fat good guys and can do things like help with balanced brain and nervous system function. MCT's in appropriate amounts can contribute to weight loss and cardiovascular health and cellular regeneration.

Butter also contains butyric acid, which helps keep your digestive bacteria happy and healthy; so it is a great option for people trying to manage chronic digestive inflammation and ailments; including IBS and Crohn's Disease. Of course, the caveat is, we are talking moderation and quality ingredients. The latest craze is putting Butter or coconut oil in coffee, the truth of the matter is, it is going to depend on a person's specific metabolic structure and body type to determine whether that will be a healthy option for them. For some people it will prove an absolute disaster and for others a complete gem.

DAY 295 – MAPLE SYRUP

Maple Syrup is sweet and earthy with hints of caramely goodness. Maple Syrup is traditionally made from the sap of a maple tree. The nuances of flavor can change depending on the type of maple tree and also what time of year the sap is extracted. According to archeological records and oral tradition the first production of Maple Syrup from the sap of the maple tree originated in North America by Native peoples indigenous to the Northeast.

During the winter the maple tree stores starch in its roots, as the season changes and temperatures begin to rise with the onset of spring, so rises the sap from the roots to the branches of the tree. The trees can be 'tapped' and the sap is collected and then processed by heating and boiling under just the right conditions to form an invert, thickened syrup.

The classification system for Maple Syrup has recently changed so that currently syrups that fall into a Grade A category can have a pretty wide variation in flavor and coloring, so long as they contain the basic appropriate flavor. Anything that does not meet the flavor standard is classified as either Processing grade or Substandard grade; neither is allowed to be sold to the public.

From a culinary perspective, real Maple Syrup is a delicious addition to just about any meal sweet and savory. What's not to love about pouring delicious maple goodness over some pancakes, waffles, or oatmeal, or baking it into cakes or pies. It is even a scrumptious addition to savory meals like maple baked ribs or sausage. It is one of my favorite sweeteners in various raw dessert recipes and it makes a great marinade for wild game. One recipe in particular calls for marinating, then slow cooking venison in Maple Syrup. I haven't tried that one yet, but I will.

From a health perspective ,Maple Syrup is interesting. The pop culture health world touts that it is far superior and more healthful as a sweetener than other sweeteners. While there may be some truth to that, it is still a sugar so it's best enjoyed in moderation. For the most part Maple Syrup has only a minimal amount of minerals like zinc, iron and manganese, however from a phytonutrient point of view the prospects for nutrient benefit expand pretty well. Studies suggest that pure Maple Syrup is packed with antioxidants and phenolic compounds that help manage things like oxidative stress, systemic inflammation and metabolic function.

Research on specific phenolic compounds demonstrate that the chemical composition of genuine Maple Syrup has an anti-proliferative effect on colon cancer cells, while also encouraging defective cells to self-destruct. The caveat? It has to be the real deal; not maple flavored sugar water, which is what many of the cheaper products are. If it says maple flavored, avoid it. The only ingredients on the list for real Maple Syrup should be, well, Maple Syrup.

DAY 296 – WILD BOAR

Dense and slightly musky, with a savory, earthy flavor that hints of the forest, Wild Boar is a well-respected addition to my dinner plate. Most of the Wild Boar sold in the United States is actually not 'wild', rather it is a hybrid of Wild Boar and feral pig that is domesticated and raised in much the same way cattle or bison are. Genuine, roaming around the forest, Wild Boar is a special treat worthy of a place of honor on the dinner table. As a game meat it has a distinct flavor that is a reflection of its wild habitat.

According to historians Wild Boar are not really native to the U.S. and have had a relatively new and intermittent history on the landscape. They were, apparently, introduced to the wilderness in the 1500's in the New England regions by European settlers, then hunted to extinction. A new group was then introduced accidentally when a few escaped from a farm and began populating the surrounding wilds. This occurred several more times until ultimately over time small pockets of Wild Boar are now pretty much across the U.S.

In some States they are even considered an "invasive species" and are, sadly, treated as such. However, with the increase in consumer demand, Wild Boar is making a comeback and the species is becoming better tolerated in the surrounding wilds of many communities; not least because they represent a commodity. Personally, I feel eating wild game meats is far more humane and in many cases healthier, than consuming domesticated conventionally farmed animals. I especially feel a deep and abiding respect for the Wild Boar, marveling at their stature and tenacity.

From a culinary perspective, Wild Boar is denser with an earthier almost musky flavor compared to domesticated pork. It tolerates stronger combinations of herbs and spices and makes a hearty cold weather meal. When preparing Wild Boar I like to think of the wilderness that it comes from and pair my cooking herbs and flavors with what might have been in the similar environment. That being said, my absolute favorite Wild Boar dish of all time is Pappardelle al Ragu Di Cinghiale; otherwise known as

Wild Boar Ragu with pappardelle.

From a health perspective, Wild Boar, like most game meats, has a higher nutrient density than its conventional counterparts. It is a higher quality, relatively lean protein, rich with essential fatty acids and vitamins and minerals.

DAY 297 – CAPERS

Salty, pungent and puckery with a dense and interesting mouthfeel; Capers add an extra dimension to culinary endeavors. Capers are actually the flower bud of the Caper bush. If the buds are allowed to flower they continue to mature past the flowering stage and into a Caper berry, which is slightly larger than the Caper bud. Both the berry and the bud, which is usually the one that is called simply a Caper, are typically eaten pickled. The origination of the Caper bush is uncertain but it can be found in semi dry climates around the world. It seems to be a very adaptable plant and quickly adapts to variations within its environment. Capers are a popular ingredient in cultural cuisines found in semi-arid and arid climates. It is a main feature in many Italian, Greek and Middle Eastern dishes.

From a culinary perspective Capers can be an interesting addition to salads and small plates. They can basically be used in any recipe that features pickles. They are a distinct addition to dishes like Chicken Piccata, Puttanesca, Lentil salad and Nicoise salads.

From a health perspective Capers are a great source of micro and phytonutrients. Nutrients like quercetin, selenium, rutin, zeaxanthine, quercetin, kaempferol, astragalin, the list goes on. All that nutrient density makes them have a significant beneficial impact for your health. Research shows that consuming Capers, both the bud and the berry, can help decrease cardiovascular issues, including heart disease, increase bone density, boost immune function and decrease oxidative stress. They will also help decrease the risk of various cancers...namely prostate and lung (as far as studies are concerned). Traditional medicine from various cultures highlights the use of Caper buds and leaves for things like gut inflammation, rheumatism, and digestive disorders.

DAY 298 – BECHAMEL

Creamy, rich and buttery, Béchamel sauce is one of the "mother" sauces, or *sayces meres*, of French cuisine. There are several theories about the origination of this sauce, with the earliest being in 14th century Italy. Over the next few hundred years it made its way to France and on to other global cuisines. Béchamel sauce is a versatile foundation sauce for other recipes. Its basic ingredients are butter, flour, and milk.

From a culinary perspective, Béchamel sauce is made by mixing a roux of flour and butter; whisked gently and not allowed to brown. Then boiled milk is slowly whisked in until the sauce is smooth and creamy/thick. Once you have a basic white sauce you can then add other ingredients, spices, vegetables, and/or lighter meats. Béchamel sauce is also a great base for various veggie dishes like veggie lasagna.

From a health perspective, Béchamel sauce is probably one of those things you want to just enjoy in moderation as a special treat. Obviously the healthful qualities will be totally based on the ingredients uses. Grass fed butter and milk and stone milled flours from heritage grain will more than likely reveal a flavor most similar to the early days of béchamel. It's definitely worth a try if you're up for experimenting.

DAY 299 – TIBICOS (WATER KEFIR)

Zingy and slightly sweet but also tangy with a hint of fizziness water Kefir is refreshing and fun to sip on. Water Kefir is made from water Kefir grains, also known as balm of Gilead, California bees, and Japanese beer seeds are a "symbiotic culture of yeast and bacteria" that live and grow in what is called a microbiogleae. Their scientific name is Tibicos and they basically look like little yellow, gummi crystals.

Water Kefir grains are not the same as the Kefir grains used to make dairy based Kefir, although they do contain some of the same types of gut friendly bacteria, such as bifico bacterium, lactobacilli and a host of other Bacillus relatives. It's challenging to isolate exact cultures because they change with environmental influence during the fermentation process. Interestingly, researchers seem to be in disagreement about exactly where Water Kefir grains come from; several sources speculate they come from the 'leaves' of a cactus fig plant but others disagree.

For all their mystery Water Kefir grains are pretty interesting and easy to work with if you are trying to increase your intake of probiotics and belly friendly foods. They are especially desirable for people with dairy issues because they provide very much the same bacteria without the dairy. Here's a quick and easy Water Kefir recipe:

2-3 Tbs Water Kefir Grains (I ordered mine from the "culturesforhealth.com")
6 cups of filtered water
¼ cup plus 2 TBS of sugar (I use Rapidura but any sugar will work)
½ lemon (or just the juice)
2 unsulphered dried figs
A couple of drops of trace minerals (I use ConcenTrace)

Melt the sugar in two cups of heated water then pour into a jar large enough for six cups of water. Add the rest of the water, the figs, the trace minerals, the lemon (or lemon juice) and finally the Kefir grains. Secure a cheesecloth over the top of the jar so nothing can get in but the mixture can breathe and ferment. Let sit in a quiet location for two or three days; depending on how fermented you would like the drink to be. The longer the fermentation the less sugar and more bacteria, however studies show that past 72 hours it begins to become higher in acetic acid and other volatile compounds that detract from the flavor and the beneficial bacteria. The optimal fermentation time is between 24-48 hours.

Once the desired fermentation time has passed, place a strainer over a bowl and drain off the liquid from the grains and other ingredients. Remove the figs (they are tasty even if they look funny) and rinse the grains with filtered water. You can either store them or put them right back into a new batch of Kefir. If you store them for just a few days then you can do so by adding a little bit of sugar to some of the liquid you just made and keeping them in a jar in the fridge. If you want to store them for longer, you can freeze or dehydrate them.

Okay so now you have a jar of lovely Kefir… you can enjoy as is or if you want to make fizzy soda you can place a lid on the jar and let it sit out for a day or two. This increases the natural carbonation. This is also a good time to flavor your Kefir if you're interested in making it into a "cider". I just made a batch of apple ginger. I minced about an inch of fresh ginger and chopped ½ of a fuji apple, tossed them in the Kefir, put the lid on and let it all sit for two days. It's fizzy and yummy!

From a health perspective, while there is limited research out there, what's in peer reviewed, scientific journals is really pretty cool. Studies have shown that just a tablespoon a day of this awesome little fermented beverage can help keep your gut bacteria happily populated with digestive good guys. Other studies have found that ingestion of Water Kefir beverage has been beneficial in the prevention of multidrug-resistant myeloid leukemia, as well as a preventative and chemotherapeutic intervention for various cancers.

Still more research suggests that daily intake of beverages containing lactobacilli are beneficial in the prevention of periodontal disease. Don't forget also that a balanced gut microbiome means balanced mood, increased cognitive function, enhanced immune system function, digestive wellness, and just all around goodness.

One caveat: most store purchased Kefirs are required to be pasteurized with flavor and ingredients added back in after pasteurization; unfortunately this tends to increase the sugar content and decrease the happy bacteria content. If you drink fermented beverages, it is well worth making your own. It's quick. It's easy. It's cost friendly once you have the grains.

One last caveat: These are meant to be tonic drinks, sipped in small quantities for health and wellness. They are not big gulps, sodas, super-sized soft drinks…. More is not better; just enough is just right.

DAY 300 – ROQUEFORT

Tangy and slightly pungent with a hint of salty sweetness, Roquefort is a type of sheep's milk blue cheese. Roquefort blue cheese has a protected Designation of Origin, which means it can only be given the name Roquefort if it is aged in specific caves in the Roquefort-sur-Soulzon in France. To me, Roquefort has a distinctive flavor that separates it from other bleu cheese relatives. That is due in part to the milk, which can only come from the Lacaune, Manech, or Basco-Bernaise breeds of sheep. The other distinctive influence is the particular strain of mold that is found in the soil of the Combalou caves.

Roquefort like all blue cheese is created by adding the mold *Penicillium* to fermenting cheese so that it creates a blue, green or gray vein of mold through the cheese.

I love blue cheese on its own or as a side with a nice savory game, like venison or Wild Boar. It is also amazing with bolder vegetables, like broccoli or kale. Roquefort is often made into sauces or dressings, its mild tangy, sweet, salty flavor adding a complex and distinctive flavor.

From a health perspective, blue cheese is actually a very heart healthy food. Research demonstrates that blue cheese in particular has a very anti-inflammatory impact, so it helps relieve oxidative stress, systemic inflammation and increases cardiovascular health. Side note and total bonus: As I've identified before, research also indicates that pairing the blue cheese with a good red wine increases the heart healthy potential and the yum factor incrementally. I'm sure it's all about moderation but really, could there be a better pairing for your health? (:

DAY 301 – SUCCOTASH

Succotash is fun to eat, with its variety of textures and mouthfeels; sweet corn kernels mixed with lima beans. According to historians the word 'Succotash' comes from the Narragansett language. The Narragansett are an Algonquian Native American tribe living in the Rhode Island area of New England. There is speculation that the Native Americans shared the recipe for Succotash with the colonials as it was a staple in the Native American diet, a casserole of corn, beans, and fish or game. The combination of corn and beans provides a complete amino acid combination; coupled with a full protein the dish provides a simple meal that is hearty and nutrient dense.

From a culinary perspective I don't know about you but I have made a concerted effort to avoid Succotash at all costs ever since childhood. Then I had the opportunity to taste a simple casserole of fresh ingredients and it was delicious. The basic ingredients can serve as a versatile foundation for a hearty and traditional Fall meal.

From a health perspective, Succotash is a nutrient dense meal. The beans are an amazing source of fiber, protein, and various minerals and vitamins. Research suggests that lima beans have a significant amount of isoflavones and plant sterols that help protect against breast and prostate cancers. They also lower cholesterol and balance blood sugar levels.

Research also demonstrates that beans are significant sources of L-Dopa, which is a precursor to Dopamine in the brain and can protect against Parkinson's Disease and various dopamine dependent mood disorders. Couple that with corn, which is high in fiber, vitamins, and minerals. Also a good source of vitamins A and B and minerals like zinc, magnesium, copper and iron. It provides quite a variety of antioxidants that help eliminate oxidative stress and decrease risk of cell mutation that leads to degenerative disease and cancers.

One caveat: traditionally, corn is a staple food and has served humanity well as one that fortifies the body. I believe that heritage and unadulterated varieties of corn still do provide more of a health benefit than not. Unfortunately, we are inundated with variations of GMO corn product in almost every kind of foodstuff. The result is we get an over-abundance, most often without even realizing it, of corn in our diets and it does take its toll. Fresh, unadulterated corn is what you want to use if you are making this particular dish.

DAY 302 – SOUL CAKES (RECIPE)

Sweet and spicy with hints of saffron, Soul Cakes are a delicious way to connect with a bit of tradition this Halloween season. It's Halloween and in honor of the day I wanted to find a traditional flavor that would suit. Soul cakes seemed like just the thing.

There are various theories about the origination of Soul Cakes for Samhain/Hallowe'en celebration, however, after the 8th century there is a more or less agreed upon symbolism. Soul cakes were given to the Mummers as they danced through the streets in costume on Samhain night driving the evil spirits and guiding the souls of the dead out of town.

Mummers actually gave us the word to 'mum' or 'mime' that is to act/dance/play silently. Soul Cakes were some of the original treats for "trick or treating". They were also given to "beggars" on All Soul's Day in return for prayers for the souls of the dead.

There are a variety of recipes for Soul Cakes. The one that I made today was simple and delicious. They have a texture somewhere between a snickerdoodle and a biscuit. The spices and saffron give them a subtle yet complex flavor. They were easy to make and my kitchen smelled divine with nutmeg, saffron and cinnamon wafting through the air.

SOUL CAKES:
2 cups all-purpose flour
1/2 teaspoon nutmeg, ground fresh if possible
1/2 teaspoon cinnamon, ground fresh if possible
1/2 teaspoon salt
Generous pinch of saffron
1/2 cup milk
1 stick (8 tablespoons) unsalted butter, softened
1/2 cup sugar
2 egg yolks
1/2 cup currants

For the Glaze:
1 egg yolk, beaten
Preheat oven to 400 degrees.
Combine the flour, the nutmeg, cinnamon and salt in a small bowl. Mix well with a fork. Crumble the saffron threads into a small saucepan and heat over low heat just until they become aromatic, taking care not to burn them. Add the milk and heat just until hot to the touch. The milk will have turned a bright yellow. Remove from heat.

Cream the butter and sugar together in a medium bowl with a wooden spoon (or use an electric mixer with the paddle attachment). Add the egg yolks and blend in thoroughly with the back of the spoon. Add the spiced flour and combine as thoroughly as possible; the mixture will be dry and crumbly.

One tablespoon at a time, begin adding in the warm saffron milk, blending vigorously with the spoon. When you have a soft dough, stop adding milk; you probably won't need the entire half-cup.

Turn the dough out onto a floured counter and knead gently, with floured hands, until the dough is uniform. Roll out gently to a thickness of 1/2 inch. Using a floured 2-inch round cookie or biscuit cutter, cut out as many rounds as you can and set on an ungreased baking sheet. You can gather and re-roll the scraps, gently

Decorate the soul cakes with currants and then brush liberally with the beaten egg yolk. Bake for 15 minutes, until just golden and shiny.

DAY 303 – CHICORY

Woody and bitter with a hint of earthiness, which is enjoyable as a digestive bitter and tea or coffee substitute. Chicory is a perennial, with several variations that fall under the general name of "Chicory". The Chicory for today's flavor is known as Chicorium intybus, subspecies Sativum. While the leaves and flowers can be used in salads and various other culinary endeavors the part of the plant most significant to this article is the root. Chicory has widely been used as a coffee replacement. The root of the Chicory plant is baked, dried, and then ground or crumbled into pieces to be used in coffee, tea or digestive tonic.

While the origination of Chicory as a coffee substitute is slightly hazy, there is reference to its use in both colonial America and in France. My first experience with Chicory coffee was in New Orleans accompanied by a freshly fried beignet. I later learned that Chicory is an awesome bitter in teas and tonics, promoting digestive health and balanced liver function. I currently enjoy dandelion root and Chicory on a regular basis. (In fact, I'm enjoying a cup right now as I type)

From a culinary perspective, Chicory root is mostly used as a substitute for coffee or in teas and tonics, however, chicory root powder can be used in any recipe that calls for coffee or a dark, earthy flavor, even as a replacement or a complement to dark chocolate.

From a health perspective, Chicory root has long been recognized as a digestive aid. In ancient Roman medicine it was used to increase bile production and cleanse the liver. It is still used that way today. Chicory is also high in inulin. Inulin is both a soluble fiber and a probiotic. Consumption of Chicory root helps promote balanced glucose and blood sugar levels as well as contributing to healthy gut microbiota.

Chicory is a great resource for antioxidants, which means helping you to eliminate oxidative stress and systemic oxidation. It's also an amazing antifungal, antimicrobial source. Studies show that chicory root is toxic to particular strains of salmonella and helps to eliminate fungal activity in the gut. A nice mixture of burdock root, Chicory, fennel, and dandelion makes an amazing detox, digestive tonic. Could be worth a try as the cold winter months are on their way...

DAY 304 – BITTER MELON

Bitter Melon is true to its name, with a bitter flavor and an astringent quality if not well prepared. Bitter Melon is a fruit, actually part of the gourd family. It looks like a cucumber with a severe case of warts. There are quite a few varieties with variations in their own sub-tropic or tropic climates around the world. Bitter Melon is a common ingredient in almost all Asian cuisines and plays a significant role in traditional medicine as well.

From a culinary perspective, Bitter Melon may be challenging to cook with if you have not done so before but it's not impossible. It can be cored, seeded, and blanched in water to remove some of the bitter quality or it can be prepared similarly to eggplant by salting it and allowing it to rest. Once it's been quickly blanched or salted and rinsed it can then be used any variety of ways. It can be added to soups, stews and stir-fries; it can also be made into desserts, even tea.

From a health perspective, Bitter Melon has quite a history in the world of traditional medicine. For centuries it has been used as a digestive tonic, including treatment for things parasites and other microbial issues. It has also been used as an intervention for diabetes, menstrual disorders, and respiratory issues. From a western medicine perspective, studies show that Bitter Melon can have an impact on blood glucose levels however, there have not been consistent findings to suggest it is an appropriate replacement for medication or other therapeutic interventions. Bitter Melon can be a stomach irritant if too much is eaten or it is not prepared well.

CHAPTER 11 - NOVEMBER

DAY 305 – RED KURI SQUASH (RECIPE)

Dense and "meaty" with a nutty, earthy flavor, mashed Red Kuri Squash is a delicious way to settle into the onset of colder weather. Red Kuri Squash looks very much like a small Pumpkin, just not quite as round. It is part of the Pumpkin family, Curcubita maxima, but definitely has its own unique flavor and even mouthfeel. Red Kuri Squash is a popular squash in Asian cuisine, especially Japanese, but it's also getting much more popular around the rest of the world. It grows on a vine, like its other squash and gourd relatives, and tends to thrive in warmer, drier climates. It grows very well in full sun and drier soil.

From a culinary perspective Red Kuri Squash is versatile, delicious and nutritious. It is great in both savory and sweet recipes. It has a nutty almost sweet flavor, which invites a different level of complexity to dishes. Its density makes it great to cook and bake with. It makes delicious soup, stew, "Pumpkin" bread, cookies, curry, stir-fry, and on and on. Today's flavor was inspired by a baked Kuri Squash with butter and cinnamon topping (see the recipe below) .

From a health perspective Red Kuri Squash is full of good stuff. It's lower in carbohydrate content than other winter squashes but higher in fiber. It is also lower in calorie than its winter counterparts. It is packed with beta-carotene, which helps reduce the risk of certain cancers and other ailments like macular degeneration. It is a good source of vitamins B and C as well as A.

Red Kuri also contains a significant amount of pectin, slightly less than a Kabocha Squash but still a significant source. Pectin helps your body in a variety of ways; it contributes to lower cholesterol levels, helps to clear the body of heavy metals, contributes to tissue repair in the gastrointestinal tract, and is useful in glucose regulation. Studies have demonstrated that consuming foods high in pectin can also help reduce the risk and occurrence of prostate cancer. It's another one of those foods that induces apoptosis in mutated cells while helping the healthy cells get healthier.

Here's a simple recipe if you want to give Red Kuri Squash a try:

1 small Red Kuri Squash (organic because you can leave on the skin)
1 clove garlic
broth or water
dash of salt and cinnamon

Scrub the squash well to remove any dirt or wax. Slice the squash in half and scoop out the seeds. Cut the halves into 1-inch slices, and then cut the slices into chunks that are roughly 2 inches in size.

Heat a skillet over medium-high heat. Add the oil, followed by the squash, and cook for a few minutes, stirring occasionally. Stir in the garlic, then add ¼ inch of water to the skillet and bring it to a boil.

Cover and reduce the heat to a simmer. Cook until the squash is fork tender, about 10 minutes. You can also simmer off the liquid to create a caramelized effect which is delicious. Season with salt and/or cinnamon or whatever else suits your fancy.

DAY 306 – SHERRY

Sharp and dry resolving into a sweeter flavor with a full mouthfeel, Sherry is delicious to sip or sauté with. Sherry is a fortified wine, similar to Marsala and Port. In Europe, Sherry has protected designation of origin status, which means anything bearing the name "Sherry" or Xeres has to come from what is known as the "Sherry Triangle" in Spain.

Jerez de la Frontera, Sanlúcar de Barrameda and El Puerto de Santa María bound the Sherry triangle. Each area has its own microclimate, which imparts the grapes from each vineyard with a specific terroir and flavor.

Sherry is produced from white grapes, fermented to a certain stage and then fortified with a grape spirit, typically brandy, which gives it a deeper flavor structure, helps cultivate the creamy mouthfeel that sherries are famous for, and imparts different alcohol percentages depending on how much longer they ferment after fortification. This is where the varieties of dry to sweet, creamy to velvety. The color typically signifies whether it will be drier, which is lighter, or sweeter amber or mahogany.

From a culinary perspective, there is a cooking sherry that is specific to the kitchen. It typically not only is fortified but also has an amount of salt added as a preservative. This separates it from the other Sherries, which are distinctive for their sipping quality. I like to keep a bottle of sherry in the kitchen to sauté with or add to soups/stews or casseroles. It's especially welcome in fall and winter, adding a complexity to warming dishes that delights the palate.

From a health perspective, Sherry is made from white grapes and brandy, so I think this is just one of those things to enjoy occasionally in small amounts and call it a day. (:

DAY 307 – BROCCOLI RABE (RAPINI)

Bitter with a chewy texture, Broccoli Rabe is more or less an acquired taste. Broccoli Rabe also goes by the name Rapini and as a mustard family member is related to both the Cabbage and the turnip. Whether or not it is palatable often depends on how it is prepared. The Broccoli Rabe that was the inspiration for today's flavor was sautéed with leeks and a little bit of Absinthe. The Absinthe and a dash of salt helped decreased the bitter flavor and softened the texture while still keeping it dense and chewy rather than soft and slimy.

Broccoli Rabe is a popular vegetable in Italy and is growing slowly more popular in the U.S. and other parts of Europe. The leaves, stems, and small "flower" clusters are the parts eaten. The small clusters actually resemble miniature heads of broccoli, which is where it gets its name. It is definitely a bitter so can be a bit daunting for someone new to its charms, however, once you've figured out a few tried and true methods of preparation, it really does add well to mealtime and to your health. My favorite way to prepare Broccoli Rabe is to simply dice it as small as possible and sauté it. Typically, I use sherry to finish it, which further eliminates bitterness and also brings out the lightly earthy quality making it a great side for game and even starchy root vegetables.

From a health perspective, as a brassica, Broccoli Rabe is an amazing source of good stuff. High in vitamins and minerals, like Vitamin A, C, and B, as well as magnesium, calcium, and manganese. The micronutrients are plentiful and the phytonutrients are even more plentiful. It has chemical compounds that help eliminate systemic inflammation and oxidative stress, as well as increasing immune function and protecting against bacterial and viral infections. Studies have shown that including Broccoli Rabe in your diet can help regulate blood sugar and insulin levels and actually helps cellular detox and repair at the DNA level. It could be worth being adventurous and giving it a try.

DAY 308 – HIJIKI

Chewy and a little bit salty with a hint of the sea, Hijiki is a type of sea vegetable. It has been part of the Japanese diet for centuries. Historical references state that Hijiki became a mainstay in Japanese cuisine because it provided such a wealth of vitamins and minerals, most of which were a compliment to the land grown vegetation. Hijiki is still processed much the same way it has always been; first it is harvested by hand with a sickle, then it is allowed to dry out. Once it has air dried, the Hijiki is then taken to a processing facility where it is steamed and reconstituted and then rinsed and cleaned thoroughly. This also removes any potential bitterness and excess salty or sea taste. It is then dried again and packaged and sold.

Hijiki has a long history as a health product and has made its way around the world into other cultures. It became very popular in the U.S. with the onset of macrobiotic diets and has remained on the list of "health" foods while also taking a prominent role as an accompaniment in Japanese cuisine. From a culinary perspective Hijiki is fibrous and nicely chewy. It can be tossed into soups and stews, or reconstituted and made into nice chewy salad. Today's flavor was inspired by a lovely bit of Hijiki salad in a black bean sauce; part of my macrobiotic platter. Delicious.

From a health perspective, Hijiki is high in minerals and vitamins; especially calcium, magnesium and iron. There is more iron in a serving of Hijiki than in spinach or other green leafy iron rich vegetables. It is also high in Vitamin A. Research indicates that the chemical compounds found in Hijiki have an anti-mutagenic effect, which means they prevent mutation of rogue cells that could contribute to disease. Hijiki also aids in repairing tissue in the gastrointestinal tract, decreasing the potential for small bowel disease and/or colon cancer.

The down side is that Hijiki has been identified by several countries' food safety administrations as having relatively high levels of inorganic arsenic so people are cautioned to eat it in small amounts.

DAY 309 – VACHERIN (DU HAUT-DOUBS)

Tangy with hints of sweet grass and earthiness; Vacherin is soft cow's milk cheese that is delectable. There are a few varieties of Vacherin including; Mont d'Or, du Haut Doubs, and Fribourgeois. The Fribourgeois is made in the Valais region of Switzerland. It is denser and has a heavier texture and flavor. Mont d'Or and du Haut Doubs are technically the same cheese only one is pasteurized and comes from the Swiss side of the Jura mountain range and the other, the du Haut Doubs, is raw milk from the French side. Today's flavor comes from a nice wheel of du Haut Doubs.

Vacherin is considered a winter cheese and is produced from August to March and typically sold from September to May. Once it is ripened it is packaged in a little spruce container, which adds a hint of flavor and protects the outer rind of the cheese.

From a culinary perspective, Vacherin is delicious and creamy and can be served much the same way that Brie is served. Heated, baked, room temperature, with bits of fresh baked bread or fruit, and crackers. It is a treat on your cheeseboard.

From a health perspective, Vacherin is a good source of protein and vitamins and minerals. Eating the rind as well as the inside creamy stuff gives you a good dose of Vitamin B1, B12, and B7 as well as some zinc to help boost immune function. There's also some Vitamin A, D, and K2 which is a very important nutrient for heart health and bone density. The bacteria in Vacherin are also a healthy addition to your digestive flora and fauna and contribute to gut balance. So other than the obvious reasons like allergy, adding some delicious Vacherin to your dietary repertoire could be good and good for you.

DAY 310 – BERGAMOT ORANGE

Citrusy and slightly sweet with hints of earthiness, Bergamot is the oil found in Earl Grey tea. Enjoying a nice cup of Earl Grey on a cold, rainy day, I am struck by the intensity of the volatile oil known as Bergamot. Earl Grey is one of my favorite teas and I realize I know very little about the flavor of Bergamot, which launched me on an investigation. I must admit I have always assumed that Bergamot found in the tea was made from the herb known also called Bergamot; however that is not the case. The volatile oil found in Earl Grey tea is actually a citrus oil derived from the Bergamot Orange.

Bergamot Oranges are a hybrid citrus fruit, a type of orange, cultivated in the region of Calabria, Italy. Bergamot trees are believed to have originated in Asia, with the original tea blend known as Earl Grey reported to having come from a blend of Chinese and Bergamot rind either intentionally or accidentally created. Currently Earl Grey tea is typically made from the essential oil rather than the rind. The essential oil is made by cold pressing the skin and extracting the volatile oils.

From a culinary perspective Bergamot Orange is inedible, however, the essential oil can be used to flavor a variety of things both sweet and savory. It is especially delicious when added to baked goods or custards.

From a health perspective, bergamot orange oil has been used first and foremost as an aromatherapeutic intervention. Aromatherapy is often discarded as an intervention for health in the U.S. however its value is recognized in many other countries around the world. Aromatherapy works on the premise that the olfactory lobe is directly connected in with the brain and nervous system, without needing to be influenced by the cognitive section of the brain. This allows scent to directly stimulate the brain and body. From aromatherapy perspective Bergamot elevates the mood, it also contributes to increased immune function. It can also be used for its antibacterial, antiviral, antifungal properties (as are most citrus family members). Bergamot is also useful as a digestive tonic, an immune stimulant, and an analgesic.

It's important to note that Bergamot is NOT edible and is toxic as the fruit itself. It also creates a photosensitive effect so if it is used in body products can make you more sensitive to the sun.

DAY 311 – KNACKEBROD

Crisp and crunchy, with a tangy, nutty flavor, Knackebrod makes the perfect foundation for my afternoon snack. Knackebrod is Swedish for crispbread or hardbread. It is typically flat and light like a giant cracker, made from Rye meal, salt and water.

Traditional recipes used sourdough Rye starter as the foundation, giving the cracker bread a tangy flavor and a naturally longer shelf life. Knackebrod originates in Sweden; however, there are many variations throughout most of the Scandinavian countries. It was an easy way to make bread for your meals that lasted longer and was easier to store. Historically, Knackebrod was made with a hole in it so it could be stored on a pole across the kitchen or pantry.

From a culinary perspective Knackebrod is easy to make, easy to store, and even easier to enjoy with a meal. Since it's basically a Rye cracker it can be used anywhere you enjoy a cracker. You can also use them in place of bread.

From a health perspective Rye is a cereal grain in the wheat family and does contain gluten, albeit less than wheat but still for someone who has celiac disease, Rye would not be a good option. Rye, especially sourdough Rye, is a good source of minerals, vitamins and phytonutrients. Research demonstrates that the type of fiber found in Rye combined with its specific chemical composition make it a great resource to help minimize erratic blood sugar.

It also appears to signal the satiation triggers in the gut, helping you feel satisfied and fed longer than other grains. Studies also show that Rye has a significant impact on intracellular metabolism, contributing the repair and optimal functioning of mitochondria and genetic function. That means, healthy genes stay active and healthy and damaged ones get shut down.

DAY 312 – SHORTBREAD

Crisp and sweetly buttery with just a hint of salt, shortbreads are an, oh so, delicious treat with afternoon tea. Shortbread is the name for a crisp cookie made from butter, sugar and flour; occasionally other ingredients are added but for the most part traditional Shortbread is just those simple but delicious ingredients. It is believed that Shortbread originally was made from the bits of leftover bread dough after a loaf was made. It would be sweetened up, flattened into small disks, and then dried out in the oven until they were crisp.

In time, they became their own recipe minus the leavening agent (whether sourdough or yeast) and bumping up the sweet factor. This made them a bit more expensive to make and they became occasional treats during holidays or special events, like weddings. For celebrations the dough was prepared and then pressed into large earthenware pans decorated on the bottom so when baked and tipped out the shortbreads would have a design or decoration appropriate to the occasion. Shortbreads are thought to have originated in Scotland and enjoy a wealth of historical recognition, however, there are examples of other similar recipes throughout Britain.

From a culinary perspective, Shortbread is relatively easy to make. The trick is to start with chilled butter and cutting it into the flour and sugar until crumbly and then forming it into balls to be rolled out and cut or pressed into an appropriate pan.

A basic recipe for shortbread is 1 part sugar, 2 parts butter, 3 parts flour (you can add a variety of flours depending on the texture you desire). You can also add a variety of flavors such as lavender, lemon or orange zest, or perhaps some hazelnut. So basically if you have 1 cup of sugar, you would mix in 2 cups of butter, to 3 cups of flour (which would be kind of an enormous batch of Shortbreads but you get the picture). You then chill the dough for about 30 minutes before pressing it out and cutting it with cutters or pressing it into a pan. Bake at 350 for about 15 minutes.

From a health perspective, well they're basically sugar cookies, so clearly moderation is key as well as the need to use good quality ingredients. A quality, non-bleached, non-adulterated flour, with a good quality grass fed butter, and some Rapidura or Turbinado Sugar will give you a different, more traditional, flavor as well as a more healthful option. Although again, I think they are just something to be fully savored in small amounts and enjoyed as the occasional sweet treat they are meant to be.

DAY 313 – SCALLIONS

Sharp and zesty, with a slight hint of earthiness, Scallions add a zesty flair to your meal. More than just a garnish, which is usually where you find them, Scallions, also known as green onions or Welsh onions. They are esteemed members of the allium family, specifically, Allium fistulosum, and very much their own variant of allium despite that some resources will try to convince you they are simply premature yellow onions.

Welsh onions do not form a bulb at any point in their development and they have hollow leaves and scapes, which are the dark green 'stems'. Although, they are referred to as a Welsh onion, they do not originate in Wales, nor are they particularly popular there (the leek is more prominent in Welsh cuisine). There are various theories on how they came by their name but none seem to be in total agreement.

From a culinary perspective Scallions have a lighter flavor and bright green leaves so they make a great garnish for both their mild potential and their color. You can toss them in salads, on soups/stews, throw them in baked dishes, really anywhere that needs a little zesty, lightly oniony pick me up.

From a health perspective Scallions are in the allium family and as such possess the beneficial qualities of other alliums. Scallions are a good source of Vitamin A and K, and a multitude of minerals like potassium, magnesium and copper. They have anti-inflammatory properties and can also help alleviate pain and irritation if used topically. Like leeks and other alliums Scallions are packed with plenty of phytonutrients that enhance health.

For example, allicin, which studies show decrease cholesterol, lower blood pressure, and contribute to liver health. They are also antifungal, antibacterial, and antiviral. Research also demonstrates that the chemical compounds in Scallions contribute to increased immune function and prevent cellular mutation. They are a quick and easy way decorate your plate and boost your health.

DAY 314 – GINGERBREAD

Moist and chewy with the warm spice of ginger and hints of burnt caramel. Gingerbread can actually refer to either moist, chewy cake or crisp biscuits and cookies. It's more the flavor combination that dictates the name. Ginger and other warming spices are the main ingredients for Gingerbread and molasses and/or honey are typically the traditional sweetener.

Gingerbread has a rich history throughout a variety of cultures; with one of the first recorded recipes found in 2400 BC Greek writings. Ginger is initially a spice imported from China. Over time it made its way via the Silk Road throughout Europe. One of the first known culinary uses of ginger in European culture was as a heating spice to disguise the flavor of meat that was beginning to turn. Prior to that it was utilized mostly as a medicinal intervention.

The Gingerbread found in the Greek culinary records was most likely made from honey, ginger, and barley flour. It appears they were mostly used in ritual settings or as celebration cakes. In time Gingerbread found its way around the world, with each region refining and adapting ingredients to suit their palate and availability.

From a culinary perspective, Gingerbread has so many variations of ingredients, textures, styles that really it seems like the sky is the limit to finding a recipe that might be most suited to your palate. Once you find a flavor combination that suits, you can then adjust other ingredients to make either a moist and chewy cake, or some crisp ginger cakes…or even more fun with the holidays approaching, some Gingerbread people and houses.

From a health perspective, besides being ceremonial cakes in early history, ginger cakes were also baked as medicinal interventions. It was recognized that ginger had several healthful properties, including boosting the immune function, aiding in digestive balance, fighting bacteria, parasites, and food poisoning. Current studies show that ginger can help decrease the symptoms of asthma and lower cholesterol. Research also shows that the chemical properties in ginger are effective cancer fighting agents. They down-regulate the bodies ability to metastasize cancer cells and then effectively kill them off.

Could be worth making a batch of Gingerbread…cake, people, house… something.

DAY 315 – LEICESTER (RED)

Firm in texture, cheesy and nutty, Leicester cheese is one of my new favorites. Leicester, also known as Red Leicester because of its rich orange color, is named after the city of Leicester in England. It is made in a similar style to Cheddar and has a similar flavor although a little nuttier, in my opinion. Traditionally Red Leicester derived its color from added beetroot or carrot juice, however today annatto is the typical coloring agent.

From a culinary perspective Red Leicester cheese is mildly flavored with a firm texture. It crumbles and melts easily and is easily used anywhere other cheeses of similar texture, such as Jack and Cheddar.

From a health perspective cheese is often seen as an indulgence to be avoided by the health conscious; however, it has its benefits (if it's real cheese and not cheese product). Cheese is a good source of protein, calcium, Vitamin B12, and if it's from grass fed cows, it contains even more good stuff. If it's from heritage breed cows then it has the added power of the A2 casein molecule, which has a variety of health benefits. Cheese is umami and satisfies the palate. Research suggests it also helps regulate blood sugar.

One caveat; if you're going to eat it make sure it is full fat and naturally processed so you are really getting the benefit of the cheese without the contamination of additives and chemical processing.

DAY 316 – VENISON

Bold and slightly gamey, Venison sautéed in a bit of garlic and red wine makes a much appreciated seasonal meal. Venison is the meat of a deer, although traditionally the term 'venison' applied to all hunted meat that was not fowl or fish. Venison is a seasonal game, best eaten in November, December, January and February. I think many people think only of fruits and vegetables as seasonal but meat is as well, including fish and fowl. Venison is best hunted and eaten during the onset of winter and through the winter months. The meat is more mature and flavorful during these months and culling the herds through conscious hunting practices can help the rest of the deer survive through the winter.

From a culinary perspective Venison is a wild game so it tends to have a little bit stronger flavor than domestic meats. It has a lighter and leaner texture even with its bolder flavor. Venison comes in many of the same cuts as beef and can be used in much the same way. Venison steaks, roasts, burgers; I've sautéed some squares of Venison thigh in garlic and red wine, served it up with some roasted barley, peas, and squash to make a delicious and healthy dinner.

As for your health? Venison is a game meat; which means a higher quality protein. It is also higher in Iron and B vitamins. As a wild foraging game, the phytonutrient density will vary depending on the environment as will the flavor. Overall Venison is a great choice for quality protein and other nutrients if you are an omnivore.

DAY 317 – ECCLES CAKES (RECIPE)

Sweet, buttery and flaky; an Eccles Cake is the perfect treat to savor while wandering around the farmer's market. While, there seems to be varying theories about the origin of Eccles Cakes, there is general agreement the first person to actually make them available as a product for sale to the public, was a baker named James Birch in the town of Eccles around 1780. Eccles akes are little cakes filled with a sweet raisin mixture and baked in a flaky buttery crust. They are not yet protected to origin so an Eccles Cake can pretty much be produced anywhere with a certain foundation of ingredients and called an Eccles Cake.

From a culinary perspective, the exact ingredients vary from recipe to recipe, except for the flaky crust and the raisins/currants. Some recipes call for other candied peels and fruits to be added and others call for spices like nutmeg, cinnamon, and vanilla. The most delicious Eccles Cake I've had was simply, sweetened raisins wrapped in a buttery, flaky crust with a tiny sprinkling of sugar on the top.

From a health perspective, of course, any potential healthy impact will be influenced by the quality of ingredients. Quality butter and milled, heritage flour, with organic or sustainably grown raisins or currants, and Demerara or Muscovado sugar then at least your little treat will be more a more consciously crafted culinary indulgence.

ECCLES CAKE

Filling:
6 TBS unsalted Butter
1 cinnamon stick
1 teaspoon ground nutmeg
1/2 teaspoon ground cloves
Peel from 2 lemons
Peel from 2 oranges
2 cups dried currants
1/2 cup golden raisins
2 tablespoons brandy
1/4 cup fresh-squeezed lemon juice

Melt the butter in a small saucepan over medium heat. Add the spices and peel and fry until they are fragrant in the butter. Add the fruit, brandy, and juice. Simmer for ten or fifteen minutes, stirring occasionally. Let cool, then put in the fridge overnight to let the flavors really meld.

Pastry
1 pound (4 sticks) unsalted Butter
4 cups flour
1 teaspoon salt
Between 1 and 1/2 cups ice water

Take three of the sticks of butter and slice them in half lengthwise and then again widthwise. Arrange them into a rectangle on a large piece of wax paper. Put another piece of wax paper on top and roll them the Butter out into a 9x12-inch rectangle between the sheets of waxed paper. Chill for at least four hours.

Put the four cups of flour into a food processor. Cut up the remaining stick of butter and add it, bit by bit, to the flour and pulse into dusty crumbs. Dump the butter-flour crumbs into a big bowl and add ice water gradually, stirring, just until the dough comes together. Knead for a couple minutes until smooth. Wrap and refrigerate four hours or overnight.

Roll the dough out into a 1/4-inch-thick rectangle and place the butter rectangle on top. Fold the corners of the dough over the butter and roll out to its previous size. Fold the sides of the dough up to the middle, like folding a piece of paper into thirds, then fold it again in half — like closing a book. You're working the butter into the dough in finer and finer layers; the butter if it stays cold will puff the pastry up in delicious and spectacular ways when you're finished. Wrap this parcel well and put back in the fridge for at least an hour or two.

Take the dough out and roll the parcel out into the rectangle again, then repeat the folding process. This is working the butter into the pastry in finer and finer layers. Continue this process - rolling out, then folding. These are called turns. Do at least four turns - six or more is even better. It's very simple: the longer you let the dough rest and chill between turns, and the more turns you do, the lighter and flakier your pastry will be.

Finishing touches:
1 egg, beaten
Coarse sugar

Heat the oven to 375°F. Line a baking sheet with parchment paper. Take a third of the puff pastry dough from the fridge. It should be very cold and firm, but not hard. Roll it out to a thickness of about 1/8-inch.

Cut small circles – a biscuit cutter is perfect with four-inch circles. Put a small dollop of filling (about 1 teaspoon) in the center of each dough circle.

Fold in half, like a pot-sticker dumpling, and seal the edges with your fingers. Now bring the two pointy edges up and fold them in the center, on the curved seam. Flatten out the little pouch with your fingers, and roll it into a small circle - just thin enough that the filling shows through the dough a little. Try not to let it leak out, though. Make two or three shallow slashes in the top of the finished round cake.

Brush with beaten egg, and sprinkle with sugar.
Bake for about 20 minutes, or until golden brown and puffy.

DAY 318 – SUCANAT

Sweet, with hints of caramel or molasses, Sucanat is a complexly flavored sugar. Sucanat stands for Sugar Cane Natural. It is made from dehydrated cane juice and as such is in its most natural state. Sucanat is sweet but with a slightly less sucrose content that its refined counterparts. It is also slightly more nutrient dense, with more vitamins and minerals like iron, potassium, and vitamin B6. However, truth be told, the nutrient count in any kind of sugar is truly negligible. The thing that makes Sucanat the most attractive to me is the lack of processing and refining. The occasional use of sugar in baking and other culinary endeavors feels more wholesome when using minimally processed and sustainable options.

From a culinary perspective, Sucanat can be used as a replacement for white and brown sugars. It has a more complex flavor, with the natural hints of caramel and molasses so it influences the flavor of whatever it has been added to.

From a health perspective, well, it is sugar. Historically, sugar was a precious commodity so when something was baked with sugar it was only an occasional treat reserved for special occasions. I imagine it was really quite a treat when it wasn't readily available as an ingredient in almost every manufactured food item, both savory and sweet. Because it is so prevalent in the typical diet, sugar is really something that should be avoided, however, if it is something that you only consume upon occasion, then it could be worth getting your hands on some unrefined Sucanat and giving it a try.

DAY 319 – BROCCOLINI

Crisp and crunchy with hints of sweet grass and earthy goodness, sautéed Broccolini is one of my favorite wintertime veggie choices. Broccolini is in the Brassica family, along with broccoli, Cabbage, and Brussels sprouts. It is often misidentified as young broccoli, which it is not. It is its own variation of brassica, a hybrid of broccoli and a vegetable called Kailaan.

Broccolini is new to the vegetable scene, being first developed in 1993 by the Sakata Seed Company and it is growing in popularity around the world. The small tender stalks of Broccolini are actually the off-shoots of a much thicker and larger stalk; sort of the way Brussels sprouts grow on a larger stalk and are removed when harvested. Broccolini season is from November through April, although it is quickly becoming more available year round.

From a culinary perspective Broccolini are pretty easy to add to a meal or be a meal. They don't need to be peeled or even necessarily chopped up. I love to quickly parboil them then finish them off in a quick garlic and olive oil sauté. They are delicious steamed, sautéed, stir-fried, and even grilled.

From a health perspective they are in the Brassica family so they are full of all the lovely nutrient goodness you'll find in Brussels sprouts, broccoli and Cabbage.

As a cruciferous vegetable, with all the benefits of its kin, Broccolini is high in vitamin C, K, an A. Research demonstrates that the flavonoids in Broccolini increase colon health and decrease the potential for colon cancer (and other cancers). It is beneficial for cardiovascular health and helps lower blood pressure.

Studies suggest that sulforaphane, a chemical compound found in most brassicas, including Broccolini, can also help repair and prevent damage to small blood vessels caused by diabetes. Broccolini also has the amazing ability, like its parent broccoli, to detoxify the body on a cellular level due to a unique trio of phytonutrients. If you haven't tried Broccolini yet, I highly recommend giving a chance in your kitchen (:

DAY 320 – JERUSALEM ARTICHOKE

Crunchy, dense, and earthy with a hint of grassy sweetness, Jerusalem Artichokes make great pancakes! Jerusalem artichokes are also called sunchokes or sunroot. They are the funny looking, knobby tube root of a species of sunflower; very similar in appearance to ginger root. Native to the North American continent they are growing in popularity and being cultivated in appropriate climates around the world. They were initially cultivated across the U.S. and Canada by the Native populations and shared with the arriving Europeans who then took them back home.

Jerusalem Artichokes are tubers, which are different from root vegetables. They are a good source of protein and lower in starch although very high in inulin. Inulin is a naturally occurring polysaccharide that is a prebiotic, so great for the gut. It also works as a good source of fiber, retaining fluid in the gut and assisting with motility and tissue repair. Research suggests that consuming foods with inulin can assist with lowering cholesterol, balancing blood serum levels, and boost immune function. As a prebiotic it helps populate the gut with friendly bacteria, which in turn balances not only digestion but also mood and cognitive function.

Jerusalem Artichokes are sort of, but not entirely, similar in texture to potatoes. When they are raw, I actually find them to be a little more like jicama root; sort of sweet and earthy, with a juicy crispness. Cooked they can take on more of a potato consistency. However, they can also become a little bit gummy if overcooked. I think that's due to the lack of starch. One of my favorite ways to enjoy Jerusalem Artichokes is as a "latke" or potato pancake. Grate them, add the egg, and some herbs and spices, and fry them up. You can also dice and roast them, then use them in things like "potato salad" or mash them and enjoy with Butter.

One caveat about them, since they are very high in inulin, they can cause abdominal discomfort for people who are unable to absorb or assimilate fructans or for people who typically eat a low fiber diet. If you're going to give them a try, I suggest introducing them slowly so your gut has time to adjust and enjoy all of their delicious healthful qualities.

DAY 321 – JICAMA

Crisp and dense, almost chalky but sort of sweet with hints of earthiness; Jicama is also known as Mexican Yam Bean. It is the root of a bean vine, which produces very lovely but poisonous flowers. The root is the only edible part of the plant. Even though I typically think of Jicama as a spring and summer food because of its juicy and crisp qualities, it is actually traditionally harvested in Fall. Once harvested, if kept in the right environment it will last for several months, retaining its refreshing and juicy quality.

Jicama is native to Central and South America, although it has been cultivated in appropriate climates around the world. It is a funny looking root, very much resembling a turnip but larger and denser. Jicama has a high water content, is a good source of fiber, with moderate carbohydrate content. It is a good source of Vitamin A and C. It is also a great source of inulin. Inulin is a belly friendly prebiotic and gastrointestinal balm so long as it is eaten in moderation.

From a culinary perspective Jicama has a similar texture to water chestnut and can definitely be used in soups and stir-fries. It seems to be most popularly enjoyed raw, cut into salads or even just eaten in slices topped with lime and chili. This is one reason I think of Jicama as a spring or summer food, when the weather is warm Jicama with a touch of lime and some chili is a delicious and refreshing treat.

DAY 322 – MULLED WINE

A lovely way to chase away the oncoming winter chill, spicy, warm, tangy Mulled Wine. Mulled wine is made by warming red wine with a variety of spices; like cloves, cinnamon, anise, sometimes sugar and vanilla. Almost every culture has examples of spiced and heated wine. In German it is called Gluhwein; in Norwegian and Swedish it is Glogg. Historically, Mulled Wines were common as first Fall and then winter set-in and were considered medicinal.

From a culinary perspective, Mulled Wine is an easy holiday treat and depending on the length of heating time and temperature it can be alcoholic or non-alcoholic. Traditional recipes call for a sachet of spices like cinnamon sticks, orange peel, anise seed stars, and cloves. I typically put the wine in a slow cook crockpot and toss in the spices, letting it slowly heat and 'mull' for a few hours before serving. Some recipes call for adding sugar, although I don't recommend it and it doesn't seem to be an ingredient in more traditional recipes.

From a health perspective, interestingly, initially Mulled Wine was a health intervention. Typically, drinking wine was healthier than drinking water, especially in populated areas, so tossing in some antiviral, antimicrobial, and antifungal spices, like cinnamon, cloves, ginger, anise, etc... was a great combination for immune boosting and disease destroying. They weren't far wrong, in moderation, red wine by itself is a rich source of antioxidants and other phytonutrients. Resveratrol is among the most popular being in the limelight of pop culture health and fitness. Research suggests that resveratrol decreases incidence and potential of cardiovascular disease as well as balancing cholesterol and reducing the formation of blood clots.

Resveratrol also protects against cell damage and mental decline. The ellargic acid found in red grapes also contributes to metabolic increase and increases the body's fat burning potential, mostly by decreasing the body's ability to produce new fat cells and delaying the growth of fat cells already present. Remember that even if you are mulling wine and it is tempting to go for a cheaper wine, but it's worth your while to stay with something consciously produced. Old world wines from France, Italy, and Spain tend to have more stringent fermentation. The rest of the health benefits will depend entirely on the type and amount of spices added. Cinnamon, cloves, ginger, anise, a hint of nutmeg all have health benefits. When the temperature dips and Jack Frost is nipping at your nose and toes, a cup of Mulled Wine can be just the holiday treat.

DAY 323 – CHERVIL

Lightly licorice in flavor with hints of earth, sweet, and a tiny bit of zest; Chervil is an uncommon herb, worth introducing to your culinary repertoire. Chervil is similar to parsley in appearance except it has a lighter, more feathery quality to the leaves and stems. Chervil is a member of the carrot family, hence the feathery leaves and soft texture which almost resemble a carrot top. You may not recognize the name if you live in the U.S. but it is part of the combination called "fines herbes" so it maybe in your kitchen at this moment unbeknown to you.

Chervil is native to Northern Europe but has made its way across Europe, into Asia, and around to Northern America. It is a popular herb in Europe and the U.K. but only moderately used and recognized in the U.S. Chervil is known for its medicinal and symbolic qualities; symbolizing new life and sincerity. It is also recognized as a digestive aid and skin purifier in traditional writings.

From a culinary perspective Chervil's subtle flavor goes really well with lighter dishes such as fish and cream based soups. Although, today's flavor comes from a heartier dish of venison and chestnut puree, with Chervil topping it off for a subtle unexpected complexity.

From a health perspective Chervil has a little research supporting its use as a digestive aid and also as a blood purifier. Nutritionally it contains a wide variety of vitamins, minerals, and phytonutrients. It is a fantastic source of vitamins A, C, and D as well as K. It has expectorant qualities, helping to clear the chest and lungs of phlegm. It is anti-inflammatory and helps decrease oxidative stress. It also helps the gastrointestinal tract repair and replenish, along with aiding the kidneys, bladder, and urinary tract in fighting bacteria and other disease causing issues.

DAY 324 – GREEN BEANS

Crisp with a sweet, grassy flavor, a handful of raw Green Beans make a delicious snack. Green beans, specifically the variety Phaseolus vulgaris, will be found on many a Thanksgiving Day dinner table across the U.S. They originated in South and Central America. Archeologists have found cultivated varieties in cooking vessels that carbon date around 7000 BC.

This particular variety of Green Bean seems to have made its way to the European continent and through the Mediterranean via Columbus' voyage in 1492. According to historians an entry in the travel diary dated November 4th, 1492 discusses the discovery of cowpeas, fava beans, and this particular variety of Green Bean. Further discussion in culinary texts can be found in British cookery books around 1543, demonstrating successful cultivation.

Fresh Green Beans can be a culinary delight. They have a subtle flavor and impart a nice crisp texture, of course they can also be a culinary nightmare if overcooked or canned. They can be steamed, sautéed, stir-fried, boiled, grilled, or even enjoyed raw. I love to use them on veggie trays during the holidays, as they are great for dipping.

From a health perspective Green Beans are a great source of fiber and nutrients like vitamin C, K and manganese and folate. As a phytonutrient source they are rich in chlorophyll and believe it or not, they are a great source of carotenoids and neoxanthins; nutrients typically found in red and orange vegetables. Carotenoids, flavonoids, polyphenols, leucoanthocyanins and catechins help with things like cardiovascular disease, systemic inflammation, and insulin management. Interestingly, green beans also contain a chemical compound that assists in the utilization and management of carbohydrate starch. Several studies have demonstrated that regular consumption of an extract derived from the bean Phaseolus vulgaris resulted in weight loss and decreased fat mass, while maintaining or increasing lean muscle mass.

Thoughts: If you are used to having the infamous (and often dreaded) Green Bean casserole as part of your Thanksgiving Day meal, it's worth making it from scratch, using fresh beans and other fresh ingredients.

DAY 325 – CRANBERRY

Tart and mouth puckering, Cranberry season is here. Cranberries, specifically the variety Vaccinium oxycoccos, come from small, evergreen shrubs that are indigenous to the Northern Hemisphere; growing wild in swamps and bogs. It is a member of the Heather family. In North America, wild growing Cranberries were part of Native American culture, used not only for food but also as a medicinal intervention and a fabric dye. Historical records suggest that Cranberries were introduced to pilgrims around the year 1620. First reported domestic cultivation of Cranberries, via Cranberry bogs is reported to be around the 1800's.

From a culinary perspective Cranberries are a traditional and seasonal treat. They are typically harvested around October and end up finding their way to the dinner table throughout the holiday months. Because of their strong and astringent flavor cranberries are typically used in smaller amounts or as a condiment. Cranberries can also be juiced, producing a tart and astringent power-packed juice. As a berry you can add them to baked goods, sautéed, stir-fried, cooked into compotes and sauces.

Creative culinary endeavors abound if you're feeling adventurous. Here's a delicious Cranberry Sauce recipe that is a bold twist from the traditional:

CRANBERRY PORT SAUCE

Sauté 1/3 cup minced red onion in 1 tablespoon Butter over medium heat until softened.
Add 1/2 cup ruby port; simmer until reduced by half.
Add 1 cup cranberries
3/4 cup chicken broth
2 tablespoons each sugar and orange juice
1/4 teaspoon mustard powder
Simmer, lightly smashing the berries, until thickened, 10 minutes. Season with salt and pepper.

From a health perspective, cranberries are considered a super fruit. They are a rich source of vitamins, minerals, and phytonutrients. They are high in Vitamin C, Manganese, and even fiber. The phytonutrient content is fantastic, with Cranberries being beneficial for decreasing oxidative stress, systemic inflammation and having significant antibacterial/antiviral/antifungal qualities. It has long been demonstrated they are useful in preventing bacteria from adhering to the walls of the urinary tract, aiding in the relief of bladder and urinary tract infections. Research also demonstrates that the chemical compounds in Cranberries are highly effective against the helicobacter pylori bacterium that contributes to ulcers and other stomach and gastrointestinal tract issues.

The caveat? Research is demonstrating that it is the entire Cranberry that is most effective in these medicinal situations, rather than as first believed, extracts and isolated nutrients. In other words drink the whole berry in a juice, eat the whole berry in your foods, don't rely on supplements.

DAY 326 – GUACAMOLE

Creamy, zingy, and spicy, Guacamole is a delicious addition to any number of dishes. Traditionally made with avocado, as the foundational ingredient, Guacamole is a dish that dates back to the Aztecs. According to historians, it made its way to the rest of the world via the Spanish who quickly developed an affinity for the avocado. The Aztecs thought that Guacamole had an aphrodisiac quality and the "sauce" was a frequent part of meals and celebrations.

While the basic ingredients tend to be the same, there are variations depending on location and availability. Each region in Mexico adds its own little localized twist to the basics. Since becoming more popular in other cultures there have also been recipes created that do not contain avocado at all, rather the foundation is some other green vegetable such as green chickpea or spring peas.

From a culinary perspective, Guacamole is pretty easy. Avocado, onion, garlic, Jalapeno, cilantro, some lime, some salt, some pepper all up for variation in amount and ingredient. It is then served up as a side dish or even used as a spread or sauce.

From a health perspective, the idea Guacamole was an aphrodisiac isn't too far wrong. Guacamole is packed with nutrients like vitamin E, magnesium, potassium, beta-carotene, oleic acid, all of which enhance reproductive health, as well as cardiovascular, gastrointestinal, and neurovascular health. The ingredients in Guacamole have antibacterial, antifungal, and antiviral qualities, as well as the ability to help decrease oxidative stress and systemic inflammation. Could be worth mixing up a batch and enjoying the healthful and delicious qualities.

DAY 327 – CARDONE

At first glance it could be very easy to mistake Cardone for an interesting looking Celery. Don't be fooled, Cardone is actually related to the artichoke and while it has a slightly similar texture to celery, it can't be eaten raw and it has its own distinctive flavor. I came across a bunch of Cardone in my local market and decided I had to bring it home and give it a try. First, I had to do a little research and figure out what it was.

Cardone is a member of the thistle family, so it is sometimes referred to as artichoke thistle. It is native to the Mediterranean but has made its way to appropriate climates around the world. It was apparently first domesticated by the Romans and then spread across Europe and the Middle East during the Middle Ages. According to historical data, written around the 15th century, it was a highly prized addition to the table and figured prominently in the dietary repertoire of Europe, the Mediterranean and even in time, with the pilgrims to the "New World". According to written records the Quakers first introduced Cardone to America. It was then first cultivated in the gardens of Monticello by Thomas Jefferson. So, in its own way, it is a perfect flavor to find during the Thanksgiving holiday.

From a culinary perspective, Cardone is interesting. Although, it resembles celery it is not as easily prepared as celery. It is a thistle and as such contains tiny barbs in the stalk, which are quite bitter in their raw state. To prepare them, it is recommended that they are first either soaked in salt water for an hour or two, or parboiled in salted water. Once they are prepped they can then be cooked in a variety of ways. I've prepped mine by soaking in salt water. I then diced up a small section of the stalk and sautéed it in butter to have with eggs for breakfast. It was delicious, earthy and dense but also a little crunchy; all in all a great addition to the meal. I will be making the rest of the stalks into a Cardone au Gratin. Really once they are prepped they can be fried, baked, stir-fried, boiled, or any number of other options.

From a health perspective, Cardone is a great resource for nutrients and phytonutrients. It contains things like potassium, magnesium, and copper, Vitamin C and folates. It's a great source of fiber, with most of it being in the form of inulin, making it highly beneficial for your gastrointestinal health. From a phytonutrient perspective, it is fantastic. Since it's in the thistle family, it contains things like silymarin, caffeic acid, and luteolin; all of which help with cellular detoxification and regeneration.

Silymarin is the chemical compound found in milk thistle, which research suggests can help the liver repair and prevent further damage. Studies have shown that people suffering from liver damage due to consumption of NSAIDs (non-steroid anti-inflammatories, like ibuprofen and aspirin) experienced regeneration of healthy liver tissue. Silymarin and other chemical compounds found in all the thistle relatives have a chemopreventive effect while also aiding in the reduction of oxidative stress and systemic inflammation. In other words, artichokes and their relatives are yummy stuff.

DAY 328 – SAVORY (WINTER)

Earthy and sharp, a bit like thyme with a citrusy twist, Winter Savory adds a nice dimension to holiday food. Winter savory, Satureja montana, is a relative of other woody, evergreen herbs like thyme and rosemary. There are two types of savory used in the culinary world, a summer variety which is lighter in flavor and the winter variety, which I've chosen to include in my herb bouquet for holiday dishes.

According to historians, Winter Savory is so named (Satureja) after satyrs, which are mythological creatures, half man and half goat that lived in meadows full of the herb. The volatile oil of the herb was said to ignite passion and was used as an aphrodisiac. Savory was so commonly used in early culinary endeavors that flavorful food became known as "savory";

reflecting the quality of the herb.

From a culinary perspective, Winter Savory has a stronger flavor and goes really well with games, legumes and root veggies; basic wintertime fare.

From a health perspective, Savory is in the mint/thyme/rosemary family; which gives it similar volatile properties. It has antioxidant and anti-inflammatory qualities. It is great for circulation and skincare. It is antiviral, antifungal, antimicrobial. It is also great for digestion and immune function. Research suggests that Savory increases brain health and is effective in fighting free radicals that contribute to disease. It's no accident that Savory is referred to as the herb of happiness; the volatile oils give it a refreshing quality that lifts spirits. This makes it so very useful in mood disorders like depression.

DAY 329 – CHAYOTE

Crisp, refreshing with the texture and color of a granny smith apple but with a mildly earthy flavor similar to a zucchini. Chayote is a member of the family cucurbita, which makes it a relative of zucchini, cucumber, and other melons and gourds. It is native to Mexico but has made its way around the world in appropriate growing climates. Chayote is a popular ingredient in cuisines found around the world ranging from Asia/India, South and Central America, the Caribbean, and the U.S. Southern States.

From a culinary perspective, Chayote is an interesting ingredient. It is subtle in flavor and maintains its texture and density even after it is prepared. It can be added to stir fries, stews, soups, sautéed, boiled, baked and even enjoyed raw in salads or as a side dish or garnish. Because its flavor is subtle and kind of sweetly earthy, it can be a great addition to dishes both savory and sweet.

From a health perspective, Chayote is a really great source of vitamins, minerals and some great phytonutrients. All parts of the Chayote plant are edible; fruit, seed, stem, leaves, and roots and they all seem to have some medicinal property. It has all the benefits of the other cucurbita relatives. It's a great source of vitamins C, B, and A, as well as a wide variety of minerals including potassium, magnesium, manganese, iron, copper, phosphorous, and calcium.

Studies have shown significant benefit to eye and vision problems including degenerative diseases. The fiber and phytonutrients are beneficial to digestive health and immune function. Research has

demonstrated a beneficial impact on blood glucose maintenance, making it a valuable resource for insulin resistance and diabetes. Chayote has a reputation for its cellular regenerative and anti-aging properties. Additionally, it appears to have the ability to help cells not only repair damage produced by cancer but also stimulates the mutated cells to deconstruct.

DAY 330 – NOPALES

With a texture similar to roasted chilies, Nopales add a southwestern flair to a meal. Nopales are the pads from the Opuntia cactus, otherwise known as the Prickly Pear. They are a common ingredient in Mexican cuisine and are a versatile addition to dishes both sweet and savory.

Nopales have been part of the western human diet for thousands of years, with earliest recorded use around 1000 BC. They are indigenous to the western hemisphere but have since made their way to appropriate climates around the world. Records suggest that Columbus carried the cactus back to Lisbon in 1493 as part of his discovery cargo. The Opuntia cactus is a very versatile plant, with edible pads and fruit (just remove the spines) and tough fibrous membrane that can be used for a variety of domestic ventures, including fabric. The pads of Nopales have also be used as a type of water storage since they are easy to carry once de-spined.

From a culinary perspective, Nopales are interesting in texture. Once they are skinned and de-spined they can be used in stir fries, sautees, scrambled with eggs, diced into stews and soups. I find them to be a little bit like okra in their texture once cooked, so as far as I'm concerned a little bit goes a long way. They have a subtle flavor that can be enhanced by grilling.

From a health perspective, Nopales are a great source of nutrients; macro, micro, and phyto. They are high in fiber and things like pectin, which help the gastrointestinal tract repair and replenish. They are a great source of Vitamin C and B complex. They are high in minerals like magnesium, potassium and even calcium.

DAY 331 – GORGONZOLA

Tangy and slightly sharp but with a sweet edge that makes Gorgonzola a uniquely delicious variety of blue cheese. Produced in the Northern regions of Italy, namely the Lombardy region, Gorgonzola is both a Protected Designation of Origin (EU) and designated origin (DOC) in Italy. These designations require Gorgonzola cheese be made in a very particular way. It is made from unskimmed cow's milk and has several different strains of bacteria lending the blue and green hues. Younger gorgonzola has a sweeter flavor, named Gorgonzola Dolce, it is typically aged a year or less. Older, sharper flavored Gorgonzola is called Gorgonzola Piccante.

From a culinary perspective, Gorgonzola cheese is a delight and versatile. It can be used in both sweet and savory dishes. It is delicious melted into risotto, turned into a sauce for pastas, steak, and/or veggies. It is also great on a cheese platter accompanied by fruits and nuts.

From a health perspective, as a blue cheese, Gorgonzola is actually a very heart healthy food. Research demonstrates that it helps decrease systemic inflammation and it helps relieve oxidative stress. It increases cardiovascular health by decreasing blood pressure and fighting bacteria that contributes to imbalanced cholesterol levels. If you haven't had a chance to enjoy a bit of Gorgonzola, I highly recommend finding some and giving it a nosh.

DAY 332 – EGG NOG (RECIPE)

Rich and creamy sweetness, with hints of cinnamon and nutmeg, it's that time of year for some holiday deliciousness. Real Egg Nog is also known as Egg Milk Punch and that's basically just what it is; eggs and milk with some spices tossed in. Sounds simple enough and maybe not even that delicious, but trust me when it's made correctly it is scrumptious.

According to culinary historians Egg Nog is technically a variation of stirred custard which accounts for its thick creaminess. Many historians theorize that the origination of Egg Nog is actually a posset, which is a type pudding or custard like sweet dessert, which was infused with rum back in the day in British history. Despite its British influence Egg Nog is apparently an American endeavor becoming a holiday favorite as milk, eggs, and rum were plentiful. True Egg Nog is actually an aged delicacy; sitting anywhere from a month to six months in a cold environment. The combination of alcohol, milk sugar, egg proteins and time, combine into a thick and creamy delicacy.

Real Egg Nog is a culinary endeavor that is absolutely worth the attempt.

If you don't have the time or wherewithal to age it, you can always make a shorter version that is just as delicious. Trust me, what you purchase in the store is nothing like the real deal homemade version.

From a health perspective, well, there is a certain amount of health benefit to egg yolks and real milk. Zinc, vitamin A, B, and D, lutein, zeaxanthin are all healthy components of the egg yolk that will be imparted to the Nog mixture. Of course, the addition of rum or bourbon sort of creates its own dimension of health risk. If you are going to make Egg Nog minus the alcohol you will need to do the shorter version since the aging process doesn't work without alcohol.

TRADITIONAL EGG NOG:
12 eggs, separated
6 cups milk
2 cups heavy/ thickened cream
2 cups bourbon
1+ 1/2 cups sugar
3/4 cup brandy
2 tsp ground nutmeg

In a large bowl and using a mixer, beat the egg yolks together with the sugar for approx 10 minutes (you want the mixture to be firm and the colour of butter).
Very slowly, add in the bourbon and brandy - just a little at a time.

When bourbon and brandy have been added, allow the mixture to cool in the fridge (for up to 6 hours, depending on how long before your party you're making the eggnog).
30 minutes before your guests arrive, stir the milk into the chilled yolk mixture.
Stir in 1+ 1/2 teaspoons ground nutmeg.

In a separate bowl, beat the cream with a mixer on high speed until the cream forms stiff peaks.

In yet another bowl, beat the egg whites until stiff peaks form.
Gently fold the egg white mixture into the egg yolk mixture.
Gently fold the cream into the egg mixture.
After ladling into cups, garnish with the remainder of the ground nutmeg.

DAY 333 – PEPINO MELON

Refreshing, dense, slightly sweet; a Pepino Melon is just the thing if you're trying cleanse your palate. Pepino melons are actually not a melon at all, being more closely related to a tomato or other members of the nightshade family. That being said, their flavor and texture very much resembles a cantaloupe or even a papaya.

The Pepino is indigenous to Peru and Chile but, as with so many other growing things, has made its way to appropriate climates around the world. Pepino is the Spanish word for cucumber; as such they are sometimes referred to as tree cucumbers or tree or bush melon. Pepino season runs from fall to spring and the bushes they grow on are, even though nightshades, also evergreens.

From a culinary perspective, the Pepino is used in much the same way melons or pears. They can be baked, broiled, sautéed, or better even just eaten raw. Pepinos are not really as sweet as melons but this is what makes them so versatile, in my opinion.

From a health perspective, Pepino melon is in the nightshade family and as such very closely related to the tomato. Pepinos are rich in vitamins and minerals, especially Vitamin C. Even better, though, they are an amazing source of phytonutrients and antioxidants; rutin, lycopene, zeaxanthine, quercetin, kaempferol, beta-carotene, the list goes on.

All that nutrient density makes them have a significant beneficial impact for your health. Research shows that consuming tomatoes can help decrease cardiovascular issues, including heart disease, increase bone density, boost immune function, decrease oxidative stress, and decrease the risk of various cancers...namely prostate and lung (as far as studies are concerned).

DAY 334 – QUINCE

Dense and fleshy with a slightly sweet, slightly earthy flavor, Quince has a mild and unassuming flavor. It looks like a cross between an apple and a pear, vibrant green skin with a pale inner flesh. Quince is native to the Middle East but they have been cultivated in appropriate environments around the world. Many historians believe the Quince was domesticated and cultivated long before the apple and is the fruit given to Aphrodite as a token of love making it sacred to relationships, marriage, and honeymoons. It is also theorized that in the bible the apple mentioned is actually a Quince.

From a culinary perspective, even though the quince resembles a pear or an apple, it doesn't really taste like one and depending on the variety can sometimes be too astringent to eat raw. The flesh is dense and hard so lends well to cooking. It can be baked, boiled, made into jam or jelly. They make a great pie ingredient and are also high in pectin giving them a natural thickening quality. Marmalade was originally made from quince, being derived from the name Marmelo, which is the Portuguese word for Quince. In France and Italy, Quince is also made into beverages, digestives, wines, and liqueurs.

From a health perspective, Quince is a great source of nutrient density. They are high in Vitamin C, A, and B complex. They are also rich in calcium, magnesium, and potassium. The high pectin combined with the astringency makes them amazing for gastrointestinal repair. They do help with digestive issues and also help heal the tissue within the intestinal tract. They are also great for decreasing systemic inflammation. The chemical compounds found in the Quince are antiviral and antifungal. Studies suggest they are beneficial in the treatment of cystitis and also in treatment of inflammatory conditions and viral flare-ups.

DAY 335 – KOMBUCHA

Tangy with a slightly effervescent, zippy earthiness, Kombucha can be a refreshing tonic when you're feeling slightly peaky. Kombucha is traditionally considered a tonic made from fermented green or black tea. The tea is brewed poured into a suitable glass container, mixed with sugar and then, what is called a scoby, is added as the fermentation medium. The mixture is then allowed to sit for a few days to a week to ferment into a brew that is purported to enhance health. Kombucha is often referred to as "mushroom tea" but the scoby is not a mushroom, it is an active community of bacteria and yeast that feeds on the sugar and continues to grow. The zippy fermented quality is a bi-product of the sugar conversion; sucrose is converted into things like acetic and gluconic acid.

From a culinary perspective, Kombucha is an interesting endeavor. On the one hand it's pretty easy to prepare and pretty low maintenance once the fermentation process is underway. That being said, I think it is important to note that there are things that can go horribly wrong if all the conditions aren't supportive to the process; instead of health invigorating drink you can end up with a hepatotoxic brew. However, if you are mindful of sterilization and appropriate ingredients, you should be just fine.

To make Kombucha tea the first thing you will need to do is secure an appropriate scoby; which isn't as challenging as it sounds since you can order them from Amazon or even Williams-Sonoma (who knew??). If you do order a scoby from an online source, be sure that it comes in a scoby liquid, that it has not been refrigerated, and that it has not been dehydrated. You may also want to be sure and purchase an organic one. Once you have your scoby you are ready to make some brew.

   4 cups of boiling water
   1 cup of evaporated cane sugar
   4-6 tsp of loose leaf black or green tea (you can use 4-6 teabags)
   1 cup of scoby liquid
   1 scoby

Boil the water, remove from heat and add tea. Let steep for 5-10 minutes (longer than 10 mins tends to be too tannic). Strain and pour into an appropriate glass container (pitcher, beaker, or large jar) then stir in the sugar until all has dissolved. Let the mixture cool to about room temperature and then stir in the scoby liquid and add the scoby. It should eventually once it makes itself at home, float on top of the liquid. Cover with a cloth because you want to keep insects and things out but you definitely want airflow and place in a quiet, relatively dark place to ferment. A cupboard or back shelf does really well. Allow it to ferment for about 7-10 days.

Once it is ready to drink, you can pour the liquid into suitable jars, saving a little bit for the scoby and either begin a new batch which can be fermenting while you are sipping your completed product over the next week. As you get more comfortable with the process, you will find that you can add other ingredients to your finished product to change the flavors and qualities. You never want to add anything other than tea and sugar to your scoby mixture. If you ever find mold on your scoby you want to be sure to discard it and the liquid. There is really no way to save the colony once harmful molds and bacteria have set in. One thing to keep in mind – the scoby is a living colony of bacteria and yeast, as such, it needs sustenance and happy vibes to thrive and do well.

From a health perspective, there are a multitude of caveats where Kombucha is concerned. Chances are you've seen in on the shelf in your local market or heard a various health "gurus" sing its praises as the heal-all tonic. I think first and foremost the key word is TONIC so consume it only in small amounts; not quart jars at a sitting. Slurping on a Kombucha with supersized big gulps is not going to help your health. In fact, it is more than likely going to create some serious health issues. People who have over-consumed Kombucha have ended up with some pretty serious liver damage and/or kidney acidosis.

So, if you are going to drink Kombucha, don't fall for the hype, make your own and sip in small amounts. One small amount per day is plenty. Second really important caveat: the FDA requires that commercially produced versions of Kombucha must be pasteurized. That means the original bacteria are killed off before it is placed in jars. Once it has been pasteurized the bacteria is reintroduced, flavoring is added, and it is sealed up and ready for you to consume from the refrigerator section of your market.

The only problem? More often than not the reintroduced bacteria aren't the same bacteria and enzymes that you would get from a homemade non-pasteurized version, so you aren't necessarily getting the health benefits from traditional Kombucha. Studies have demonstrated that the commercial Kombucha compared to traditional tonic Kombucha have a wide difference in bacteria, yeast, and even sugar content.

Kombucha has been consumed as a tonic drink in Asian culture for centuries. It is purported to increase longevity and is sometimes referred to as "immortal tea". Over the past decade Kombucha has gotten a reputation as a brew that heals everything from cancer, aids, diabetes, to the common cold. To date there are no studies involving human trials to confirm the efficacy of Kombucha. There are a variety of studies examining various components, like the acids and enzymes found in Kombucha, for their benefit to health. These studies are challenging to duplicate because there are so many variables in each batch of Kombucha. At the very minimum Kombucha has pre and probiotic qualities and can indeed help repopulate the gut with beneficial bacteria, which in turn can help boost immune function, mood, and cognitive ability.

CHAPTER 12 - DECEMBER

DAY 336 – PHEASANT

Gamey and earthy, Pheasant most definitely does not taste like chicken. It's that time of year; Fall is moving into winter and game hunting is in season. Taxonomy suggests that the Pheasant is native to Asia, however, it has been widely bred as a game bird for the past few hundred years and many varieties can now be found all around the world in various environments. Male Pheasants tend to be quite ornate with very colorful plumage while females tend to be more easily camouflaged with browns and greys in their plumage.

From a culinary perspective, preparing Pheasant can be a bit of a process. They must be hung for a few days before they are ready to cook. The length of time, whether or not the feathers are left on, and whether it is a cock or a hen, will all impact the flavor of the bird. Once it has hung the appropriate amount of time and been appropriately cleaned, it can then be prepared in any way that you might cook any other kind of bird. Pheasant have a lower fat content than chicken so whatever you end up doing with it, whether grilling, baking, roasting, frying, sauteeing, making into sausage, etc... you will want to be sure to use other ingredients that complement the gamey flavor and preserve the moisture content of the meat.

From a health perspective, as a game bird, Pheasants provide nutrient density based on what they forage in the forest. They are often, as with most game, higher in nutrient content than commercially raised birds. They are leaner in fat, and a great source of iron, zinc, and B vitamins. They are also a great source of Selenium, which helps balance metabolic function and boosts your immune system.

DAY 337 – AMARANTH

Small and dense in texture, Amaranth has a nutty, earthy flavor that makes a delicious morning porridge. Amaranth is a heritage/ancient grain that has been part of the human diet for over 8,000 years. It is native to South and Central America and historians theorize it was first domesticated and cultivated in the Peruvian landscape.

Because Amaranth is only ever referred to as "Amaranth" it can be easy to miss the fact that there are actually over 60 different species. Each species varies slightly in flavor and nutrient density; obviously this will also be due to terroir. Each species also, of course, has its own variation of the amaranth name, my favorite being the Amaranthus Hypochondriacus, which leaves one with the image of some chronically worrying plant; "oh no, is that blight on my right leaf?".

Amaranth has a very interesting history. First of all, it isn't really a grain even though it is often lumped into the grain family. It is a pseudo grain. From a taxonomy perspective, Amaranth comes from the same plant order as the beet, certain varieties of cacti, and believe it or not, carnivorous plants like the Venus fly trap. It was a staple food for the Aztecs, used not only in their daily diet but also in ceremony. Historians report that for ceremonial purposes Aztecs would mix blood and honey with the grain, form them into shapes of the gods and then eat them during rituals. This practice was put to a stop when the Spanish overran their population and for a short time Amaranth was a forbidden grain.

From a culinary perspective, Amaranth is easy peasy to work with. It has small seeds, smaller than quinoa making it a versatile addition to a variety of foods both sweet and savory. I soaked mine then cooked it for a breakfast porridge, to which I added honey and a small amount of Kefir. Super delicious. It can be added to baked goods, soups, stews, stir-fries. It can be a substitute for really any grain as an addition to a meal. Amaranth is gluten free so it doesn't really adapt well to baking flour if you are hoping to find a bread replacement.

From a health perspective, Amaranth is highly toxic in its raw state as are quite a few nuts and grains. It should not be eaten raw and is always best if soaked first, rinsed and then used in cooking. The soaking will help break the cell wall and remove the phytates that cause such a problem for our digestive tract. Once properly prepared, amaranth is a really nutrient dense food. It contains a significant amount of protein, is lower in carbohydrate than most other grains and contains a higher healthy fat content. It also is rich in minerals, vitamins, and amino acids.

It is a great source of lysine, zinc, iron, potassium and magnesium. On the phytonutrient spectrum, amaranth is packed with polyphenols and anthocyanins; which help reduce oxidative stress and system inflammation significantly. They are also beneficial in the prevention of cell mutations, which can lead to cancer. The anthocyanins especially work from within the cell, fortifying the healthy activity and encouraging the mutating stuff to self-destruct. How cool is that?

DAY 338 – PECANS

Crunchy, nutty and slightly sweet, Pecans are one of my favorite nuts. I love their ridged surface and meaty texture and I find that they are slightly sweet in flavor. Pecans are a type of hickory nut. The get their name from the Algonquin Indian word "pecane", which basically translates to "nut the needs to be cracked with a stone". Which sort of fits the description of all hard shelled nuts but since the pecan is native to North America and was first cultivated by the Native Americans, it makes sense that the Pecan would end up with this very descriptive name first.

According to historians, cultivation and use of the pecan in the diet remained almost exclusively a Native practice until the 1700's. Then in 1775, Thomas Jefferson (who was an avid gardener and naturalist) became enamored of the nut on a trip to the Mississippi Valley. He returned to Virginia with a store of nuts and some seedlings, which he shared with George Washington. They immediately set about cultivating them on their farms and the Pecan began to make its way more thoroughly into the American diet. It is now the second most popular nut in the U.S.

From a culinary perspective, the Pecan is super-versatile. It is commonly used in dishes both sweet and savory, especially in southern cuisine. Of course, probably the best-known uses are Pecan pie and Pecan Praline, both of which are southern delicacies. I love to use Pecans in raw food recipes or as a nut-based crust in desserts and puddings. I also add them to a variety of dishes both sweet and savory. I've been known to scatter them over sweet potatoes, toss them into oatmeal, shake them onto a salad, chop them into Brussels Sprouts, you name it. I love them because they are pretty mild and very flavorful. They don't tend to have the bitter aftertaste that can sometimes accompany other nut flavors like walnuts and hazelnuts.

If you want to make a quick and easy and relatively healthful piecrust you can try blending some Pecans with a few soaked dates and a pinch of sea salt and dash of cinnamon and/or vanilla. Blend in a food processor until it begins to clump together and take on a rolled quality. Then press them into a pan and voila...pie crust. You can pour in any no bake ingredient or if you are going to bake, just make sure it is at lower temperatures so the nuts don't burn.

Basically one cup of pecans and 3 or 4 dates is all you need to give you a full pie or tart crust.

From a health perspective, Pecans are amazing. I find it interesting that almonds tend to top the media-driven health food list when Pecans actually pack more of a balanced dietary punch. They are a great source of healthy fat, protein and fiber. Almonds may have higher protein content and a few more minerals, however, the Pecan actually wins out in the phytonutrient arena, making it a fantastic addition to your diet if you are trying reduce oxidative stress and systemic inflammation (which truthfully, we should all be paying attention to). The chemical compounds in Pecans enhance glutathione production, which means a happier brain and nervous system.

DAY 339 – MAPLE BUTTER

Creamy, maple flavored goodness-infusing; a perfect accompaniment to homemade barley cakes. Maple Butter is nothing but maple syrupy goodness. It's made by heating the syrup to a certain temperature, then whipping it as it cools until it takes on a creamy, buttery texture. There is no actual butter in the ingredients but don't let that fool you, this stuff is amazing and creamy and scrumptious. Historians believe that, in part, Maple Butter was created because it made it easier to transport and increased the shelf life. Raw maple sap and even some grades of syrup are incredibly perishable and by turning it into butter it just gives the Maple Syrup lover more options.

In the kitchen, Maple Butter is actually very versatile and can be used anywhere one might use honey, sugar, or syrup. It adds a yummy dimension to dishes both sweet and savory. I made some fried barley cakes and gave them a slather of Maple Butter and it was seriously heavenly. I've also used it to roast root vegetables in lieu of the honey that I typically use. You can make your own maple Butter if you have the time and energy to do so. America's Test Kitchen has a great video on how to make it step by step.

From a health perspective, studies suggest pure Maple Syrup is packed with antioxidants and phenolic compounds that help manage things like oxidative stress, systemic inflammation and metabolic function. Research on specific phenolic compounds demonstrate that the chemical composition of genuine Maple Syrup has an anti-proliferative effect on colon cancer cells, while also encouraging defective cells to self-destruct.

The caveat? It has to be the real deal; not maple flavored sugar water, which is what many of the cheaper products are. If it says maple flavored, avoid it. The only ingredients on the list for real Maple Syrup should be, well, Maple Syrup. So if you are going to make your own maple butter or if you purchase, make sure your ingredients are the real deal; real cream butter and real maple syrup.

DAY 340 – FREEKEH

Toasty, nutty goodness, Freekeh is fun to chew and packed with complex flavor. The name Freekeh applies to end result of a very specific process for wheat grain. It also applies to a dish that is called Freekeh because it is one of the main ingredients. To make Freekeh, the grain is typically harvested while still immature. Apparently, the quality of the product rests completely on the exact right harvest time. When the leaves begin to yellow and the grain is just starting to harden but still contains a milky, creaminess is the time to begin to start cutting the wheat.

Traditionally, it is then left out in the sun for a day and on day two the chaff and stems are set on fire. If the grains are moist enough it keeps them from catching fire in the process. What is left of the plant then gets threshed and rubbed while the grains continue to sun dry. This gives them a roasted quality and also begins to break them down into smaller granules. Once all the chaff and hulls have been removed the grain processing is complete and you have a roasty, toasty flavored grain that can be used in any number of dishes.

Freekeh is a popular ingredient in Middle Eastern and some African dishes. In some countries barley is used instead of wheat but the processing is the same. To make the dish Freekeh, typically involves braising some type of meat with spices, then adding in the Freekeh with more spices to finish it off. It can also be made vegetarian style, similar to any other 'pilaf'. Cook the grains in some liquid, add whatever spices suit you, cook until the grain is soft and the liquid is gone, and viola... you have something that is 'Freeken' delicious. (I had to say it).

From a health perspective Freekeh is wheat. So all the goodness of wheat will be in the grain and because it's a young grain it will be less "toxic" and easier to digest. Research suggests that green wheat has a nutritional value very close to that of oats. It is high in protein, high in fiber (if the whole grain is used) and high in vitamins and minerals. It contains a specific carbohydrate known to boost immune function and contribute to balanced blood flow, contributing to appropriate clotting and tissue repair for wounds.

It is also a significant source of calcium, copper, lithium, magnesium, phosphorus, potassium, selenium, sulfur and zinc. The green wheat grains are high in phenols and other phytonutrients that help decrease systemic inflammation and oxidative stress. They also contain other phenols and catechins, including also gallic acid, which is the same compound found in foods like blueberries and green tea, notable in the way it helps protect the liver and provides protection against carcinogenic influence of free radicals.

WARM FREEKAH SALAD
1/4 cup extra virgin olive oil
2 shallots, chopped
1 1/2 cups Freekeh
1 3/4 cups vegetable stock
2 teaspoons orange zest, finely grated
1/3 cup orange juice, freshly squeezed
1 teaspoon allspice, ground
1/2 cup figs, dried, thinly sliced
Kosher salt and black pepper, freshly ground
3/4 cup walnuts, toasted, chopped
1/2 cup parsley, flat leaf, coarsely chopped as a garnish

Warm the olive oil in a large saucepan over medium heat. Add the shallots and cook, stirring, until soft, 3 to 4 minutes.
Add the Freekeh and stir to coat the Freekeh with oil. Add the stock and 1 cup water. Add the orange zest, orange juice, allspice, figs, salt and pepper to taste. Bring to a boil and reduce to low.
Add half of the walnuts, cover, and cook for 15 minutes.
Remove from the pan from the heat, place in a serving bowl and garnish with the fresh parsley and remaining walnuts.

DAY 341 – POMELO

Sweet and slightly tart, the Pomelo has the flavor of a very mild grapefruit. The Pomelo looks like very giant, light green, grapefruit. Pomelos are native to Asia and seem to be the ancient relatives of the grapefruit. They can range in size from something similar to cantaloupe size up to about 25 pounds. They have very thick pith, which is the white stuff just below the surface. The pith can be inches thick depending on the size of the Pomelo in question. They tend to have sweeter fruit, with a sweet tart pith and a slightly more bitter skin. The Pomelo can also be found growing wild in Fiji and nearby islands.

From a culinary perspective, it can be used anywhere that one would use a grapefruit, just count on the flavor being slightly more mild. They can be peeled and pieced similarly to their citrusy cousins, so can be tossed in salads, broiled with a hint of sugar, or juiced. They can be eaten raw and make a great snack.

From a health perspective, Pomelos possess all the goodness of their grapefruit relatives. They are one of the most hydrating fruit choices, second only to watermelon and contain ample amounts of vitamin C and fiber. They are a great resource for athletes because they are high in potassium and other vital minerals.

Research suggests they are helpful in regulating blood sugar, lowering cholesterol and decreasing the potential for arterial plaque and other cardiovascular issues. For a while, like the grapefruit, the Pomelo was touted as a weight loss gem; in fact, research suggests that this might just be true. The phytonutrients, hydrating qualities, and fiber all contribute to balancing metabolic function for most people

DAY 342 – MINCEMEAT

Tangy and sweet, with a mouthfeel that has an adventure in every bite; traditional mincemeat is a delight to the palate. Historically, mincemeat has included actual meat, either beef or game (mostly venison) however these days it tends to include simply the suet rather than chunks of meat.

Historical versions have included meat, suet, dried fruit, cinnamon, nutmeg, and cloves along with a healthy dose of spirits, either brandy or rum. Historians disagree on the exact origination of Mincemeat or how it came to be such a holiday staple.

I believe, based on the combination of strong spices and spirits that it came into being as a way to serve meat that might have been less than fresh. I'm guessing it was what came to the table from the food cellar in the dark of winter when stores needed to be stretched but still enjoyed. Recipes for spiced meat are not uncommon throughout a variety of cultures and the spices not only mask the taste if it is close to spoiling but also kill bacteria that might lead to food poisoning. Remember the meat that was carried over the Swiss Alps in wine amphoras to create Sauerbraten? The spirits were a preservative, making it possible to carry the meat long distances without spoilage.

Today's Mincemeat is made from dried fruit, suet, spirits (brandy or run) and cinnamon, cloves and nutmeg. According to the History Channel, Mincemeat became a holiday treat because of the "trinity of spices"; cinnamon, cloves, and nutmeg.

Another interesting tidbit of information from the history of mincemeat pies? Apparently, they were the "twinkie defense" of the 1800's. Due to the combination of fruit, protein, and sugar, mincemeat was considered a digestive nightmare generating extreme indigestion and brain disruption which lead to any number of violent deeds that people committed.

From a culinary perspective, if you are going to make Mincemeat yourself, you actually need to start at least two weeks earlier than your mealtime. It might be easier to find a quality mincemeat option and use that if you have gone past the two-week period. Once you procure your Mincemeat, it can be used to fill pies, which is the traditional method or it can be baked into cookies, muffins, and breads. With a little surf of the internet you will find any number of interesting recipes, from tarts and cinnamon rolls to a really delicious looking African casserole.

From a health perspective, the virtues of Mincemeat are pretty variable. Traditional recipes are much healthier from a basic real food perspective; real meat, real suet, spices and even the spirits in small amounts. Later recipes that just contain fruit rely heavily on sugar content. Often, they contain candied rather than dried fruit and ample amounts of sugar. I just can't really get behind those ingredients with any peace of mind. That being said, it is possible to find un-candied, low sugar, more traditional recipes that don't contain the actual meat but are still very delicious and much better for you. If you are up for trying your hand at your own recipe, here's a good one from the 1700's:

TRADITIONAL MINCEMEAT RECIPE
1 lb beef (I used ground, grass-fed beef)
3/4 tsp salt
1 1/2 lbs apple, peeled and chopped (about 3 cups)
8 Tbs beef suet (Butter will work if you can't find a good source of suet)
2 Tbs Brandy or Rum
¼ cup of cider
1/2 Tbs cloves
1/2 Tbs cinnamon

1/4 Tbs nutmeg
8 Tbs (1/2) cup raisins (or 1 full cup if not using currants too)
8 Tbs (1/2 cup) dried currants

First, combine the raisins, currents and apples in a bowl with the brandy and cider. Then cook the beef on low, once it is browned, add the suet and allow it to melt. Stir in the spices. Remove from heat and combine all ingredients. Then place in a jar (quart jar works well) to sit for anywhere from 2 days to 2 weeks. You can then use the mincemeat in any recipes that you find interesting. If you are going to make a pie, you will need a lovely crust, pour in the ingredients and then bake in a 400 degree oven for about 45 minutes, or until the crust looks golden brown.

DAY 343 – PECORINO (ROMANO)

Salty, zingy, and sharp. Pecorino cheese is a very tasty addition to winter dishes like barley stew. Pecorino Romano is an EU protected designation of origin (PDO) which means in Europe and countries within the European Union it has to be made by specific guidelines and with specific ingredients. Sadly, the U.S. chooses not to recognize the PDO, so if you are purchasing Pecorino Romano cheese in the U.S. how it's made and what it's made from is anybody's guess.

However, if you choose an import or you live within EU influence, your Pecorino Romano is made from sheep's milk and follows guidelines that have actually been in place for thousands of years. Pecorino Romano is one of the more ancient cheeses in human history. Pecorino Romano is a hard, white cheese, easily grated and easily added to a variety of dishes. Pecorino cheese is mentioned in Roman writings, including Pliny the Elder and Hippocrates, and was a traveling staple among the Roman troops, known as the Legionaries.

To earn the name Pecorino Romano, it must be made from sheep's milk, in particular regions of Italy, it should be dry salted by hand and aged anywhere from 8 to over 12 months. This is what makes it dry and hard... and delicious.

From a culinary perspective, Pecorino Romano is often used as a substitute or in addition to Parmesan. It has a zingy robust flavor, plenty of umami going on, and it is hard and easy to grate. To me it has a little bit more of a complex flavor than Parmesan and I love that it's made from Sheep's milk. It's definitely one of my favorite cheeses.

From a health perspective, Pecorino is a dry, white cheese, which seems to be more beloved by the medical establishment. It's good to note that Pecorino is among the type of cheese that is a good source of protein, calcium, Vitamin B12. Pecorino cheese is umami and satisfies the palate. Research suggests it also helps regulate blood sugar. Sheep's cheese has a slightly different molecular structure and is easier for on the human digestive system. For that reason, it tends to provide higher nutrient content, simply because it is easier to digest.

Grate a little Pecorino over your winter stew... you won't be disappointed.

DAY 344 – CARAMEL

Sweet, salty, with a buttery slightly burnt or umami aftertaste, Caramel is a decadent wintertime treat. Caramel is basically cooked sugar. The process of caramelization is similar to the Maillard Reaction. When sucrose begins to break down from the sustained heat, it thickens and becomes a sweet sticky treat. Anything with the right amount of sugar can be caramelized, onions, parsnips, even carrots. It adds a delicious sweet and umami component to food. Caramel itself is really nothing more than sugar that has been melted and browned until it reaches a thickened, caramelized texture. Heaven knows when the first food was caramelized or even when the first Caramel candy was created, however it appears that the first caramel candies for commercial consumption were made and sold around the 1800's.

From a culinary perspective Caramel is a delicious treat all by itself. Bringing sugar up to the appropriate heat and allowing it to thicken and brown to a bubbly sticky scrumptious goodness is actually pretty easy. You just need some sugar, a heat source, and a candy thermometer. You can vary the thickness, stickiness, and stiffness of Caramel by heat and length of cooking time. Caramel can be a liquidy topping or a thick and chewy candy and anything in between. If the cooking time is less and heat temperature slightly lower, it will give you a nice liquid caramel; you can pour this over any number of delicious desserts. If you cook it slightly longer and a slightly higher heat point you can make a denser version of caramel. Using a thermometer you can cook it to the appropriate heat then, preparing a cookie sheet, you can pour the caramel mixture out onto the buttered surface and spread it out with a spoon. Once it cools you can cut it into little cubes or chunks and then wrap in wax paper. Enjoy.

From a health perspective caramel is sugar so all the rules of sugar consumption apply. That being said, if you use a quality minimally processed sugar, like demerrera or turbinado and eat in moderation, then a small amount of caramel consumption isn't going to make or break your

THE COTTAGER AND ARTISAN.

READY FOR ACTION!

holiday diet.

DAY 345 –PLUM PUDDING

That's right, it's that time of year for a scrumptious, sweet, moist, and dense Plum Pudding. Plum Pudding is a traditional pudding found in the U.K. It is also referred to as Christmas pudding denoting it as an included part of traditional Christmas dinner. There are many variations of Plum Pudding but it is generally agreed that traditional versions didn't ever include plums. Rather, the word plum in medieval England, typically meant raisins. To that end Plum Pudding is actually a steamed cake, with raisins, candied fruit, and a variety of spices. The variations of ingredients are plentiful, although the raisins are always included. Traditional Plum Pudding is made with raisins, candied fruit, suet, eggs and a bit of treacle or molasses. Throw in the trinity of spices, cloves, nutmeg, and cinnamon and some spirits and you have a Plum Pudding.

Once the ingredients are combined they can be carefully pressed into an appropriate pan and preserved for several weeks, even months before steaming to perfection. The first recorded reference to Plum Pudding can be found in writings from the 1400's. It has been a part of holiday meals ever since. As a holiday custom a trinket or coin is typically baked into the holiday pudding. The finder of which is assured luck and prosperity for the upcoming new year.

From a culinary perspective, traditional Plum Pudding is on the one hand, quite easy to make but on the other hand quite labor intensive. It's definitely an endeavor that involves time if nothing else. Plum Puddings can be made way in advance of the holiday season, in fact, in many instances the pudding for the next year is made during the holiday season of the present year. All the ingredients are carefully combined, then scooped into a piece of cheesecloth or cotton sackcloth, then formed into a ball and tied.

From a health perspective Plum Pudding, if made form quality ingredients, is actually not that bad for you. Unsulphered, manually dried fruits, organic eggs, brandy and you've got some quality ingredients that are worthy of the occasional consumption.

DAY 346 – BRANDY 'HARD' SAUCE (RECIPE)

Smooth and creamy with a heady Brandy zing; Brandy 'Hard' Sauce is just the thing to complete your Christmas Pudding. It's not really a hard sauce at all since there's nothing crackly about it, in fact, it's more like brandy butter (which, confusingly, happens to be another name for it). The first recorded recipe of Brandy Hard Sauce seems to be found in the culinary records from the kitchens of King George I in 1714. Plum pudding and Brandy Hard Sauce were on the menu of the first Christmas feast of his new monarchy.

Historians are quite sure that things like brandy, rum, and sherry hard sauces existed well before this but record of them is apparently non-existent. Couple that with the fact that for a time sugar was extremely hard to come by and extremely expensive, and it would have been a pricey and challenging recipe.

Brandy Hard Sauce is really just butter, sugar, and, well, brandy. You whip the butter until smooth and creamy and then begin adding the sugar until it all begins to be fluffy and creamy and then slowly drizzle in the brandy (or rum, or sherry). Once it's to your taste preferences consider yourself done. It is then slathered atop a nice warm plum pudding and voila Christmas dessert extraordinaire.

> BRANDY HARD SAUCE
> 2 sticks plus two tablespoons unsalted butter, softened
> 1 1/3 cups powdered content_id:162397942 sugar
> 6 tablespoons brandy
> (interesting variations: add 1 teaspoon vanilla extract or orange zest or use rum or sherry instead of brandy)
> Whip Butter until creamy, slowly add in sugar and whip until smooth and fluffy, drizzle in brandy.

From a health perspective… let's not even go there. Just enjoy the simple dip into a traditional holiday favorite, in moderation of course, and call it a day.

DAY 347 – GOOSE

Rich and slightly gamey, Goose is a tasty alternative to turkey for your holiday table. In the U.S. if you're looking for something more sustainable and healthier for your holiday meal, a nice Goose just might be the ticket. As of yet, geese are free from added hormones and antibiotics and tend to be raised in pasture settings since it is very challenging for them to thrive otherwise. *Be aware that this is only true for geese being raised for consumption; geese being raised for foie gras undergo a very different and very horrible fate (unless otherwise specified).*

It's interesting how history can reverse itself; in Victorian England, Goose was the more affordable option for the masses, while Turkey was more expensive. On today's table, as you well know, turkey is commonplace. This is in part due to the hybridizing of the breed and the mass production factory farm operations. Turkeys are undergoing the same or similar unhealthy mass-produced fate as chickens. Thankfully, this is not the case for the average goose….*although seriously I cannot stress enough that this does not apply to geese raised for foie gras.*

From a culinary perspective, if you were to read a recipe from the 1800's or early 1900's you might be quite daunted as to the preparation and cooking of a Goose. Partially, this is because back then, the geese were often older and more mature, making them tougher and gamier with a higher fat content. Today, the geese sold are often a couple of months younger, so they don't require the tenderizing processes prescribed in early recipes. The one thing to be very aware of, is that Goose is a much fattier meat, so it will need to be roasted in a pan deep enough to catch the fat (which you will want to keep because it is quite delicious to cook with and lasts for several weeks). Because of the fat content, any stuff placed in the Goose will be that much more flavorful and also find its way into the meat.

From a health perspective, Goose meat is a very good source of protein. It is higher in fat that other fowl, however it also higher in nutrient density. The fat in Goose fat is about 52% monounsaturated fat making a relatively healthy choice for cooking. Typically, goose fat and meat is higher in omega 3 fatty acids due to their foraging diet. The meat of a goose tends to be a little earthier and rich in texture because of its higher fat content with darker meat throughout.

DAY 348 – SALSIFY

Earthy and slightly sweet Salsify is an obscure little tuber that can add an interesting twist to your winter meals. The name 'Salsify' is actually used to describe a similar, yet quite different, root vegetable. One has dark skin and to me looks a little bit like burdock root; this is the one I tried. The other is a lighter skinned root and looks like a skinny parsnip. They are both related to the sunflower, which means they are also related to the Jerusalem artichoke. Black Salsify is native to Southern Europe and regions of Asia, it has however made its way around the globe. Historically Salsify has been used in Europe as a food and as a medicinal intervention.

From a culinary perspective Salsify is not as straightforward to cook as it looks and there seems to be disagreement on how to prepare it. Of course, this may be due in part to the shared name, making it challenging to know which root the recipe is referring to. Black Salsify is best cooked and peeled. It is suggested that it be boiled first for an amount of time and then cooled and peeled at which point it will be ready to be used in any number of dishes containing root vegetables or tubers, including "French fries".

From a health perspective, because it is in the "sunflower" family it contains many of the same nutrients as the Jerusalem artichoke, Yacon and other relatives. They are a good source of protein and lower in starch although very high in inulin. Inulin is a naturally occurring polysaccharide that is a prebiotic, so great for the gut. It also works as a good source of fiber, retaining fluid in the gut and assisting with motility and tissue repair. Research suggests that consuming foods with inulin can assist with lowering cholesterol, balancing blood serum levels, and boost immune function. As a prebiotic it helps populate the gut with friendly bacteria, which in turn balances not only digestion but also mood and cognitive function.

DAY 349 – FRUITCAKE (RECIPE)

Sweet and chewy, with just enough crunchy nuts in each bite to be a texture and taste delight; the updated version of Aunt Thelma's Fruitcake is amazing. I realize people typically groan a little when Fruitcake is presented, that's because they've never had that chance to try Aunt Thelma's Fruitcake. Yes, there really is an Aunt Thelma and her recipe, which was already quite delicious, has been carefully re-crafted by Chef Rex (my dad). The new version is actually closer to a more traditional version, with wholesome, organic, and sustainable ingredients where possible. This version is an absolute WIN with me. It's sticky and chewy and not too sweet… it gives fruitcake a whole new meaning.

	Original Recipe	Updated Recipe
Dry Ingredients		
	1 ½ cups flour	1 ½ cups organic stone ground whole grain flour*
	1 ½ cups sugar	1 ½ cups organic Demerara sugar*
	1 tsp. baking powder	1 tsp. aluminum free baking powder*
	1 tsp. salt	1 tsp. salt*
Fruit and Nuts		
	2 – 7 ½ oz packages of dates	15 or 16 ounces of organic Medjool Dates*
	1 lb diced candied pineapple	1 lb. of *unsulfured* candied pineapple*
	2- 16 oz jars Maraschino cherries	2-16 oz. jars of organic Maraschino cherries*

	18 oz . (5 ½ cups) pecans or walnuts	18 oz. (5 ½ cups) pecans or walnuts*
Wet Ingredients		
	6 eggs	6 large free range eggs*
	1/3 cup dark rum	1/3 cup dark rum*
	½ cup light corn syrup	½ cup light syrup*
Original Instructions	Updated instructions and notes*	
Grease 2 loaf pans, line with foil – grease foil	I used two loaf pans, Buttered and floured, and they slipped out on to a serving plate without coaxing. If you want to use the foil, tightly fold the foil over the outside of the loaf pan, then slip it inside. This makes a shape conforming insert that tightly fits the loaf pan with a lot of wrinkles and crease that will adhere to the fruitcake.	
Sift dry ingredients together.	Measure ingredients into an appropriate sized bowl and just whisk them together to insure a uniform dispersal of the ingredients.	
Add fruit and nuts, toss until well mixed.	The point here is to make sure that the dry ingredient mixture is dispersed uniformly among the chunky fruit and nut mixture. I tried using the paddle and dough hook attachments on my stand mixer to mix these, they both worked about the same. However, they both crushed some of the ingredients which results in a denser, more uniform textured fruitcake. The original version is a composite of intact chunks of fruit and nuts that makes in stand out from other cakes. They are equally tasty.	
Beat eggs until smooth, mix in rum add egg/rum mixture to fruit and dry ingredients. Mix well.	Again I can't over emphasize that a large spoon gently tossing the ingredients until well mixed is the way to go. I used Myers Dark as it has a great molasses flavor which sets of the caramel tones of the Demerara sugar.	

Pack into loaf pans Bake at 300 F for 1 ¾ hrs. or until a tooth pick Inserted into center comes out clean.	Don't skimp on the time, I recommend using the full 1 ¾ hours as the center can still be a bit sticky even if the toothpick comes out clean.

Fruitcake has a long history as a wintertime treat with recipes dating to Ancient Rome including things like pine nuts and pomegranate seeds. All across Europe there seems to be some variation of the fruitcake.

DAY 350 – TALEGGIO

Savory and decadently umami, Taleggio is another favorite cheese that I only get to enjoy occasionally. Since it's the holidays, I say bring out the stinky cheese! Taleggio is definitely stinky but absolutely worth getting past the olfactory insult because it is delicious and creamy. Taleggio gets its name from the caves of Val Taleggio in Italy. First recorded history of Taleggio cheese is around the 9th century. Although, it was not always called Taleggio, originally it was name *Stracchino quadro di Milano*, it isn't until the 1900's that it became known as Taleggio and acquired the Protected Designation of Origin. It is made from cows milk and aged in caves.

One interesting thing about Taleggio is that it is made into squares, not rounds or wheels. It is also what is considered a smear-ripened cheese. Sounds a little gross, but really it just means that the outside is washed with a solution containing a particular strain of bacteria. This is what contributes to the unique flavor that develops as it ripens the interesting color of the rind.

From a culinary perspective, Taleggio is interesting. The smell suggests that it will have a strong flavor and fool one into serving it up with bits and pieces that will handle the insinuated palate. However, don't be fooled, it is actually quite mild, although it has a very complex flavor pattern. Taleggio is a soft white cheese so it can be added to just about any recipe calling for a soft white cheese. It is delicious melted on sandwiches and into risottos or cheese based culinary creations. My favorite way to eat Taleggio? With a hunk of freshly baked warm sourdough bread and maybe even a glass of red wine. Seriously, a treat to be sought out.

From a health perspective, because Taleggio is ripened in a similar way to blue, it has many of the same properties for health. It is a great source of vitamins and minerals, namely B vitamins, phosphorous, calcium, magnesium and potassium. It is heart friendly and contributes to a decrease in oxidative stress and systemic inflammation. It also has a teeth whitening quality, helping to decrease plaque and support healthy gums.

Caveat: unfortunately, in the U.S. we do not honor the protected origin, so if you are buying U.S. produced "Taleggio" it isn't really Taleggio. What makes Taleggio what it is, is the bacteria and yeast found in the Lombardy region. This doesn't mean that the cheeses produced here are any less tasty, it just means they aren't as authentic. I highly recommend going for a traditional PDO Taleggio from Italy at first, then if you want to try some local brands, by all means give it a go.

DAY 351 – ORANGE

Refreshing, zesty and juicy, Oranges are an uplifting addition to any meal or snack. They also have a rich traditional history that is easily forgotten since they have become so commonplace on the table. Oranges have been part of human culinary history for thousands of years. Chinese records suggest cultivation of the Orange as early as 2500 BC. It appears they originated in Eastern China and parts of India and have since made their way around the globe. Oranges are one of the most widely cultivated fruits and definitely one of the most popular; even more popular than the apple.

Orange trees are evergreen trees and how they reproduce depends entirely on whether or not they are sweet or bitter oranges. Oranges are actually a wintertime fruit, even though they can be found year round in just about every market around the world. This is one reason they are part of holiday tradition in European and U.S. culture. There are several theories of why we have found Oranges in the toe of our Christmas stocking for years; one being that the Orange represents prosperity and good health in the coming year; another that the Orange represent bags of gold. There is a story about Bishop Nicholas throwing bags of gold into the windows of houses with young women too poor for a dowry. The bags of gold ended up in their stockings, hung by the fire to dry. For at least a century, if not more, Oranges have made their way into the toes of stocking representing these bags of gold. Of course, Oranges would have been an exotic and delectable treat in the cold of winter, so I imagine they were a truly appreciated gift. They were also an assurance of good health, loaded with vitamins and minerals that were scarce in the cold, short days of winter.

From a culinary perspective, Oranges play a pivotal role in many aspects of dietary and culinary endeavors. Orange juice for breakfast, Oranges as a snack, Orange slices in dishes both sweet and savory. In fact, as I mentioned the Orange is, unfortunately, so commonplace it is easy to miss out on how amazing it truly is. One way I like to use Oranges is as a base for brown rice. I squeeze the juice, including the pulp, into an equal part water and then add rice and steam. It adds an amazing dimension that is refreshing and delicious and can be used for sweet or savory dishes.

From a health perspective, Oranges of course are an excellent source of vitamin C. They are also an amazing source of antioxidants, helping to decrease oxidative stress and systemic inflammation. Their phytonutrients boost immune function, enhance heart health by lowering blood pressure and cholesterol. They also neutralize free radicals and decrease the potential for cell mutation and cancer. Because they are citrus they are also packed with volatile oils that stimulate the olfactory response to balance mood and increase serotonin production. Research has also demonstrated that the kumquat can be a beneficial addition to your diet if you are trying to get rid of gallstones or liver inflammation.

DAY 352 – PLANTAIN (GREEN)

Starchy and dense, with a mild flavor, Green Plantain chunks are an interesting twist to my bowl of Tortilla/Avocado soup. Plantains have been part of human diet for hundreds of years, especially in tropical regions where they originate. The Plantain and banana are in the same family, however Plantains are typically larger, denser and less sweet. This makes them perfect for cooking, they hold their shape and texture pretty well.

The Plantain is actually a type of berry and there are actually several hundred varieties throughout the tropical regions across the globe. Plantains have a higher starch content and lower sugar, and they are really only palatable if cooked. Some varieties have an extremely high latex content making them challenging to peel and requiring a soak in salt water prior to cooking. In some cultures Green Plantains are dried and ground into flour, then used to make flatbreads and or as a thickener to soups and stews.

From a culinary perspective, depending on the type of plantain you have, they are pretty easy to work with in the kitchen. As a tropical culinary mainstay, they can be used anywhere a potato or root veggie might be used. They can be fried, baked, roasted, added to soups or stews. They can be a stand alone or integrated into a recipe.

From a health perspective Plantains are slowly digested starch, which means regulated impact on blood sugar. They are also high in fiber and things like oligosaccharides, which keep the bacteria in your gut happy. The Plantain also contains specific chemical compounds that help decrease cholesterol and lipids in the blood. One study used green Plantain flour as the base for yellow noodles and noted a demonstrated reduction in digestive issues, unhealthy cholesterol issues, and bowel health, which resulted in balanced weight loss and decreased systemic inflammation. Plantains are rich in vitamins and minerals, like potassium and Vitamin A. They are also a great source of tryptophan. This makes Plantains and bananas a good mood food as the tryptophan is a precursor to serotonin production.

DAY 353 – PINTO BEANS

On their own Pinto Beans have a dense texture and mildly earthy flavor. Add them to a soup or stew and their starchy quality enhances whatever the other ingredients have going on. Pinto Beans are a winter season food and one of the most common beans in the U.S. and Mexico. They get their name from the "painted" quality they have before they are cooked. Pinto Beans are part of the "common bean" family originating in Peru and spreading across the globe. It is typically the pinto bean that is used in refried beans or other stews and chilies.

From a culinary perspective, you'll want to soak your Pinto Beans at least overnight before using them to cook with. This will help break down the cell wall and eliminate phytates that can be irritable to the digestive system. Once they are soaked they can then be slow cooked or boiled to the texture desired. The cooked beans can be added to soups, stews, chilies, and casseroles. They can be smashed and refried with lard and herbs and spices.

From a health perspective the Pinto Bean is a great source of fiber, protein, slow digesting starch and vitamins and minerals. They are an excellent source of folate, copper and manganese. Because of their mineral and fiber content, they are a heart healthy food, helping decrease the potential for cardiovascular disease and lowering cholesterol. They help stabilize blood sugar and, if soaked first, help repair the gastrointestinal tract, decreasing the potential for bowel issues and colon cancer. The trace minerals in Pinto Beans can help detoxify the body after consuming sulfites; a preservative found in many processed food and drink. The folate in Pinto Beans makes them a great resource for increasing iron storage and transport in the body.

DAY 354 – ORACH (RED)

Slightly chalky, with a flavor and texture similar to chard or raw spinach; Red Orach adds an interesting dimension to a winter salad. It's also known as Mountain Spinach and is a relative of Amaranth. Red Orach is really a lovely addition to salads not only for its flavor but also because it is really aesthetically lovely. Deep red leaves add a festive quality to dark leafy greens.

Red Orach has a long history as part of the human diet. In fact, it was a main go to green (or red) before spinach really became a hit. Orach actually has many variations that also result in color differences. When cooked the leaves color whatever they are cooked with and have historically been used for just that purpose. In Italy it has been used for centuries to color pasta. Orach is a versatile plant and can be found in a variety of landscapes around the globe.

From a culinary perspective Orach is great as an add-in to raw salads and garnished small plates, both for its beauty and for its flavor. It can also be added to any variety of cooked dishes that call for leafy vegetables. Just keep in mind that the red and purple leaves will change the color of whatever culinary endeavor you are undertaking.

From a nutritional perspective Orach is a great source of a wide variety of vitamins, minerals, and phytonutrients. The green leaves contain phosphorous, calcium, magnesium, and iron. The red leaves contain anthocyanin, which, if you remember from other red colored fruits and vegetables, is a chemical compound that acts as a preventative measure against oxidative stress and the development of different types of cancer. It is also the compound responsible for relieving the potential for muscle strain after a workout. Red Orach isn't that easy to come by in the marketplace, but it is a winter vegetable so keep a lookout as the days cool and nights lengthens.

DAY 355 – MIZUNA

Astringent and peppery, Mizuna reminds me of arugula as it flavors up my winter salad. Mizuna is part of the brassica family; and more specifically the Brassica Rapa family, which also contains things like Napa Cabbage and Bok Choy. Mizuna has the texture and appearance of leaves similar to mustard greens (again, same family) or arugula. The greens are popular in Japanese cooking and in Japanese cuisine are often pickled and then added to foods.

From a culinary perspective Mizuna has a similar texture to the mustard green or arugula. It can be added to salads as an exotic and flavorful green or sautéed in stir-fries, and added to soups and stews.

From a health perspective Mizuna is in the brassica family and as such contains all of the nutrient density that its brassica relatives contain. Calcium, potassium, phosphorus, iron, all contribute to healthy bones, tissue, and blood, as well as nervous system balance. Vitamins A, C, and K and beta carotene contribute to overall health and wellness. Adding it to your diet can help manage systemic inflammation, oxidative stress, and boost immune function.

DAY 356 – IMAM BAYILDI

Spicy, sweet and savory with an exotic Middle Eastern flair that livens up my holiday palate. Imam Bayildi hearkens back to the Ottoman Empire according to historians. The literal translation of this delicious little dish is, "the Imam fainted". I'm imagining he fainted from such an extraordinary flavor combination, which is, as I later learned, the gist of the story behind the name. There is also another version, which implies that not only did the Imam faint from the scrumptious flavor but also from the exorbitant price of the ingredients back in the day.

Traditionally, Imam Bayildi is basically deliciously stuffed eggplant. However there are new recipes that offer slight variations of preparation making it easier to make and to eat. Imam Bayildi is meant to be served at room temperature and can be either a small plate part of an array of other dishes or a main entrée. The combination of sweet, spicy and savory with the texture that is a variant makes this dish an interesting and delightful treat.

From a health perspective, Imam Bayildi is made from some fantastic ingredients; eggplant (aubergine), onions, tomatoes, olive oil, cumin, allspice, garlic and parsley (of course recipes can vary). It is a heart healthy dish that also contributes to a decrease in systemic inflammation and oxidative stress.

DAY 357 – EGGPLANT (AUBERGINE)

Earthy with a hint of bitterness, Eggplant is one of those veggies that people either love or hate. Eggplant is a member of the nightshade family and is actually considered a fruit. It appears to have originated in Asia and, upon domestication, made its way around the world. There are many varieties of Eggplant ranging in size, shape and color.

The uncooked fruit is quite bitter and often requires presoaking in salt to decrease the bitterness and better prepare the fruit for culinary endeavors. The seeds when raw can be quite toxic and even can have a hallucinogenic quality. After soaking the fruit in salt, it can then be rinsed and used in a variety of ways. There are a wide variety of cultures that feature Eggplant as an ingredient in signature meals. It can be found most frequently in Middle Eastern, Italian, Asian, and Spanish.

From a culinary perspective, it is the variety and size of the Eggplant that will dictate whether or not you will need to soak in salt first. Once this has been decided and the fruit has been adequately prepared it can then be used in a variety of ways. One of my favorites, is to smoke or roast the whole fruit, including the skin and then blend them with a variety of appropriate spices, turning them into Baba Ghanoush; a deliciously complex middle eastern "dip".

From a health perspective Eggplant has often gotten a bad reputation because it is part of the nightshade family. Yes, as a raw fruit it can be toxic to the body and can contribute to increased histamines or inflammation in the body. When prepared appropriately it contains a decent amount of macro and micronutrients; manganese, magnesium, Vitamin B and copper, along with protein and fiber. What the Eggplant lacks in micronutrients it makes up for in phytonutrients; not the least of which is anthocyanin; a chemical compound that helps reduce oxidative stress and systemic inflammation.

DAY 358 – PORT (TAWNY)

Sweet and astringent with the warm burn of alcohol, a sip of Port is a traditional finish to a traditional meal. Port is a fortified wine, which means it is initially made from grapes but then after fermentation it has brandy added to it before bottling. According to historians, Port originates from Portugal, in the Douro Valley. Unfortunately, it does not have a protected origin so Port can be produced in other places, although they will not have the same influence of terroir found in the Douro Valley.

Port is consumed towards the end of the meal as a digestive aid. It's made from late harvest grapes and Tawny ports are fermented in wooden barrels allowing the grapes to age and oxidize producing a nice amber color. First recorded shipment of Port from Portugal is in the 1600's and it has continued to be shipped around the world, increasing in popularity and varieties.

From a health perspective, there are some benefits to the moderate or occasional consumption of both red and white wines, including fortified wines like Port. One study listed in the Journal of Internal Medicine found that drinking a moderate amount of fortified wine, either while fasting or eating a meal, had no significant impact on blood sugar levels. So, perhaps, Port and other aperitifs and digestifs are meant to just be consumed for the sake of themselves and enjoyed in moderation or on special occasions where they can be incorporated into a meal and appreciated for their own unique qualities.

DAY 359 – MUSTARD GREENS

Sharp and slightly spicy with a hint of earth, mustard greens are a nice deviation from the typical dark leafy green. There are several varieties of mustard green, all of which are members of the brassica/cruciferous family. That's right, they're related to broccoli, brussels sprouts, and cauliflower to name a few.

The flavor of your mustard 'green' will vary depending on which mustard family it belongs to. Three basic families; white/yellow, brown/indian, and black provide different nuances and influences that change the quality of spiciness, texture, and appearance. As mustard greens have gained in popularity there are even wider variety of colors available in the market place. Don't be surprised if you notice purple or red mustard 'greens' gracing the produce aisle.

From a culinary perspective, my favorite way to prepare mustard greens is sauté. A little bit of bacon, a little bit of garlic, toss in the greens and sauté until tender. You'll be serving up a side dish worthy of any holiday meal. Of course, you can toss mustard greens into any dish to which you might add other greens; soups, stews, stir fries, even salads for a bit of palate invigoration.

From a medicinal perspective, mustard greens contain all the amazing nutrients and phytonutrients of their namesake family. The glucosinolates in mustard greens assist in protection of the digestive tract, helping to support cell health. Research also demonstrates that mustard greens help balance the microbiotic community that lives in the lower gut. Add that to the ability to decrease oxidative stress and systemic inflammation, regulate blood lipids (good vs. bad cholesterol) and mustard greens present a pretty amazing picture to add to your dinner table.

DAY 360 – HAM

Salty, smoky, with a slightly chewy texture, real ham from a quality source is quite a treat. Most ham found in the grocery market today is not traditionally prepared ham, rather it is pork pieces-parts shmooshed into ham shape…not really delicious and not the ham discussed in this entry.

Real ham is typically the hind quarter of a pig that has been preserved either by salting, smoking, or curing. The method of preserve will give your end result a potentially different flavor and texture. The first recorded reference to preserved pork is in Chinese text from about 5,000 years ago. Later, Rome was a huge influence in the spread of preserved pork on the dinner table. However, salted and cured meats have been part of human history for thousands of years, in almost every culture. I imagine there has been some form of preserved pork in other ancient cultures not dependent on written word.

From a culinary perspective, ham is quite versatile. Because it is preserved it can be served up for just about any occasion at just about any time. Snack, horsdovre, main course, picnic, whatever you can imagine.

From a health perspective, pork is quality, higher purine protein, which makes it a good option as a protein source. The caveat being, avoid conventional pork at all costs. Most conventional pork in the U.S. has been given some form of pharmaceutical called ractopamine. Ractopamine is a growth stimulant used to increase muscle mass and body weight. Unfortunately, it also causes increased cardiovascular stress, hyperactivity, aggression, muscles spasms and tremors, and any number of other issues. Typically, it results in 61% of the 'herd' becoming what is referred to as a 'downer' meaning the animal seizes and collapses, unable to walk, and so, well, I'm sure you can imagine what happens next.
I cannot stress enough that consuming conventional pork is bad for them and bad for you.

DAY 361 – YORKSHIRE PUDDING

Chewy and savory, with a texture much like a thick crepe, Yorkshire

Pudding is a traditional Sunday dinner favorite. Historically Yorkshire pudding would have been referred to as a "dripping pudding"; meaning it cooked underneath meat roasting on a spit in order catch the drippings and fat. Although, called a pudding, Yorkshire Pudding is not in the least bit sweet. It is, rather, made from a batter similar to a soufflé and when cooked, the fat collects at the bottom while the top remains fluffy and light.

While the origin of "Yorkshire" pudding is unknown or at least no agreed upon by historians, it is generally accepted that it originates in Northern England. One reason for the confusion and potential disagreement is that the item existed long before the name in British cuisine. It wasn't until the mid 1700's that the "Yorkshire" title stuck, from then on becoming a beloved addition to meals of roast and gravy. At a time when meat was scarce, pudding would be served with gravy beforehand to help appease the appetite and require less meat.

The culinary perspective... Yorkshire pudding is on the one hand, at least from an ingredient perspective, quite easy to prepare. On the other hand, to truly finesse the lift of the batter and drop the heaviness of the available fat without losing texture and flavor is not as easy as one might think. The perfect Yorkshire Pudding is made from flour, eggs, water (or milk) and just the right amount of beef fat. I have not yet had the chance to try my hand at making a Yorkshire pudding. It's on the list! However, I have had the opportunity to try a few over the past weeks and there is definitely an art to it.

If you've not experienced the traditional British Sunday Roast then it's worth trying to find one... perfectly roasted beef with root vegetables, gravy, a seasonal green and a delightful Yorkshire pudding.

DAY 362 – OYSTERS (SMOKED)

Smoky, slightly salty, with even a hint of sweetness; smoked oysters have a dense, somewhat mushy mouth feel. As a person who is very sensation oriented, mouth feel often plays a bigger role in what 'tastes' good and what doesn't. These smoked oysters were a challenge initially but, once I got past the way it felt to chew them, I realized they tasted really quite nice.

Oysters are an interesting topic both nutritionally and ecologically. Oysters are packed with nutritional goodness but also in some cases depending on the water they live in, they contain things that are not so good. Despite the potential health warnings, oysters are consumed around the world in such large amounts that approximately 90% of the oyster population in our oceans across the planet have been over-harvested, creating serious issues.

Enter the concept of oyster farming! Now, for the most part the public has been inundated with messages about the woes of fish farming...and for the most part much of it is true, however, in the world of the oyster, farming seems to be a symbiotic relationship; one that is sustainable and beneficial to all parties involved (although one could argue that being someone's dinner at the end of the day may not be the Oyster's most desired outcome). Being the complete research geek that I am, I have searched databases high and low attempting to find the most up to date and unbiased information about Oysters and Oyster farming and it appears that farmed Oysters are indeed healthier all the way around, for you, for them, and for the planet.

From a culinary perspective, the oyster is like many other foods in that its taste will vary depending on its environment. Although I have yet to acquire a taste for raw oysters I now understand how people can spend precious time perusing an Oyster menu as though they were attempting to choose a fine wine... they are! Oysters can be eaten raw, cooked, baked, grilled and in soups, stews, and sauces. They are actually quite versatile and present an interesting challenge for culinary endeavors. I will be giving the Oyster more respect from here on out and attempt to discover more healthful ways to enjoy them in my diet.

From a nutritional perspective, despite the admonitions to avoid crustaceans and mollusks because they are garbage filters (pleasant thought??) they do offer some significant benefits to health. Oysters are high in zinc, which makes them highly beneficial for neurological functioning, cardiovascular health, immune function, and reproductive health for both men and women. The zinc level is one reason Oysters are considered an aphrodisiac food. Oysters are also an impressive source of iron, calcium, copper, and selenium making them highly beneficial for metabolic function and blood and bone health. They are a good source of protein and omega 3 fatty acid; which helps decrease systemic inflammation and oxidative stress.

DAY 363 – FLEUR DU MAQUIS
Creamy and earthy, encrusted with an herb blend of rosemary, fennel, and juniper, giving it an almost intoxicating ability to excite the palate; sweet,

savory, piquant, creamy, earthy…oh my. No wonder this little cheese also goes by the name of Brin d'Amor (Breath of Love). Indeed it is an experience to savor.

Fleur du maquis; flower of the 'maquis' named because the Lacaune ewes that supply the milk for this cheese, feast on the flowers of the hedgerow in the landscape. Thickets incidentally said to provide cover for highwayman and robbers lying in wait for innocent passersby.

From a culinary perspective, Fleur du Maquis is delicious in every stage of its maturity. As a young cheese it is bright and earthy, reflecting the herbs and grasses that the sheep feed on. As it matures it becomes even earthier and tangier, taking on more and more of the flavor of the herbs it is packed in. Best way to eat? As is, and maybe even paired with a nice red wine.

From a health perspective, it is a sheep milk cheese, so supplies different nutrients than dairy. Sheep milk tends to have more nutrients than cow's milk, often higher in iron, zinc, phosphorous and calcium as well as, vitamins A, D, E. It also is a significant source of Omega 3 fatty acid based mostly on the sheep's diet of grass. Sheep milk also tends to be easier to digest and assimilate than other dairy.

DAY 364 – LIVERWURST

Dense and savory, Liverwurst is a treat that harkens back to days of frugal and efficient, use of everything from nose to tail. It is also called liver sausage, although there are slight variations in recipe, consistency, and ingredients between spreadable wurst and more dense sausage. Liverwurst is made from, you probably guessed, the liver, and sometimes other organs, of an animal. Most recipes call for pork liver and other herbs and spices, but there are those that contain a mixture of beef and pork. Often the ingredients will be dictated by country of origin. There are examples of liver sausage in almost all cultures that consume meat.

I grew up eating Liverwurst without a second thought. Then sometime in my late teens and early 20's when the "nonfat" diet madness hit the scene, I shunned it heartily. Now, however, as I've learned to listen to my own body and have grown to understand what it really takes to be healthy and well, along with the health and wellness of the planet; Liverwurst has found its way back into my diet. My favorite is just simply liver and spices like garlic, nutmeg, salt, pepper, onion, ginger, and coriander. The organ meat and the spices are all mixed together, sort of pureed and then baked.

It can then be served cold or warm, sliced for sandwiches or snacks, or as a main ingredient to a healthful and delicious dinner. In today's world people often turn their nose up at the thought of Liverwurst, however, it is, in my mind, an important addition to our dietary repertoire if one is a meat eater. Respect for the full animal and what it has given requires finding ways to utilize all parts.

From a health perspective, organ meats are very beneficial to the body. Traditionally, they were prized and cherished parts of the animal almost over the muscle meats that tend to be the only ones we consume. Archeological digs and even observation in current day hunter-gatherer peoples demonstrate the preferential consumption of the internal organs.

The caveat, of course, being that the meat should be quality. Raised with care and in a healthful environment, living the life it is supposed to live. Eating organ meats from conventional animal feeding operations (CAFO's) will simply add to your ill health and potential for disease, especially liver since it is one of the main "cleaning" organs in the body. (Not to mention, adding to the continued misery and suffering found in these types of operations.) All of that being said, if you do get your hands on some quality Liverwurst, you are in for a healthful treat; packed with nutrients like vitamins A, B12, D, and K2. It's also a good source of minerals like iron, calcium and potassium, as well as, essential fatty acids, including omega 3's.

DAY 365-BLACK EYED PEAS

Getting ready to bring in the new year with traditional flavors. Earthy and dense, black eyed peas also are very good at taking on the flavors accompanying them in the pot. The tradition of black eyed peas seems to go back at least 1,500 years and spans various cultures and ethnicities. As a crop, they can be found all around the globe in warmer climates and according to historical data were introduced to the U.S. in the 1700's.

While they are found in a wide variety of ethnic cuisine, it is only in certain cultures that they are revered for prosperity and luck at the turning of the year. The earliest recorded reference to them as a symbol of luck can be found in the Talmud, around 500AD, eating them for Rosh Hashanah brings a prosperous year filled with merit. In the Southern U.S. various methods of preparation including beans, pork, and some green leafy vegetable, typically collard greens or chard, are served up on New Year's Day as a symbol of luck for the coming year. Depending on the traditional preference, you might find a penny in your bowl of beans and greens or you might need to eat exactly 365 beans to insure the potential of prosperity.

From a culinary perspective, black eyed peas are a legume, also called a cowpea. They are easily prepared by cooking them in liquid for an amount of time, much like other beans or peas. I recommend soaking them first, even if they are fresh. I soak mine overnight. If you are making them to ring in the new year, soaking them overnight can be a great way to collect your thoughts and intentions to add to the pot when ready to cook them.

From a health perspective, black eyed peas are nutrient dense and a great addition to your celebratory meal. They are high in fiber, a good source of protein, and an excellent source of potassium. They are also rich in iron and zinc and make a good 'healthy heart' option for your bowl. Ringing in the new year with a hearty bowl of black eyed peas is good for your heart and your soul.

THE END... OR MAYBE THE BEGINNING

This concludes 365 Days of Taste and Flavor. It is my earnest hope that you have been at the very least, entertained and the at the very best, inspired to deeper understanding and relationship with your palate and your food world.

Bon ♡ appetit

ABOUT THE AUTHOR

Dr. Stephanie Shelburne is a Food/Mood Doctor and an Integrative Health Educator, Writer, and Researcher. She provides scientifically supported and intuitively implemented protocols for Optimal Well-Being. She is passionate about food and eating for health, wellness, and enjoyment. Dr. Stephanie travels, teaches, speaks, and works with clients internationally and is always excited to share experiences with pure, simple, and life-enhancing tastes and flavors.

CPSIA information can be obtained
at www.ICGtesting.com
Printed in the USA
LVOW12s0746261217
560710LV00002B/172/P